Movement
Behavior
and
Motor Learning

HEALTH EDUCATION, PHYSICAL EDUCATION, AND RECREATION SERIES

Ruth Abernathy, Ph.D., Editorial Adviser

Chairman, Department for Women,
School of Physical and Health Education
University of Washington, Seattle, Washington 98105

Movement Behavior and Motor Learning

BRYANT J. CRATTY, Ed.D.

Associate Professor and Director Perceptual-Motor Learning Laboratory
Department of Physical Education, University of California
Los Angeles, California

SECOND EDITION

Lea & Febiger

PHILADELPHIA 1967

This book is dedicated to

DARREN

Foreword

THIS Second Edition represents another step in the attempt to bring together data relevant to the understanding of human movement with particular reference to learning. It reflects the findings of more recent research and increasingly mature theoretical formulation. The task of examining correlates of observable behavior is not a simple one, and Doctor Cratty is to be congratulated on his effort to explore, synthesize, and report in a meaningful way some of the increasingly complex data in this area.

The insistence on focus on movement as *observable, purposeful,* and *broadly volitional* is needed. While many authors are attempting to clarify terminology, it is felt that the differentiation of *movement behavior* and *motor performance* is sound—in spite of the relatively simple limitation of the latter term to a "purpose-duration" aspect of the former. The differentiation among other terms is equally helpful. The implicit as well as explicit definitions that appear throughout the text should contribute to the understanding of the various aspects of the problem of movement analysis.

The additions, revisions, and deletions materially increase the usability and interest of the text. The chapters dealing with perception and the stated limitations on coverage should be of particular interest to students in the field. The discussions of maturation, motivation, and stress in relation to movement should lead to a greater interest in the investigation of aspects of movement behavior. For example, the need for studies relating to role perception, to aspiration and to performance level, utilizing female subjects in various age groups, is a case in point.

"Personal equations" in movement should be of great interest to those attempting to find verification in the class or instructional situation. The idiosyncratic aspects of movement all too often overlooked are of particular interest to the teacher concerned with identifying "cues." Individual differences in movement have been grossly identified by teachers of Physical Education and utilized in qualitative judgments. The broader coverage of movement behavior is enhanced by the chapter on communication through movement. It is hoped that further attention will be given to creativity and movement exploration in future editions. The introduction of the four-part theory of perceptual-motor performance seems appropriate. This view of components is of interest both for the factors included and those excluded. Such a presentation at first glance appears simple, but the problem is indeed most complex. Further research should serve to make explicit some of the implicit dimensions.

RUTH ABERNATHY

(vii)

Preface

THE widespread acceptance of the first edition plus the growing list of research findings relative to motor behavior prompted the writing of this second edition. Several new chapters have been added to the book, including a review of research dealing with the neurology and biochemical theories of learning and retention, a discussion of some "personal equations" in movement, as well as material explaining the role of "social motives" in the modification of movement behavior and motor learning.

All of the chapters contain new material from recent research to help bring the graduate and undergraduate scholar "up to date." New information relative to kinesthesis, visual-space perception, motivation, and learning has been placed in appropriate sections of the book.

This second edition has been re-organized into a more lucid presentation of material dealing with, first, perceptual factors, then a discussion of variables influencing the state of the performer, and finally various components of movement behavior and motoric functioning caused by the resultant of these perceptual and organismic factors. In this re-organization the chapter on instructions was more properly placed in the section dealing with perception, rather than within the section dealing with learning. With these and similar shifts in material, it is believed a more accurate S-O-R (Stimulus-Organism-Response) format has been adhered to.

In books of this nature attempting a broad survey of literature dealing with a variety of human functions, authors must not only select but reject certain research findings for inclusion. This material is a result of this selection and rejection process, and thus many findings may have been overlooked or were not deemed important or conclusive enough for discussion within these pages. Generally material has been included which attempts to explain the structured and unstructured movements of human beings who are relatively free from some kind of psychic or physical abnormality. Emphasis has been placed upon the factors which explain the manner in which healthy human beings learn motor skills.

I would like to express my thanks to Dr. Jeffrey Lombardi who constructively criticized the chapter dealing with the Biochemistry and Neurology of Learning and Retention, and to members of the Departments of Psychology, Psychiatry, Education, and Pediatrics at the University of California at Los Angeles who extended their academic help as well as their emotional support during the preparation of this second edition. Similarly I would like to thank Misses Lockie Swengel and Wendy Bock for their efforts in editing and typing the final manuscript.

BRYANT J. CRATTY

Los Angeles, California

Contents

SECTION III.   THE PERFORMER

xiv **Contents**

SECTION I
INTRODUCTION

Progressive changes of behavior brought about through practice and termed "learning," have been the subject for extensive experimentation. Learning has been studied as a function of the type of sensory stimuli available or the meanings individuals attach to their learning situation. Learning concepts are usually illustrated with fluctuations in measures of performance, which take the form of "learning curves." Psychologists differ upon two main points when discussing the learning process: (1) the nature of sensory factors which influence an organism's response, and (2) rewards (reinforcements) within a situation which cause some patterns of behavior to become stereotyped and others to be discarded.

Earlier investigators concluded that learning and human performance are based upon reactions to discrete sensory stimuli and that learning takes place as bonds are strengthened between stimuli and the organism's responses. Other theorists contended that environmental stimuli are organized into patterns and that subsequent performance is based upon the meaning or the significance attached to the total field of experience.

One school of thought holds that in order for an act to be learned, some type of reward has to be present within the learning situation, although this may be only relief of an individual's "tension-level." Others feel that learning may occur merely because stimuli and response occur at the same time.

Some learning theories deal extensively with the *motor performance* of various organisms, indeed many are based upon research involving movement behavior. Other theories merely make reference to the "type" of learning called "motor learning," while still others virtually ignore the means by which skilled movements are acquired and focus primarily upon intellectual-perceptual behavior.

More recent learning theories compare man's performance to that of the electronic computer. Whereas several years ago computers were considered so complex as to be almost human, several contemporary theories imply that man is so complex that he is nearly machine-like! Thus, computer terms such as "memory drum," "input-output," "channel capacity," and the like are used within some contemporary theoretical frameworks.

Learning theories are concerned with the explanation of several levels of behavior. Some attempt to elucidate all the possible modifications of human functioning, others outline the general nature of the acquisition of complex tasks, while a third is concerned with specific types of learning: "reasoning," "motor learning," "verbal learning," and the like.

The psychologist has not ignored the motor performance and learning of healthy human beings, despite the numerous animal experiments in the literature. Generally utilizing fine motor skills, he has studied the influence of various types of practice and the role of differing sensory stimulation upon the learning process. In an effort to clarify concepts pertinent to the central focus of the text, extensive reference has been made to psychological research in motor skills and motor learning, to investigations concerned with the perceptual process, and to those eluci-dating various learning theories in the chapters which follow.

The Engineer Studies Motor Performance

Within the past fifty years, the engineer has begun to study the capaci-ties of humans to perform and to learn motor skills. Studies have usually been of an applied rather than of a basic nature and have involved manual-manipulative skills needed to perform various industrial tasks effectively.

The industrial engineer has often filmed time-motion studies through which components of manipulative performance have been categorized. This scientist has generally been concerned with practical problems and has studied movements occupying a relatively small amount of space and requiring minimal amounts of force.

More recently a "new breed" of engineer has come to the forefront to study man's capacity to learn complex movements. The human factors specialist, part life scientist and part engineer, has begun to explore human performance within complex man-machine systems. The human factors specialist generally studies perceptual-motor performance, reac-tions under various conditions of stress, and the influence of types of sensory stimuli upon decision-making. The integration of man to "machines" as simple as the hammer and screw driver has been reported in articles adjacent to those which treat human functioning in complex air-defense warning systems. The human factors engineer utilizes tradi-tional psychological and physiological research, while devising unique evaluative techniques to solve new problems.

Others Consider Motor Behavior

Man's capacity to move with accuracy has not been the exclusive con-cern of the engineer, psychologist, physiologist, and anthropologist. Numerous other disciplines have been interested in the movement behavior of human beings.

The writings of the historian often relate to the influence of historical trends upon the work and play movements of people. The emphasis upon vigorous developmental activities to harden the male youth of the European nations within the past three hundred years probably resulted from the pressures of war, rather than from more subtle factors. The dictator's use of massed physical activities to mold the minds of men into united action has been documented in historical works.

The medical profession has also been concerned with the gross move-ments involved in locomotion, as well as with manual skills. Psychiatrists, physical therapists, and prosthetics specialists are constantly studying methods of improving the movement capacities of the atypical. Re-edu-

Chapter 1

Introduction

MOVEMENT is a fundamental dimension of human behavior. Man manipulates his environment through contractions of large muscles, as internal smooth muscle acts to integrate and nourish these observable movements. Primitive man survived through the appropriate application of strong, forceful acts, while modern man has molded fine movements into vehicles for oral and written expression. Manual skill enables some to earn their livelihoods, while accurate movement of large muscles allows others to express themselves in sports and games. The analysis of movement characteristics is a means of assessing maturation and is an important method of studying the total personality.

Early theorists postulated that all human behavior involves movement. It was contended that immobile thought is accompanied by unobservable, but measurable, movements of the vocal apparatus and that these small movements are chained together as we think, remember, and learn. While later writers seemed to place "thinking" and "moving" into two behavioral niches, more recent scientific findings tend to make difficult the isolation of human functions into two discrete categories, one characterized by motionless thought, the other by observable movement. Instead, human behavior appears to lie upon a continuum from functions which seem largely "motor" to those which involve no observable movements.

Within the past century, increasing scientific interest has been evidenced by an increasing number of studies devoted to behavior located near the "movement" end of this continuum. Contemporary research has often focused upon man's capacity to move with force, speed, and accuracy and the methods by which complex skills are learned. Some investigations have been concerned with athletic performance, or with the re-education of the handicapped in the basic functions of walking and talking. Other research has dealt with proficiency in industrial skills or with the integration of man and machine. Whatever the purposes of these investigations, however, knowledge about purposeful human movement has more and more come to occupy the time and thought of the anthropologist, the physiologist, the psychologist, the engineer, and the educator.

Motor Behavior as Viewed by the Anatomist-Physiologist

The physiologist considers man as an interrelated group of functioning anatomical systems. Behavior is integrated by the nervous system nourished by the digestive system, while growth is controlled and regulated by the endocrine glands. Observable movement is viewed as a function of muscle contraction acting within a system of levers and pulleys formed by bone, tendon, and ligament. Efficient motor functioning is usually said to depend upon tissue adaptations based upon use and the body's ability to utilize nutrients and to dispel the waste products of muscular work.

A molecular rather than a molar approach is taken by the physiologist. Man is assumed to react to discrete kinds of internal and external stimuli as they effect specialized sensory end-organs. Explanation of the many behavioral variations of persons possessing relatively similar anatomical equipment is left to the psychologist.

While the physiologist studies human performance rather mechanistically, the learning process is virtually ignored. Neurophysiologists are only beginning to identify changes taking place within the nervous system during the learning process. Nerve impulses have been traced as they are received from the environment by the sense organs, areas of the brain receiving these impulses have been mapped, and the pathways carrying messages to the muscles have been isolated. Anatomical changes, however, accompanying modifications of behavior brought about through practice have yet to be clearly identified.

The Psychologist Studies Motor Learning and Motor Performance

The psychologists regard their discipline as the science of behavior. Controlled experiments are carried out, theories are formed, and an attempt is made to control or predict total action patterns. Throughout the history of experimental psychology, there has been extensive study of the motor behavior of animal subjects. Human skill has come in for somewhat less examination, but studies within this more limited area are becoming more prevalent.

During the past twenty years, in particular, there has been renewed interest in the performance of humans in various movement tasks. Impetus has been given to the study of skill by several conditions: the performance requirements of pilots during World War II, the need to understand the functioning of complex man-machine systems in industry and in the military, and the evolvement of theoretical statements which purport to account for the complexity and variability of the perceptual-motor behavior of humans.

The movements of animals have been studied for several reasons: (1) the inheritance and environmental influences upon animal behavior are easily controlled; and (2) their nervous systems are simpler than man's, thus animal reactions are generally more predictable within the experimental situation. Humans engage in complex verbal symbolism to form internal thoughts, while mice seem merely to move through the maze to food.

cating the handicapped and the influence of movement therapy upon the mentally retarded and emotionally disturbed have been the subjects of their investigations.

The psychologist has helped the musician to explore the nature of skills necessary to play various instruments. The serial-like build up of responses, from single note-to-chord-to-phrase, has been investigated.

Other members of the performing arts have also evidenced interest in specific aspects of motor performance. Dance specialists have studied the nature of creative movements. Actors have spent a considerable amount of time attempting to understand the manner by which one may best express meanings and emotions through facial and bodily movements.

The Educator and Motor Skill

While the educator would seem to be mainly concerned with behavior of an intellectual nature, many have been interested in various aspects of motor learning. Many of these skills involve man's attempts to communicate with one another. The transmission of information verbally, through writing, and with various devices such as the typewriter involves motor performance. The influence of various methods of teaching handwriting has also been studied.

Reading, although largely a perceptual act, may also be considered a motor skill. Most "reading clinics" spend a considerable amount of time training the eye to assimilate whole phrases, rather than to pause at each word, when scanning the printed page.

Child development specialists, within the field of education, have studied various motor indices of human maturation. Longitudinal studies have attempted to categorize the progressive acquisition of learned movements noted as children mature and to identify normal stages in motor development.

The educational psychologist has spent a considerable amount of time investigating the learning process as it takes place within the classroom. Much of his work has been concerned with various motor tasks. One of the principles underlying some of the recently developed teaching-learning machines involves a motor act, pressing the correct button.

Thus educators have been concerned with small as well as large movements. The child's facility in learning to walk, to talk, to write, and to move efficiently has been the subject of extensive educational research.

And What Then of the Physical Educator?

The question then arises: With what body of knowledge should the physical educator be concerned? What should be the subject of his basic research, and what kinds of understandings should prospective teachers gain? The therapist studies gross human movement, the engineer, manual skill, the physiologist, functions underlying motor performance, while the psychologist studies motor performance and learning from several standpoints. What, then, is the physical educator's unique area of concentration?

Should man's movement behavior be viewed microscopically, as by the anatomist, or should a macroscopic or molar approach be taken? Should prospective physical education teachers be interested in the teaching of sports, dance, or individual activities as ends in themselves, or should they take a more basic approach? And if so, where shall one look for knowledge—to the psychologist, the physiologist, or the therapist? Or should principles be derived unique to the field of physical education?

While helpful in the past, the traditional approach of the kinesiologist no longer seems to offer a complete explanation of variations in human movement. Describing man as a system of bony levers moved by muscles and undergirded by various physiological systems seems to place little emphasis upon individual performance differences.

School administrators want to know *what* the physical educators are doing and *why* and *how* they propose to do it. Members of academic disciplines on the university campus attempt to ascertain whether research being produced by physical education faculties might be conducted better by some other life scientist. Researchers from other fields sometimes wonder aloud whether physical educators are producing *basic* research, and if so, within what areas of human behavior?

The physical educator has often been hard pressed to provide meaningful responses to these queries. However, it appears that his professional respectability may be based upon the adequacy of his answers and upon the quality of the subsequent performance to which his responses will hopefully commit him. It is thus hoped that the statements which follow will help to clarify the central focus of the text, and might also provide some basic operating principles for the professional worker in the school and for the researcher in the laboratory.

1. Physical educators should be concerned mainly with that aspect of human behavior which is characterized by observable, purposeful, voluntary movement, movements which are task-centered and those which are reasonably complex.

2. Physical educators generally are called upon to teach healthy human beings, and thus should be familiar with all aspects of movement behavior which these individuals evidence. However, of main concern should be movements which occupy relatively large amounts of space and involve large skeletal muscles.

3. Movement behavior is worthy of investigation as a unit within itself and does not necessarily need to be related to various physiological-anatomical processes which may accompany it. A comprehensive approach should be taken to the study of motor performance and learning.

Study should be made of motor tasks measurable not solely in units of strength but also in terms of spatial accuracy.

4. Concern should be directed toward the rather permanent change of movement behavior brought about through practice, *"motor learning."* Interest should be generated in variations of practice and the influence of various factors upon learning proficiency.

5. One should not ignore but, on the contrary, utilize to best advantage research in psychology, medicine, physiology, and other disciplines to aid in gaining a thorough understanding of gross motor performance and learning.

Words and Definitions

Within the previous pages numerous terms have been presented which need definition. Such terms as *motor behavior, movement behavior, motor learning, motor skill, movement skill,* and *motor performance* require reasonably precise explanations to provide a common basis of understanding of the concepts that follow. Many of the terms defy simple definition; clarification depends upon critical examination of the experimental evidence and of various theoretical assumptions under lying learning. Words, however, stand for ideas. We are able to think with more clarity as our grasp of terms is expanded. It is thus one of the purposes of this book to expand the reader's vocabulary by presenting words which represent concepts, verbal tools with which more thorough understandings may be possible.

Movement Behavior. Movement behavior refers to overt movements of the skeletal muscle. The term *behavior* places the definition more specifically than does the word movement; thus movement behavior is *observable* movement of the body, excluding such functions as visceral changes, the conduction of nerve impulses, and circulation of body fluids. Movement behavior is *observable* and not simply *recordable* movement, for most internal fluctuations are measurable by various devices.

Movement behavior is a general term and refers to movements which might be termed skilled performance, those which indicate emotion or tension and others which seem purposeless and random. Reflex actions, movements which are elicited in reaction to some stimuli without conscious volition on the part of the individual, may also be considered a facet of movement behavior.

While acts which involve the execution and completion of an identifiable task may be considered a form of movement behavior, it is believed that these require a more precise definition. The terms *movement behavior* and *motor behavior* are used interchangeably throughout the text.

Motor Performance. Motor performance is a relatively short-term aspect of movement behavior marked by movement oriented toward the execution of an identifiable task. Inherent in the definition is the assumption that an observer can detect, identify, or otherwise discover the goal or purpose of another's movement. Motor performance is thus considered to be goal-centered, purposeful, observable movement behavior of relatively short duration.

While it might be argued that all movement involves some physiological goal, that an individual needs to move to live or that perhaps the psychiatrist or psychologist is able to give meaning to the most random of movements, it is believed that the definition presented is valid.

Motor performance has numerous dimensions usually identified through statistical analysis, as well as through subjective observation. Studies within the physical education literature have generally regarded motor performance as manifestation of the contractile strength of muscle tissue. A more comprehensive approach to the study of motor performance will be taken within these pages. Perception, motivation, and maturation, as well as other behavioral and environment factors, will be analyzed in an attempt to gain deeper understanding.

Motor Skill. Motor skill may be termed reasonably complex motor performance. While the phrase "reasonably complex" is of course subjective and somewhat vague, reference within the definition must usually be made to the nature of the task and the status of the learner. For example, an adult can hardly be said to be skilled because he is able to walk or to run; while to an eight-month-old, walking is an extremely skilled act.

The term *skill* denotes that some learning has taken place and that a smoothing or an integration of behavior has resulted. Extraneous movements have been omitted, and the performance is executed with increasing speed and accuracy, a decrease in errors, or perhaps the ability to apply greater force. A skilled act has to be learned. It is not one which might be termed instinctive or reflexive or one in which successful performance is achieved in a single trial.

Motor Learning. Motor learning may be thought of as the rather *permanent change* in motor performance brought about through practice and excludes changes due to maturation, drugs, or nutrients. The concept of learning involves two main inferences: (1) that a rather permanent change in behavior, verifiable by comparing performance trials separated in time, has occurred, and (2) that the change has been caused by practice.

"That learning takes place through practice" on the first inspection appears to be a simple concept. However, members of the psychological community have been occupied for the past one hundred years examining the nature and conditions of practice and precisely how practice produces permanent behavioral changes.

At times the terms *learning* and *performance* have been used interchangeably in the literature. *Performance,* however, is immediate and short-term in nature and subject to certain factors which fail to influence the long-term changes which take place during the learning process. Learning, however, must often be studied indirectly by inspecting measures of performance.

Studies investigating the effects of massing and distributing motor practice upon learning help to clarify the distinction between learning and performance. With the massing of performance trials little improvement will often be the result; however, with the introduction of rest periods a marked performance increase will often be elicited. This further illustrates the rather temporary state suggested by the term "performance," that suggests that "learning" is a more subtle concept that at times may be best facilitated when no performance is engaged in!

Motor learning, therefore, may also be thought of as the *potential* to engage in an efficient movement, rather than solely as a measure of performance fluctuations recorded. The complexities of various learning concepts as they apply to the learning of motor skills is dealt with in Chapters 15 to 18.

Motor Fitness. Motor fitness refers to individual *capacity* to perform a motor task. It is the potential one has to perform a motor skill, and as we shall see later, may be somewhat specific. An individual must be declared fit to perform a particular task measured by certain kinds of units within a defined situation.

. While most research in motor fitness has been based upon measures of strength and endurance, the concept as defined here includes other performance dimensions: capacity to utilize space effectively in the accurate performance of a task, as well as the application of speed and the effective combination of various factors when performing a skilled act.

Motor Educability. While *motor fitness* refers to capacity to *perform, motor educability* may be defined as the capacity to *learn.* Generally, the research has attempted to identify a general educability factor based upon the relationship between amounts of improvement evidenced as an individual attempts to learn several tasks. The term infers that individuals may be found whose performance may be easily molded and who may easily learn (be taught) several kinds of motor skills. The term motor educability is related to such concepts as "coordination" and "general athletic ability."

Fine Motor Skill and Gross Motor Skill. Dichotomous classification of these terms has been inferred by much of the previous discussion. However, a rigid categorization of skills as either "fine" or "gross" is difficult to make. Rather, it is believed that skills may be placed upon a continuum, from those which may be considered "gross" to those which may be termed "fine." To those movement performances near the "fine" end of the continuum the term *manual,* or *manipulative skill,* has usually been applied.

Classification of motor tasks into various portions of this continuum may be made with reference to the size of muscle involved, the amount of force applied, or to the magnitude of space in which the movement is carried out. Physical educators generally refer to "big" muscle activity, indicating a preference for a cataloging system based upon the muscle or force concept. Industrial psychologists, on the other hand, have devised various classifications based upon function, the spatial dimensions of the task, and/or the part of the body involved in the movement.

While a more detailed discussion of the relationship between various fine and gross motor skills is presented in Chapter 14, it should be emphasized that the main concern in this text is with performance classified near the "gross" end of the continuum. Generalizations from studies of fine motor skills are identified.

Sensory-Motor Skill and Perceptual-Motor Skill. Within recent years research has been increasingly concerned with a more comprehensive approach to understanding motor performance. While the motor "output" seemed to be the first aspect of performance drawing the attention of researchers, within the past several years the types of sensory cues influencing performance, as well as the formation of meanings from sensory experience (the process of perception), have been studied in greater detail. Thus the terms *sensory-motor* and *perceptual-motor* performance have been coined, indicating the important influence the sensory cues and the perceptual process have upon the motor act.

SUMMARY

The study of motor skills and learning is the concern of many academic disciplines. The medical profession is concerned with the motor performance of atypical individuals; the anthropologist studies motor performance within culture or as a function of evolution; the anatomist-physiologist studies motor performance as a function of structure; the psychologist uses animal subjects or employs the fine motor skills of humans to investigate many basic problems; and the human factors engineer studies manual skills in industry or within man-machine systems. The physical educator, on the other hand, has as his unique area the study of factors accompanying the gross motor performance and learning of healthy human beings. Research will be reviewed, synthesized, and interpreted so that knowledge important to the teacher in training may be presented.

Motor behavior is a general term for observable movement. *Motor performance* is observable, voluntary, goal-centered movement. *Motor learning* is the rather permanent change in motor performance brought about through practice. *Motor fitness* refers to capacity to perform, while *motor educability* is capacity to learn. *Motor skill* is performance involving reasonably complex adjustments acquired through the learning process. *Fine* motor skills and *gross* motor skills are considered as opposite ends of a continuum upon which all movements may be placed. Tho terms *sensory-motor* skill and *perceptual-motor* skill emphasize the sensory and perceptual determiners of the motor act.

A behavioral rather than an anatomical approach is taken to the study of motor performance and learning. "Flexibility" is the goal: plasticity in teacher behavior which should result in the ability to modify the motor performance of students. Throughout the book, the teacher-reader is encouraged to assess accurately the learner, the situation, and himself prior to forming a plan of action.

Student References

1. BERELSON, BERNARD and STEINER, GARY A., *Human Behavior*, New York, Harcourt, Brace & World, Inc., 1964.
2. GAGNE, ROBERT M. and FLEISCHMAN, EDWIN F., *Psychology and Human Performance*, New York, Henry Holt & Co., 1959, p. 493.
3. WELFORD, A. T., *Aging and Human Skill*, New York, The Oxford University Press, 1958.
4. WOODWORTH, R. S., *Dynamics of Behavior*, New York, Henry Holt & Co., 1958.
5. FITTS, PAUL M., and POSNER, MICHAEL I., *Human Performance*, Belmont, California, Brooks/Cole Publishing Co., 1967.
6. BILODEAU, EDWARD A., *Acquisition of Skill*, New York, Academic Press, 1966.

Chapter 2

Evolution of the Human Action System

A MULTITUDE of problems have beset those interested in the evolutionary beginnings of humans. Religious dogma of the nineteenth century
refused to concede that man, indeed all the animals, did not spring
from the powers of divine creation.[513] Inquisitive scientists during this
century, when coming upon bones which resembled the human, and yet
still the ape, were often prompted to mask their findings for several
decades, gradually leaking the news only to their close friends in the
scientific community.[539]

Also beclouding the problem was the fact that within a single primate
grouping, the skulls of the adult males might differ in texture and construction more from the adult females and from children of the same
species than did the skulls of two pre-men living millions of years apart.
Further compounding the consternation of the anthropologist were indications that more than one type of early man probably lived at the same
time. One million years ago on the plains of Africa, for example, the
meat-eating Australopithecus fought with the more primitive vegetarian
Paranthropus.[232]

The study of the evolution of movement capacities may be made only
from indirect evidence. Function may be deduced only from structure
and from the bone and stone implements that primitive men made with
their hands. Filmed studies of the manual dexterity of the Neanderthal
are as hard to come by as are data concerning the incidence of stuttering
among the Proconsul.

Further problems arise when attempting to differentiate structurally
a man from a pre-man, a pre-man from an ape, and so on. Are differences based upon cranial capacity as it changed from 750 to 1500 cc.?
Was the opposability of the thumb to the hand or the ability to remain
upright for a period of time the important criteria? The development of
dentition and of facial characteristics which permitted speech, the ability
to use tools, the ability to make them, what were the keys to the human
evolution?

What are the interrelationships between such apparently diverse
findings and functions as the size of the animal bones adjacent to primitive human-like skeletons and the development of speech? Chimpanzees
can thread needles . . . is finger opposability crucial when one defines
a primate man? Inspection of the arm-hand-shoulder regions of the ape

(14)

and of man reveal few significant differences; while the brain of the ape and of the man do not differ so much as those of the zebra and the horse.

If tool *making* is the crucial test of humanness, and many anthropolo gists subscribe to this, what then of the primates who have been found using sticks to entice ants from their mounds? Does breaking off a stick constitute making a tool? Were the first tool makers the pebble people of antiquity who chipped off one or two flakes from one end of an oval stone, held to the other end and then proceeded to knock the brains out of small game? Or was the first human the Bone-Age Australopithecine who placed an antelope jaw on the end of an antelope leg bone and attempted to perform a frontal lobotomy on his fellows and upon the hapless baboon? Some discoveries of our ancestor's bony remains do not clarify these questions, but only add to them. Instead of looking for the missing link, the anthropologists by the 1930's became acutely aware of the innumerable missing *links* which they still had to find.

Of primary importance is consideration of the interrelationships between the time taken by various portions of the action systems to evolve. Did the bony system, the face, and brain capacity evolve at reasonably even rates? Until the 1940's this was believed to be so. And yet with the Java skull were found lower limb bones that resembled those of modern man. Dart and Broom, in Africa, uncovered advanced primates who possessed ape-like brain cases, carried over man-like pelvises.[232]

And what of the relationships between erect posture, tool making and dentition changes? Do sharp canine-shaped teeth contained in a wedge-shaped protruding mouth hinder speech? Does the formation of words require a flattened molar? Was the ability to speak hastened by some change in face and dentation? Or were words developed simply because to catch larger game humans needed to communicate in more sophisticated ways with each other?

The answers to some of these questions have been made only tentatively, but within the past fifteen years anthropology together with many other disciplines has sprinted ahead. With the help of carbon and argon dating techniques some of the answers to these questions are beginning to become clear.

It is apparent that one of the early changes in the primates which produced structures similar to that of modern man was their grasping ability. This change enabled the early primates to move to the trees, while brachiation began producing a visceral system which became relatively well adapted to upright locomotion. This mammalian development has been dated as occurring about 10,000,000 years ago.

The second major change in the structure and function of man was the assumption of upright posture, evidenced by the evolvement of a rounder pelvis different from the wedge-shaped bony girdle possessed by the tailless apes. Two theories attempt to account for this. It is believed by some that the more successful of the great apes stood upright for increasing periods of time to see over the tall grass and to better sight their prey and enemies. Others suggest that these pre-men were already upright as they moved through the trees and thus simply alighted to the ground and began to move using the lower part rather than the upper part of their bodies. The rough date for the assumption of an upright posture, based upon the C-14 content of fossil remains has been placed at from 1,000,000 to 2,000,000 years ago.

Finally brain changes began to appear, the head moved directly above the spinal column, marked by the gradual relocation of the foramen magnum to the center rather than to the rear of the skull. Cranial capacity increased from 750 to 1500 cc. Speech and association areas appeared and the cerebellar cortex began to expand and to grow as man began to utilize his hand-eye action system and became able to view his world for increasing periods of time from an upright posture. These latter developments and the emergence of man possessing modern cranial characteristics have been recently dated at only 50,000 years ago!

The discovery of the order in which these changes occurred, however, presented additional problems. For example, as the great apes began to move on their rear feet, their viscera became more vulnerable to attack. Thus, those early apes who began to protect themselves best with small rocks fashioned into implements for defense were the most successful and survived. However, upright posture placed the eyes in better position for use, and thus more successful anthropoids began to gain increased head mobility. The upper limbs became able to be moved through 180° hemispheres, instead of in the narrowly restrictive space field of their immediate ancestors whose hands rested on the ground. Thus, verticality promoted the use of the hands not only for defense, but also for more extensive exploratory-manipulatory tasks. The changing visual field encouraged greater head mobility and the neck became free from the bands of the restrictive musculature possessed by the earlier primates.

EVOLUTION AND MODERN MAN

Structurally and functionally the unique features of the modern human action system includes eyes which can scan and deal with a complex three-dimensional and moving space field, a pelvis which together with locked knees affords a stable base and permits freedom of the upper limbs to deal with the environment for extended periods of time, a mobile neck and upper trunk area which permits flexibility of action, coordination between the eye-hand action system, a brain and facial characteristics which facilitates symbolic speech behavior, and development of the associative areas of the brain which mediates abstract thoughts relatively independent of direct action.

A critical question remains, however. Is man a successful animal? There is no doubt that we seem to have modified his environment to his needs (or possibly to his destruction). Upright posture has given the organism certain intellectual and functional advantages; structurally and functionally, however, man still seems to be thousands of years away from an efficient accommodation to verticality. Innumerable functional problems are believed to arise from the relatively recent assumption of an upright stance. Adults are plagued by varicose veins and hernias. Infants' large heads do not seem to fit easily through the woman's narrow birth channel. Back pains, flat feet, and other conditions stemming from the evolutionary struggle to stand up are a constant plague.

Physiologically man still seems to be a poorly adapted organism. In addition to the rudimentary remains of apparently useless organs which frequently infect, dysfunction and plague him, physiological systems are not adapting as rapidly as the environment requires. The frequency of stomach ulcers and other conditions attest to this. Are the relatively stable constitutions of the astronauts indicative of an evolutionary trend, as opposed to that of the business man with ulcers?

And most important, what are the future directions of human evolution and structural change? Will the emphasis placed upon creative thought, automation and cognition result in a reduction of muscle size and of gross action capacities and the expansion of our brain case? Is the larger child being produced during the past generations indicative of a trend to gigantism which led to the disappearance of other mammals? These and other questions are important, but the primary questions remaining and of interest to those interested in the action patterns of men is how much of an *animal* is man today? What percentage of his time should be devoted toward meeting his action needs versus intellectual contemplation. Should programs of equal vigor be developed for *all* men to drain excess animal energies which "kick back" into the constitution and destroy it? The answers to this and other questions will be found only after a thorough consideration of available anthropological evidence, together with an interdisciplinary study of the human behavior including its psychological, sociological and physiological underpinnings.

ACTION AND EVOLUTION

The carbon dating techniques contributed by Libby and his colleagues raised some difficult questions for the anthropologist, paleontologist, and geologist. For example, it became apparent that man's time on earth had been badly overestimated. He was found to be a much newer creature than imagined, posing the question of how such marked structural changes in the face region, in the lower limbs and pelvic areas could have taken place within the brief million years allotted to modern humans on the C-14 scale. Darwin suggested that evolution was a more gradual process than was revealed by the carbon dating methods. The problem then became how to reconstruct evolution to answer these questions? Man moves with muscles, but these had long disappeared from the skeletal remains of the man-like creatures. Could one produce and experimentally investigate evolution on organisms now living? The anthropologist Washburn attempted this very thing. During the last decade Washburn, basing his research on the assumption that muscle changes may have influenced bony structure more rapidly than was formerly believed, performed some unique and exciting experiments.[926]

First utilizing rats and later chimpanzees, it was found that by surgically altering the jaw muscles of the face, marked and immediate changes in the bony ridges around the jaw and over the eyes could be induced. In this way, Washburn began to demonstrate *actions* were vital to the evolution of man—as the muscles functioned so did the skeleton form itself. And most important, this formation probably took place rather rapidly.

The questions and answers that these findings raise are thought provoking and hold most important implications for those interested in the actions of modern man. Exercises for adult males could include provision for counteracting some of the effects of his incomplete and somewhat unsuccessful efforts to stand upright, and rather than concentrating upon limb strength, the body builder might well concentrate on developing musculature in the back and in the abdominal region. Programs should provide for the fact that man remains more animal-like in some of his physical and visceral makeup that he would perhaps like to believe. Furthermore, the mounting scientific evidence concerning the anthropological underpinnings of man's action system suggests that at the graduate levels specific courses might be instituted. These offerings, taught with the help of anthropologists, should begin to explore some of these problem areas.

1. How did man evolve to function in the way in which he does at the present time?

2. What functional imperfections are present in the physiological and structural makeup of man which might be taken into consideration by program planners?

3. What are the interdependencies of the portions of the action system which might have important implications for the learning of skill, and for more efficient strength-endurance programs? What primitive reflexive patterns remain, sometimes aiding and sometimes inhibiting traditional components of sports activities?

4. What are the implications for program and for teaching of the most recent neurological developments in man, *i.e.*, does verbalization and "over-intellectualization" inhibit the "animal-like" output of his action system?

These recent anthropological writings thus suggest several areas for scholarly consideration. The beginnings of the scientific movement in physical education was spearheaded by physicians who felt that vigorous action was synonymous with freedom from disease. Recent scientific excursions have had the backing of literature written by the psychologist and sociologist. It, therefore, seems reasonable that a more penetrating look at the evolutionary beginnings of the structural interrelationships which underlie man's action systems, aided by the physical anthropologist, may reveal new and exciting dimensions to the quest for knowledge about human movement.

Student References

1. Brace, C. L. and Montagu, M. R.: *Man's Evolution,* New York, The Macmillan Company, 1965.
2. Dart, Raymond A.: *Adventures with the Missing Link,* New York, Viking Press, 1959.
3. Hill, W. C. Osman: *Man as an Animal,* London, Hutchinson and Company, 1957.
4. La Barre, W.: *The Human Animal,* Chicago, The University of Chicago Press, 1965.

SECTION II
PERCEPTION

Chapter 3

The Process of Perception

VITAL to an understanding of man's movement behavior is knowledge about perception. It is the central portion of the situation-interpretation-action chain, leading to purposeful motor activity. Perception is a dynamic process, involving more than a response to sensory stimulation. It is a holistic term referring to meanings attached to an object, event, or situation occurring within spatial and temporal proximity of the individual. Perception is an ever continuing, as well as an immediate, phenomenon, dependent not only upon a situation's momentary core, but also upon the context in which the event occurs and upon past experience. The process involves organizing, feeling change, and selecting from among the complexity of events to which humans are continually exposed, so that order may be attached to experience.

Recognition of the importance of the perceptual process arose from the observation that interpretation of an event by one individual did not always correspond to the meaning another might attach to the same facet of measurable reality. At the same time, however, within limits, prediction of perceptual interpretations seemed possible by controlling the nature of the sensations reaching sensory end-organs, the context in which these sensations were presented, and/or the individual's past exposure to similar objects and situations.

Research dealing with this "order within disorder," or the study of variables which modify and influence the meanings attached to the environment, has formed the basis of much of the experimental literature in psychology, psychiatry, personality theory, human engineering, and education. Therefore, careful consideration of these studies seems **imperative for the** student interested in the "why's" of human movement.

SENSATION, PERCEPTION, AND THE IMMEDIATE FOCUS

Our perceptions are generally felt to be dependent upon immediate sensations affecting our sensory end-organs, and, indeed, extensive literature concerned with psychophysics deals with quantitative aspects of this interrelationship. Perception also has been shown to be more than an awareness of immediate sensory stimulation. Events occurring in an individual's past and internal visceral changes also seem to play a part.

In essence, *perception* is more of an all inclusive term than is *sensation;* it is usually viewed as a total pattern or "schemata" arising from many sensations and results in a meaning which is more than the sum of a total. A perception (or percept) assumes a distinctive identity, independent of the various kinds of sensations forming it.

Material elucidating perceptual phenomena is generally fragmented into portions dealing with visual-spatial, olfactory, or auditory perception. While these classifications probably are convenient, they are somewhat artificial. Contemporary scholars emphasize the interdependence of the various senses in forming perceptual meanings.

In these chapters concerned with perception, a proximal-distal approach is taken. In the present chapter an overview of the perceptual process is presented, while a following chapter deals with the manner in which humans perceive their own bodies and utilize their senses to form judgments about events in close proximity to them. The final chapter in this section deals with "event" perception, the meanings attached to dynamic happenings in distant space. Throughout this section an attempt is made to relate perception to motor output and to clarify the manner in which movements in turn form perceptions.

EXPERIMENTAL AND THEORETICAL APPROACHES TO THE STUDY OF PERCEPTION

Several avenues have been taken to the study of perception, including the philosophical, the biological, and the behavioral. This latter classification might be further fragmented to include the psychophysical, the socio-cultural, or perhaps the phenomenal or holistic approach. Each of these approaches seems dependent upon the basic point of view and the assumption as to which measurable or speculative aspects of perception are most important to the total process.

Philosophical

The main argument among early Greek philosophers was whether judgment depends directly upon the object and its direct influence upon our senses or whether imagination and the image formed from these sensations are the main determiners of meaning.

The Stoics were the first to use the example of the *tabula rasa,* the black wax tablet of the mind upon which experience writes in the form of direct sensory impressions of outer things. Later John Locke, in his *Essay Concerning Human Understanding,*[593] suggested that, while the mind may be conceived of as a blank piece of paper upon which external sensations are inscribed, our *reflections* or internal senses also aid in forming meanings from experience.

Bishop Berkeley[97] in the early 1700's argued at the other end of the continuum by stating that the mind is the ultimate reality, that ideas are primary. Despite this emphasis upon thinking, Berkeley was the first to classify sensation into the traditional five of sight, hearing, smell, taste, and touch.

It remained for Thomas Reid,[97] in the middle 1700's, to differentiate between sensation and perception. A sensation was thought to be only an impression upon an organ of sense, while a perception, although dependent upon sensation, was believed to be much more and included a conception of the object. The perception *was* the object, according to Reid.

These early philosophers eventually arrived at the concept of *associative fusion,* meaning that complex ideas are essentially built up of many sensations, perceived sights, sounds, or touch. A dog may be seen, heard, petted, and held and becomes a *dog* because of ideas inserted by several of the senses.

Two pathways were taken by those interested in perception at this point. On the one hand were those concerned with forming general behavioral categories in which to classify various perceptual phenomena. Research gained from introspective reports formed the basis of these classification systems. Descriptive categories included Wundt's[984] characterization of sensations into two attributes, *quality* and *intensity.* Kulpe[97] added *duration* as a third category, and *extension* for sensations involving vision and hearing. Tichener[890] added a fifth attribute, *clearness,* which pertained to the attention paid an object, whether it was in central focus or marginal.

However, problems arose when an attempt was made to relate these attributes to concrete perceptual situations. It was initially difficult to demonstrate their general existence among all types of perceptual events. For example, when was a touch clear, or what constituted an intense color, and, more important, how could one equate a sound with a visual impression on a meaningful scale based upon the attributes listed?

Psychophysics

A second more objective approach was taken as researchers attempted to measure more exactly the intensity of sensations affecting human beings. Psychophysical research was spurred by the scientific awakening of the nineteenth century and had as central concepts the ideas of *threshold* and *just noticeable differences.* General laws were derived by noting the point at which a majority of subjects in a controlled experimental environment could report a difference between two stimuli presented. Threshold studies included investigations of perceived changes in illumination, color, depth, and weight.

Fechner[293] and later Weber,[97] published pioneer works in this area based upon extensive studies. It was found that one sensation is reported just noticeably different from a second when it has been increased a constant percent of its total, rather than when increased a constant amount. The formula derived to explain this phenomenon became known as Weber's law. Although it was later found that the intensity of background stimulation would modify threshold measurements between two presented stimuli, in general, Weber's law held true.

Research in psychophysics is based upon three fundamental approaches: (1) Method of limits: a stimulus is gradually changed by discrete serial steps until a difference is reported by the subject. (2) The method of right and wrong cases: a stimulus is presented with a standard for comparison and a judgment is made as to whether the variable stimulus is equal to, less than, or greater than the original. (3) The method of average error: the subject is provided with a standard stimulus and with a method of changing the second stimulus. The average error is usually computed. This method of measurement is generally found in depth perception studies.

These three methods could be utilized to obtain information relative to five phenomena: (1) the absolute level of perception or the limits of audible frequency for sound or of visual color acuity, (2) the just noticeable difference or the amount of slight change to which the average subject reported being sensitive, (3) equivalents or thresholds of sensitivity in various parts of the body to similar types of stimulation involving the same kind of sensory receptor (Goldschneider,[375] for example, studied comparative sensitivity to movement in several of the joints when investigating kinesthesis), (4) sense-distance or comparison of just noticeable differences within various portions of scales of conscious judgments, and (5) sense ratios or the facility to multiply or to fragment judgments of stimulus intensity.

Studies in psychophysics marked the initial step toward quantification of perceptual judgments. In general, they were concerned with the efficiency of various sense organs, relying upon subjects' introspections for evidence.

Biological

Perception may also be studied biologically. Two main approaches are utilized: (1) identification of anatomical structures which seem sensitive to various kinds of stimulation, or (2) analysis of various physiological processes which seem to influence perceptual judgment. Research in the former category has involved tracking nerve pathways or plotting functions performed by various portions of the brain. Investigations in the latter include studies of circulatory functioning, of blood chemistry, of enzyme action and/or of hormonal secretion as affecting perceptual judgments.

Early researchers concluded that discrete portions of the nervous system, stimulated by sensory end-organ function, carried messages along specific pathways to identifiable portions of the brain. The messages were then thought to be received and to travel along labeled motor pathways producing movement. More contemporary investigations, however, seem to refute such simple explanations of behavior. It seems that, instead of single messages traveling over identifiable sensory and motor pathways, the receptors get hooked-up with one another, so that several receptors are usually communicating with the central nervous system at the same time. Further, it has been found that both broad-band and narrow-band receptors exist, the former reacting to the general nature of the stimulus, and the narrow-band receptors responding to selective aspects of the range of stimuli affecting the receptors.[673]

The picture was further complicated upon finding that one receptor sometimes inhibits a second, just as one portion of the brain sometimes inhibits other portions. So, instead of various sensory stimuli being simply added together to form a meaning in the brain, a vast number of summations and inhibitions take place concurrently to form the final sensory impression.

Thus, the neat map of areas of brain functioning, drawn by early researchers, has become somewhat outmoded since it has been discovered that motor and sensory areas are firmly connected and sometimes seem to overlap. When one area of the brain is removed or destroyed through disease or injury, others will take over its function.

Recently, endocrine function has been explored as a possible effector of perception. Weber[936] analyzing and synthesizing research in perception, movement, personality, and endocrinology, concluded that endocrine malfunction not only affects movement variables but also produces modifications in the process and organization of perceptual-motor activity.

Behavioral

The behavioral approach to the study of perception is most relevant to the central focus of the text. It is an avenue grounded in philosophy but using the experimental method to determine the effect of perception upon behavior, and also the effect of various environmental variables upon perception. Testing environments are usually created in which human subjects report their susceptibility to illusions, their impressions of events and objects, and the meanings they attach to what they see, hear, feel, smell, and/or taste.

Within the general behavioral area, several subareas may be identified. Much research activity has revolved around the influence of perceptual facility upon complex and simple motor activity. Literature of this nature is usually found within human factors and physical education journals and provides the bases for much of the material which follows.

A second subdivision of behavioral studies involves investigating the role of perception in the development of the total personality structure. It has been found that the manner in which we view and interpret the world and our relationships with reality are basic determinants of the total human character. Marked perceptual distortions of time, space, or body structure are sometimes indicative of personality disorders. Studies concerned with the relationship of distorted perceptual judgments to the abnormal personality form a substantial portion of the literature on perception.

Another subdivision of research involves the experimental distortion of sensory input and then observing the manner in which the subject functions to reorganize his relationship to the real world. Research involving inversion of the visual field by various lens arrangements, or reversal of the auditory functions of the two ears, are examples of investigations in this area. Generally, it is presupposed that the manner in which the individual reorganizes the artificial experimental situation corresponds to the manner in which he originally began to interpret the world as he matured.

Research in these three broad areas generally involves the interpretation of three types of data: (1) *Informational data,* including any simple means of informing the experimenter that a particular object, event, or situation is or is not present. This may come about through a verbal statement, a movement, nodding the head, or some simple manipulation. (2) *Response data,* including more active participation on the part of a subject, involve maze traversal, complex tracking movements, and the like. It requires more than providing a simple negative or positive bit of information. (3) *Phenomenal data,* gleaned from perceptual studies and usually collected by the clinician.

Within the present context, the primary concern is with data involving simple and complex movement responses to various perceptual events. The purpose of the present chapter is to form a structure and provide a general understanding of the perceptual process in order that perceptual determinants of movement behavior of normally adjusted human beings may be more clearly recognized.

PERCEPTUAL THEORIES

Throughout history, several theoretical positions have been advanced in the attempt to organize knowledge relating to the perception of the many facts within the complex environment. Generally these are rather broad statements representing a synthesis of philosophical thoughts and/or experimental findings. It is usually desired that such statements will result in better predictions concerning the manner in which some phenomena of man, nature, or the physical world actually functions. It is usually hoped that such formulations represent "truth," and, therefore, may eventually aid in the better control of some aspects of man's environment.

Several types of theories have been formulated in an attempt to explain the process of perception. Some are closely allied with identifiable philosophical trends. Others may be logically associated with various learning theories or to particular "schools" of psychology. Still others might be distinguished by the type of experimental evidence underlying their basic assumptions. Contemporary theories also may be grouped according to the relative emphasis placed upon the individual, the immediate context, socio-cultural factors, or past experience as molders of perception.

Within the present context, perceptual theories will be discussed in an historical framework. At the same time, the relative emphasis placed upon various aspects of the perceptual environment will be brought out. The section concludes with a chart presenting a synthesis of current perceptual theory.

Sensation to Perception

Earliest thinkers held that we learn about our world through our senses, receiving discrete impulses from objects in the environment. This viewpoint was gradually expanded to include the concept that humans also engage in imagery, in thinking about the received sensations, and that both the sensation and the integration were important. The emphasis, however, in these early theories was upon a one-to-one relation between the object or event and the perceiving individual. The importance of the context in which the object was observed, the feeling of the individual about himself, his past experiences, and his socio-cultural setting were usually ignored.

One of the first of the early theoreticians to recognize and emphasize the importance of perception over mere sensation was Wundt,[984] who, in 1912, formulated the principle of *creative resultants*. He hypothesized that the product of our sensations is not merely a "sum of the separate elements . . . but represents a new creation." Reid[97] also postulated that perception was a fusion of conceptual and sensory processes. Expanding these concepts further, Helmholtz[97] suggested that unconscious inferences might also influence perceptions of the real world.

Core-Context

Tichener's[890] *core-context theory* was a forerunner of conceptual frameworks which attempted to explain perception as a dynamic phenomenon, rather than as a static mechanical process based upon immediate sensation and situation. According to Tichener, perception consisted of a core of immediate sensations and of secondary sensations contributed by past experience. The learned context of the experience, therefore, was felt to vary considerably from individual to individual, while the immediate core remained relatively stable. Thus, variation in meanings might be attributable mainly to an individual's past experience with similar situations, objects, and events.

Boring[97] added support to the core-context theory by postulating that, while visual perceptions were initially dependent upon the retinal size of the image (the core), exact estimation of size, distance, speed, and the like depended upon the learned aspects of the context or the relationship to other objects. Woodworth[982] also felt that cues and meanings are continually interacting, even when the organism is apparently at rest, and, further, that the perceptual process is a dynamic phenomenon.

Helson's theory of adaptation level also is based heavily upon the importance of past experience in the development of meaning. It was assumed that objects and events are isolated, identified, related, and ordered within frames of references that are revealed in categorizing statements. For example, "This building is very tall," or "That is an angry man." The concept of "pooling" is central to Helson's theory. This refers to the idea that continual attempts to categorize depend upon a rough average or "pool" of past experiences which influence quantitative and qualitative judgments of things. Three separate factors are felt to be important in the perceptual process, according to Helson: (1) the stimulus or object which gains attention, (2) other objects forming the object's immediate background, and (3) the effects of previous objects in the perceiver's past experiences which formed the "pool" or *residual stimuli*. Helson bases the *adaptation theory* upon both psychological and physiological principles and was one of the first to emphasize the triad of object, background, and past experience as modifiers of perception.[438]

Gestalt Theory

Much of the experimental literature relating to perception produced within the past thirty-five years has been related to one of the 134 "laws" developed by Gestalt psychologists. The Gestalt approach to the study of perception was the first to take the purely behavioral avenue. Experimental methods were developed which were unrelated to previous experiments in psychophysics, physiology, or neurology. Principles derived from this extensive program of experimentation underlie many of the perceptual tests presently found in the literature.

The word *Gestalt* means form or shape, and, more generally, a manner or essence. Basically, the system was instigated in protest against researchers who accepted only measurable behavior as experimental evidence and also against the psychophysicists who seemed preoccupied with physiological concepts.

The importance of whole meanings, independent of sensation, to the study of perception was first conceived by the German, Wertheimer,[956] in about 1910. His paper treating the apparent movement of quickly presented pictures, as occurs in the cinema, was published in 1912 and represents the first scientific exploration of gestaltic concepts.

This apparent movement in the cinema, or as Wertheimer termed it, "phenomenonal movement" (or simply the phi-phenomenon), provides an example of the holistic gestaltic approach to the study of perceptual behavior. For what the Gestalt experimentalist would be interested in investigating is what is reported as *seen* as one views the movie, not what neurological-physiological processes cause one to see the movement. For the gestaltist, the basic data are *phenomena*, or a *phenomenal experience*. One can see movement (phi) without being able to identify the successive pictures; one can describe an individual as "angry" without naming exact behavioral attributes constituting the emotion. A square may be formed of dots, of lines, either red or black, but it is usually seen as a square, not simply a sum of the total. A whole form is usually perceived and reported, not the manner in which it is constituted.

While the gestaltist emphasized the total perceptual field, attention was also devoted to the central figure experience. The concept of *figure-ground* thus becomes important within the theoretical framework. The facility with which an individual perceives the figure (core or central object) of his experience, as opposed to his total field surrounding the object or event, was explored experimentally.

The concept of "good" form, or object consistency, is also central within gestaltic theory. It is based upon the finding that an individual tends to preserve an object's basic shape, size, and/or color, despite changes in background. For example, if an individual is quickly presented with a circle of dots (via a Tatistiscope), it is reported as a circle. Likewise, if an incomplete circle is similarly presented, it is usually reported as being completed. This tendency for perceptual consistency and completeness (closure) is fundamental to gestaltic theory.

Gestaltic concepts, so frequently validated experimentally, have caused the particular "school" of psychology to become less identifiable within recent years. Gradually many of the concepts have been absorbed into general psychology. Most experimental studies have utilized tasks involving judgments of patterns in two-dimensional space, involving vision.

The relation between various perceptual qualities, identified by Gestalt experimentalists, and accurate movement has just begun to be explored. An example is a study by Kreiger,[544] who found that the ability to distinguish simple geometric forms within more complex patterns was related to the facility with which tennis players adjusted their rackets to incoming balls.

The Sensory-Tonic Theory

Whereas the gestaltist seemed primarily concerned with the complex visual field as a modifier of meaning, Werner and Wapner, in their sensory-tonic theory, suggest looking through the other end of the camera lens by proposing that perception is equally dependent upon the general attitude (or tonus) of the perceiving individual as well as upon the visual field. The term tonus is used broadly and means "the state of organismic tension as evidenced by the visceral as well as by somatic (muscular-skeletal) reactivity . . . to the dynamic (motion) and to the static posture status of the organism."[953]

It is held that sensory experience and the status of the organism hold equal importance in the total perceptual situation. It is based upon the major assumption that tonus factors within the organism, can be shown to exert direct influence upon the formation of meaning. Experimental literature from psychiatry, psychology, neurology, and physiology are drawn upon to add substance to this theory.

Werner and Wapner, with Chandler,[955] carried out research which led directly to the formation of the theory. In a dark room subjects were placed erect with their heads immobilized and were required to adjust visually a luminescent rod to the vertical. Using the perceived vertical as a control (subjective zero), it was found that when tonus in one neck muscle was increased by stimulation of its motor nerve, significant angular displacement of the rod to that side was reported. Similar results were obtained when strong auditory stimuli were sounded in one ear. The subjects reported that the rod seemed to tip toward the side of the stimulated ear.

In another study by the same investigators, subjects were blindfolded and relied upon their sense of touch to judge rod verticality. Induced muscular imbalance and unequal auditory stimulation affected kinesthetic judgment of the vertical in the same manner as was described in the previous research. More recent research indicates that tactile sensation is also affected by postural tonus. Taken together, the results of these experiments are interpreted as indicating that perceptions could be altered significantly within several sense modalities when the tonus of the organism is modified.

A second concept important to the sensory-tonic theory is termed vicariousness or equivalence. This may be illustrated best by reference to the Krus, Werner, and Wagoner[546] experiment in which a subject stands in the center of a striped cylinder rotating around him. Two perceptions are reported in this situation: (1) As the screen is moving, the subject reports watching it and usually moves his whole body as he turns in the direction of the screen rotation. (2) When the screen is suddenly stopped, his movement also stops. However, he still perceives apparent motion of his body in a direction opposite to the former rotation of the screen and also perceives motion of a point in front of the screen in the opposite direction.

The interpretation of these phenomena is that sensory-tonic energy may be released through body movement or may be expressed in perceptual illusions of motion. This fluctuation between the sensory experience as perceived and movement as perceived is termed *vicariousness* or *equivalence* and infers that sensory and tonic factors interact to exert equal influence upon perception.

Werner and Wapner[953] suggested that the sensory-tonic theory integrates well with those emphasizing the importance of the body-image, perception of the self or of the ego in the perceptual process. In addition, research dealing with the effect of various visceral states upon perception also lends substance to the sensory-tonic theory. Thus, according to the supporters of this theory, the general tonus, the attention-set, and the state of tension assumed by or induced in the human organism seems intimately related to the perception of external objects and events.

The Transactional Theory of Perception

A more recent theory of perception is based primarily upon external psychological and situational variables rather than upon the internal anatomical-physiological fluctuations encountered in the sensory-tonic theory. "The Transactional Approach" suggests that a valid study of perception may be made only by considering all aspects of the dynamic event (or transaction) occurring between the observer and the object. It is held that the focus should be upon the unique characteristics of identifiable situations, external to but including the observer, rather than upon what environmental stimuli *do* to the individual.[485]

It is further suggested that each individual ascribes unique qualities to events within his "psychological environment," his temporary placement in time and space. These total events await perceptual interpretation for their very existence and do not achieve form as perceived, independent of real life situations. For example, it is felt that to study a batter just throwing a ball to an individual is not enough. Rather, such a study to be valid should involve consideration of the pitcher, of team members, and of other aspects of the situation as they affect the perceptions of the batter.

Although such a theory would seem to encourage research of such complex design that identification of influencing variables might prove difficult, such is not the case. Ames,[21] Ittelson, and others[485] have carried out carefully controlled studies in which many variables that might influence perception have received individual consideration. Generally, these investigations have involved either determining *discrepancies* between two events as perceived, or searching for *consistencies* among situations in slightly different contexts.

While it is felt that "physiological excitation" is requisite to perception, more important factors are held to include objects and events of which the individual initially becomes *aware* and the *significance* subsequently attached to them. These assumptions and significances, it is suggested, correspond closely to weighted averages of previous experiences (Helson's "pooling"[438]) as they relate to the present situation. For example, when studying perception of events occurring within a seascape, supporters of the "transactional theory" would deem it important to find out whether the observer believed the beach to consist of large or small pebbles and whether birds flying among the rocks were thought to be large or small. It is only as these kinds of observer-assumptions are known, it is held, that one may correctly assess the accuracy perceptions of distance-speed-time-and-size formed by an individual who is viewing the scene.

It is further advanced that whether there is accurate or inaccurate correspondence between perceptual awareness and the actual environmental situation is central to the process of living. As a result, several important kinds of investigations involving the perception of movement in two-dimensional and three-dimensional space have been carried out in keeping with this theoretical framework. Some of these will be considered in Chapter 6, in which visual-space perception is discussed.

Socio-Cultural Theories of Perception

In addition to theoretical structures emphasizing the sensory experience, imagination, the perceptual field, and the tonus of the perceiver are those usually advanced by the social psychologist which places emphasis upon the social and cultural context. These theories may employ a biological-social approach, or a gestaltic approach as found in Lewian field theory.

Initially, these theorists relied upon observation and assertion concerning the role of instinctive factors in the molding of perceptual behavior. McDougall,[634] in 1918, stated that perceptions are constructed from innate tendencies, leading to appropriate emotional responses related to survival and to physical activities involved with escaping danger.

Some social psychologists place emphasis on learned social perceptions. Experimental evidence by Munsterberg[683] at Harvard, for example, indicated that individuals in a classroom influence one another when reporting upon an objective situation, the number of dots placed on a screen. Allport,[19] following up Munsterberg's investigations, also demonstrated that group membership influenced individual perceptions, depressing qualitative judgments while adding to quantitative ones.

Sherif,[811] in 1935, supplied the first experimental evidence concerning the influence of the social environment upon perception. Using as stimulation the apparent movement of a single light in a dark room, the autokinetic effect, it was found that the individual learns to perceive as members of his group perceive and that the individual is progressively molded toward the group's perceptions of the illusion. Each group, it was found, established its own unique range and a point of reference, and, even if an individual was able to first establish his own judgments, convergence toward collective norms occurred as he was absorbed into a group. This convergence was even more marked if the individual was required to participate initially within a group. Sherif constructed curves to illustrate this convergence, or "the funnel-shaped relationship," characterizing indoctrination of the individual in group perceptual norms.

Ten years later, Schonbar[786] substantiated Sherif's findings using line-length estimation and height judgments as tasks. It was found that, when an individual was removed from the group, the collective perceptual norms persisted and that the longer an individual had been subjected to group influence the longer these norms persisted. Clark,[161] studying differences between men's and women's interpretations of material bearing upon a struggle between the sexes, and Bruner and Goodman,[117] studying the apparent size of coins as judged by children from favored and substandard backgrounds, related the influence of the socio-cultural environment to individual perceptions of events, objects, and situations. Chapter 9 contains specific ways in which movement attributes are modified as a result of this kind of social stimulation.

Anthropologists have also supplied objective evidence that individual perceptions are modified by the society in which one resides. For example, the staff of the Torres Straits expedition in 1898 found that certain native groups were much less subject to the Miller-Lyre illusion (Fig. 1). It was hypothesized that the natives' frequent use of spears,

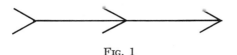

FIG. 1

the heads of which resembled part of the illusion, might have had some effect upon their responses to the tests. McDougall and Rivers, in the same report, noted that while no differences were found between standard visual acuity test scores recorded by Murray Islanders and White Europeans, rather striking superiority of the native men was noted in their ability to spot distant horizon objects and to distinguish camouflaged coral fish against their natural backgrounds.[800]

Borogas[45] studying the Chuckhee, reported that these deer-hunting people, due to little opportunity to see colors in their native environment, seemed unable to sort accurately yarns of various hues. At the same time, however, these natives were able to distinguish more than two dozen patterns within the reindeer hide, differences which were not apparent to the investigating anthropologist.

Allport and Pettigrew,[20] in 1941, found that the Zulus of Africa were not susceptible to an illusion resulting from a rotating trapezoidal-shaped window. This was attributed to the fact that rectangular-shaped windows, doors, square buildings, and the like were not normally found in their pastoral existence.

As the evidence mounted, psychologists began to use the phrase "in our culture" before generalizing about human perceptions, because it became apparent that cultural factors exert important influences upon the development of meaning. As Frank stated: ". . . in every culture the individual is of necessity 'cribbed, cabinned, and confined' within the limitations of what his culture tells him to see, to believe, to do and to feel . . ."[317]

Motivation and Perception

Initial need set, mental preparation is a vital determinant of human awareness and seems most important during the initial portion of the perceptual process. The research previously outlined, substantiating the sensory-tonic theory and the socio-cultural theories, emphasizes the importance of visceral and cultural needs upon perception. Clark's research[149] relating to the distortion of coin size by impoverished children also underscores the role of motivation upon perception.

The organism is seldom indifferent to its environment; there is usually a state of expectancy. The importance of motivation upon perceptual-motor performance is elaborated upon in Chapter 8.

Growth and Perceptual Change

The stages of growth through which humans pass seem to influence perception greatly, partly because of the changing and increasing complexity of the neuromuscular apparatus and sensory receptors and partly because of an evolving capacity to explore and to act. Developmental change and perceptual change are closely interrelated as the ability to attach meaning and to act upon various kinds of information bear a direct relationship to particular stages in development of the organism.

Siegel[814] has hypothesized that three stages exist in perceptual-motor development: (1) the motor-somesthetic, (2) the motor-visual, and (3) the visual-motor. These are generally related to the manner in which man collects evidence about his environment. During the initial stage, the infant's sense of touch enables him to gain initial impressions of his world. The second stage involves confirmation of his motor exploration with visual impressions. Movement seems necessary to add substance to reality and to afford an accurate impression of size, shape, and depth. The final and most advanced stage involves, first, gathering distant impressions via visual cues and, later, confirming them with manipulative behavior.

The prolific Swiss writer, Piaget,[728] explained perceptual development through the use of central concepts, relatively independent of discrete sensory modalities. His key concepts are presented in nine volumes, published from 1923 to the present, on child growth and development, based upon observations gathered in his research center at the University of Geneva. Although some critics have suggested that he has failed to keep abreast of contemporary statistical techniques, many provocative questions have been raised by Piaget's anecdotal records.

Piaget reported that the child passes initially through an egocentric stage during which a slow awareness of himself, distinct from a hazily perceived environment, is achieved. The emerging self, in turn, becomes the platform from which he observes and makes judgments about the world. Things and events then gain meaning in relation to his own feelings and experiences. The child's perceptual development, Piaget believes, involves the gradual emancipation from this egocentric mode of thought to what is termed the "participation stage." A more extensive consideration of various developmental theories and their relationship to perceptual-motor functioning appears in Chapter 7.

Learning and Perception

Learning is intimately related to the perceptual process. Perception gives meaning to events, objects, or situations, while learning involves a series of ongoing perceptions or *perceptual change* brought about through repeated exposure to the same or similar objects and situations. Thus, learning may be thought of as perception with a temporal dimension added

The effect of past learned experience usually is strongest during the initial portion of the perceptual process, as the preparatory set or initial attitude toward the object or event is formed. Generally, as was pointed out during the discussion of Helson's adaptation level theory, meaning is arrived at through an averaging process, a "pooling" of our past experience concerning similar situations or objects.

A second concept related to perceptual learning is *stability*. It is found that individuals generally attempt to create a stable environment, one similar to their previous experience, which they understand and in which they may function. Supporting this second concept are studies in which various kinds of sensations are reversed or distorted. The manner in which perceptual stability is relearned is noted. Examples are the experiments using inverted lenses resulting in an inverted view of the world. Generally it has been indicated that individuals can relearn the location of objects in an inverted visual field and can quickly make a readjustment if the lenses are removed.[842]

Man seems to coordinate and stabilize his environment by the integration of several of his senses. For example, in the previous study, adjustment to the upside-down world is facilitated if the individual is afforded an opportunity to manipulate the strange environment. It seems certain that the more intimate the direct contact is with objects and events the more accurate are estimations of their characteristics. We have little real concept of the size and consistency of the moon, for example, while our perceptions of the buffalo nickel are reasonably accurate.

But, in addition to direct handling of objects, we also seem to learn about our environment through "mental manipulation." Kilpatrick[524] found that the real nature of rooms, which had been purposely distorted to encourage various misjudgments of size and shape of objects within them, could be accurately estimated when the subject was allowed to view the experimenter exploring room surfaces with a long wand or throwing balls at the walls to demonstrate the actual tilt of the floors. Accurate estimation of the nature of the rooms and the objects in them was equally facilitated whether the subject manipulated the wand and threw the balls or merely *observed* the experimenter doing so.

Kilpatrick[524] thus proposed that two types of perceptual learning take place: (1) reorganization learning or the unconscious re-weighing of visual cues after an illusion or misconception has been formed, and (2) formative learning or new perceptual ideas not dependent upon cues offered by various exploratory types of behavior. It was concluded that the belief that "gross-overt action is necessary for perceptual modification is clearly wrong."[524]

Thus the perceptual process is intimately related to learning; these appear to be interacting behavioral phenomena. Learning is an attempt to organize and to give stability to the environment and may be carried out both by direct manipulation as well as by imaginal manipulation. As Hilgard pointed out: "The end result is, on one hand, a world in which we feel at home, because we know what to expect, and what we expect does not disagree too much with what we want."[52]

PERCEPTUAL TYPES

After exploring various perceptual qualities and attributes, investigators have sometimes attempted to categorize individuals according to the methods or approaches they characteristically use when structuring their space field. Although these "types" are generally related to general perceptual behavior, most of the tests upon which classifications have been based evaluated abilities relating to space perception.

One of the most frequent ways of classifying individuals has been to place them into groups labeled *analytic, plastic* (or flexible), and *synthetic*. Research by George[350] indicated that at one extreme are individuals who actively analyze discrete portions of their space field and attempt to "see through" illusions and pull apart complex situations. At the other extreme are found individuals who tend to synthesize experience, to generalize rather than to analyze. In the intermediate portion of the continuum, of course, are people who seem to employ a flexible changing perceptual framework, depending upon the nature of the event with which they are faced.

A more recently devised categorical system to describe individual differences in perception is the *visual* and *haptic* framework. In general, it has been found that some individuals characteristically perceive more easily through visual impressions, while others (the haptics) add the most meaning to their experience primarily through touch and kinesthesis.

Other researchers (Witkin) found that some individuals are primarily dominated by vision when attempting to judge rod verticality within a tipped frame, while a second group of subjects seemed less susceptible to the visual context (the frame) and made independent judgments about the space field, based primarily from impressions of the central figure. It is thus hypothesized that some individuals are primarily *ground dependent*, while others are *figure dependent* when making perceptual judgments.[974]

In 1954, Holtzman and Klein[298] suggested the terms *levelers* and *sharpeners* with which to classify individual differences in perceptual functioning. This system was based upon the observation that some individuals tend to accentuate differences between stimuli presented (the sharpeners), while others tend to minimize such differences (the levelers). The tasks utilized by these researchers consisted of judging the size of squares projected on a screen.[466]

Research by Ryan[774] and others has pointed to the existence of another dichotomy with which to classify the manner in which people organize their environment. Utilizing measures of kinesthetic after-effects and of pain thresholds, it has been concluded that there are both "reducers" and "augmenters" of stimuli. The former are individuals who reduce sensory input, who are active motorically and relatively insensitive to their environment. On the other hand the augmenters are sensitive individuals who are relatively inactive themselves, and who are acutely aware of all components of their environment.[774] Placing these two types together in the classroom through the elementary school years and then presenting the same learning experiences to them would seem to be fraught with peril, and yet this is exactly what usually happens.

Perhaps the physical educator can evolve learning experiences involving various movement tasks, which will be more helpful in educating the active male "reducer" than are the present classroom activities which would seem primarily to appeal and to aid the tranquil female "augmenter."

THE PERCEPTUAL PROCESS

As a summary of the theoretical discussion and the survey of various determinants and modifiers of perception, the following chart (Fig. 2) has been prepared. As pictured, the process is presented as containing five parts, separate in time. The initial step deals with the preparatory set formation, or postural attitudinal modifiers within the perceiver, prior to the presence of the perceived object or event. This set, as has been stated, depends upon "pooling" of the individual's past experience, the cultural and social expectations with which he is surrounded and his muscular-skeletal and visceral tonus. The preparatory set is also determined by unconscious past experiences and by visceral states of which the individual is relatively unaware.

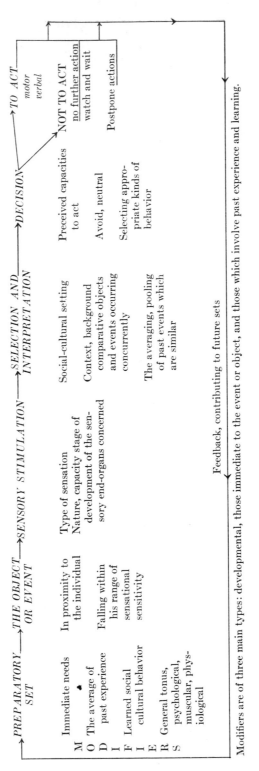

Fig. 2.   The perceptual process.

Modifiers are of three main types: developmental, those immediate to the event or object, and those which involve past experience and learning.

The second part in the process occurs as the object or event begins to assume a distinct identity or form and is brought into spatial and temporal proximity to the organism. The event may be received by distance receptors, eyes and ears, or through surface receptors, for pain, pressure, heat, and cold, or possibly through kinesthetic receptors. In any case, the object or event must assume a distinct identity and become located in time and space so that it may affect one or more of the sensory end-organs.

The third step in perception comes as the event or object stimulates one of the sensory end-organs. In order to accomplish this, the object must emit stimuli which fall in the sensory range of human receptive organs. It must not be too small, have too limited a sound or range, or move too rapidly. While formation of a perception involves more than a mere recording of sensory information, most perceptions begin in this manner. We usually do not perceive something which has not affected one or more of our sensory end-organs, although we may be stimulated without perceiving.

The fourth and vital step is termed here the selection and interpretation stage. This is the heart of the process, when the incoming stimuli are differentiated, selected, and given meaning. The object or event perceived is related to others within the immediate present and to events occurring in the past, through categorizing and classifying statements and thoughts. The average of the individual past experiences with similar objects is compared to the present situation, and a quantitative or qualitative value judgment is made.

From this fourth stage a decision is made concerning the manner in which the perceiver will interact with the event. Important at this point is the individual's perception of his capacities to act or to deal with the situation. The individual may decide to move or to act, to assume a momentary attitude of inaction, to act at some future time, or to ignore the event. In general, however, an experimenter must require some kind of reaction either verbal or motor in order to confirm whether the perceiver attaches meaning to the facet of experience with which he has been confronted. Such concepts as intelligence and motor coordination rest upon the appropriateness of the individual's choice of actions. The quality of the individual's response and the outcomes of his actions are related to his whole personality structure.

The final step in the process points to the dynamic nature of perception. It involves a reinterpretation and evaluation of the decision which feeds back to prepare the organism for future perception and activity. This feedback concerning the appropriateness of response, or lack of response, contributes markedly to the formation of future preparatory sets and to learning.

The perceptual process is thus a continuous and unending chain of events. We are continually coming into range of various objects. We select some for interpretation, ignore others, and act upon our interpretations during all waking moments. The quality of the responses contributes to intelligent behavior, movement coordination, and the total personality.

THE COMPONENTS OF PERCEPTION

Perception has been discussed theoretically as though it were a unitary concept. Experimental evidence, however, reveals that the process involves qualities measurable in a variety of tasks. Contrasting performance in various perceptual tests through factorial techniques has resulted in the identification of several groups of perceptual abilities.

Most of these qualities have been identified through tests of visual perception, but in any case they were selected for review because of their generality without regard to specific sense modalities. Some of these factors depend upon the ability to locate quickly a central object within a complex background, to remain unconfused by various illusions, or to structure an object out of fragmented parts. As a result, intelligent discussion of various perceptual components, by necessity, involves a parallel analysis of the content of tests purporting to isolate such factors.

Perceptual Selection

One of the central factors influencing perception relates to the manner in which we select central objects from their backgrounds and our relative dependency upon the central figure, or its surroundings, when making perceptual judgments. Research concerning the *figure-ground* phenomenon constitutes evaluation of the factor of *perceptual selection*.

Research in figure-ground concepts began in 1912 when the German Gestaltist, Edgar Rubin, found that the field of visual perception is normally divided into two parts. The figure is the focus of attention, and the ground or surrounding context appears further removed, less clear, and lacking in detail. The central object is seen bounded by a contour and is perceived as a whole; the ground, on the other hand, has an indefinite shape and outline. The figure dominates the ground, is more impressive, and is better remembered.[766]

The figure-ground phenomenon appears to be one of the basic organizing components of perception. It may be illustrated by experimental findings reported by Holzman and Klein[466] utilizing a task similar to that used by Wapner and Werner[922] in exploring the sensory-tonic theory. A luminous rod was suspended in a dark room, surrounded by a luminous frame. Both the rod and the frame could be rotated independently. When the frame was rotated so that it was not aligned with the rod, some subjects were still able to make accurate adjustments of the rod, while others could not. In other words, some subjects seemed to be influenced most by the context (the "ground" represented by the frame), while others were influenced most by the figure (the luminous rod) when making judgments of verticality. Some individuals were thus found to be "field dependent," and others "figure independent." These classifications seemed reliable over a period of time.

Kurt Goldstein,[378] the German psychiatrist, among others, holds that the flexibility and naturalness with which we select various objects from their background determines the consistency with which we perform motor and intellectual tasks. Perceptions of figure-ground relationships seem related to basic emotional factors and operate to determine sensory thresholds to various kinds of stimulation.

Perceptual Speed

Consistently emerging as a basic aspect of perception in most factorial studies is the speed with which perceptual judgments are made and acted upon. Individuals scoring high on tests purporting to evaluate this quality generally evidence little "blocking" of responses; their reaction times are relatively short, and their perceptual judgments are acted upon expeditiously.

Typical of tests evaluating perceptual speed is a matching task requiring the quick selection of one of five airplane silhouettes in one column which match those in a second row of five such figures.[759] A second task which is frequently used to evaluate perceptual speed involves the quick determination of words, parts of which have been erased. Rapid adaptation to the dark also seems to identify perceptual speed. Subjects were presented with an illuminated screen upon which a projected letter had been obliterated by an accompanying bright light. A score was obtained by timing the interval between the removal of the light and the subjects' correct identification of the now perceptible letter.[887]

The speed factor emerges when responses required on a perceptual test are timed. Such a quality is probably related to innate reaction time, to a general alertness quality of personality, and to the quickness with which one is able to synthesize, organize, and draw inferences about various kinds of objects and events.

Perceptual Flexibility

This factor refers to the willingness to proceed from one fixed concept or form to a second. It involves the perception of an object in a variety of positions and situations. This infers that the individual, while accurately perceiving a given structure or object, is able to imagine it in a variety of positions. Perceptual flexibility may also be termed *perceptual imagination*, the ability to "shake-off" one attitude about an object and assume another. Tests which evaluate the ability to manipulate two simultaneously presented objects, or to engage in two movements at the same time, also evaluate perceptual flexibility.

Tests which require imagined changes in position of various objects, or prediction of movement of parts in statically presented mechanical systems, are related to perceptual flexibility. The ability to manipulate mentally two-dimensional patterns and solid figures, as represented in surface-development or unfolded solids tests, involves perceptual flexibility. In tasks of this nature, one must match a solid figure with the correct two-dimensional pattern of the figure as it might look if unfolded onto a flat surface. Tasks evaluating the resistance to one form in order to visualize a second and locating pictures of geometric design in more complex pictures also evaluates perceptual flexibility. A motor task involving two simultaneously made movements is another test of perceptual flexibility. The subject is required to touch styluses, held in either hand, as rapidly as possible to two separately numbered discs. A score is obtained by totaling the number of simultaneous touches on the same numbers.

Perceptual Structuring

A fourth general component of perception involves the ability effectively to structure a task, synthesize a form, or organize a situation despite the presence of illusions and distractions or the presence of other types of conflicting forms, activities, or objects. It also refers to the ability to draw whole meanings from fragmented evidence and to differentiate accurately between various kinds of objects and situations.

Structuring occurs after the individual selects the object from its context and, in a sense, involves the final stage of the perceptual process previously diagrammed. Tasks which evaluate the ability to construct forms and obtain whole meanings from fragmented materials seem to evaluate this quality. Hilgard has suggested that an important goal of perception includes this "achievement of definiteness and stability in the environment." Perceptual structuring refers to the success with which this is carried out.[452]

The term *closure* is frequently utilized to identify a factor similar to perceptual structuring. Tests involving the identification of words and objects through reference to scattered incomplete, or distorted visual cues evaluate the efficiency of perceptual closure. Examples of tasks in this category are the Hidden Digits test in which the subject is presented with 12 squares, each containing a multitude of small dots. The object is to distinguish letters or digits, or letters written in scripts, formed within the speckled patterns. Tests of perceptual efficiency also include some evaluating perceptual speed and those which involve the distinguishing of simple geometric designs from within more complex ones.

AN OVERVIEW OF GENERAL PERCEPTUAL FACTORS

The four basic factors of speed, flexibility, selection, and structuring are not felt to be mutually exclusive, nor do they constitute a complete list. Thurstone,[888] in one of the first factorial studies of perception, identified 12 factors. Roff,[759] in another analysis, isolated 18 elements, including a verbal factor, a memory factor, and a psychomotor factor. Identification of perceptual categories, of course; depended upon the constituents of the test battery, the type of statistical treatment utilized, and the experimental focus.

The four general perceptual factors of speed, flexibility, structuring, and selection represent large *families* of elements. Their interrelationships are apparent from an inspection of the nature of tests purporting to evaluate each quality. Perceptual selection, for example, is partly dependent upon the efficiency with which the individual is able to distinguish figure-ground relationships and the speed with which judgments are made. Perceptual efficiency is also related to perceptual speed.

PERCEPTUAL MOVEMENT RELATIONSHIPS

Although the relationship between general perceptual factors and accurate movement seems obvious, relatively few experiments have been conducted which clearly illustrate such a connection. As was indicated in the previous section, most tests purporting to evaluate perceptual qualities require rather immobile responses, pencil markings, or verbal interpretations or identifications. Research dealing with the relationship of general perceptual efficiency to immediate gross movement accuracy generally indicates that between two groups comprised of extremely high and low motor performers significant differences in perceptual accuracy do exist. Identification of finer relationships, determining what percent of a motor task may be attributed to perceptual factors or predicting movement accuracy from perceptual tests, seem to be more difficult experimental assignments.

Inferential statements concerning general perceptual-motor relationships frequently have been made. McCloy, for example, states that "'closure' has something to do with 'athletic intelligence'."[630] Experimentally, however, the connection between perceptual and motor behavior usually involves discriminative tests predominantly dependent upon specific sensory modalities. Studies comparing kinesthetic awareness and motor performance and studies of visual perception of space and depth or of visual acuity and movement accuracy will be reviewed in the two chapters which follow. The purpose of the present chapter was to present a general framework in which the total perceptual process might be examined.

SUMMARY

Perception was described as the dynamic process of attaching meaning to objects, events, or situations occurring within the spatial and temporal proximity of the individual. It is a process involving organizing, feeling change, and selecting among the complexity of events with which humans are continually confronted. It involves the attention-set, an object, sensory stimulation, and interpretations with the resultant decision. Some clinicians and researchers have formulated classification systems based upon the manner in which it is purported that individuals habitually organize experience. It has been suggested that people differ in predictable ways in the amount of information they take in, as well as in the manner in which stimulus elements are organized.

Perceptual theories have evolved from those merely emphasizing sensations, and the manner in which they are organized, to those emphasizing the over-all socio-cultural context in which the event or object is perceived. Research reveals that general components of perception include perceptual selection, involving figure-ground concepts; perceptual flexibility, denoting the freedom to modify perception; perceptual structuring, involving the efficiency with which various objects are related and formed and the concepts of closure, leveling, and sharpening; and perceptual speed, indicating the rapidity with which judgments are made based upon sensory information.

Student References

Books

1. BORING, EDWIN C.: *Sensation and Perception in Experimental Psychology*. New York, D. Appleton-Century Co., 1942.
2. DEMBER, WILLIAM N.: *The Psychology of Perception*. New York, Henry Holt & Co., 1960.
3. HELSON, HARRY (Ed.): *Theoretical Foundations of Psychology*. New York, D. Van Nostrand Co., 1951, Chapter VIII, "Perception."
4. ITTELSON, W. H.: *Visual Space Perception*. New York, Springer Publishing Co., Inc., 1960.
5. WERTHEIMER, MICHAEL, and BEARDSLEY, DAVID C.: *Readings in Perception*. Princeton, New Jersey, D. Van Nostrand Co., 1958.

Articles

1. SHERIF, MUZAFER: A study of some social factors in perception," *Arch. Psych.*, #187, July 1935.
2. THURSTON, L. L.: "The Perceptual factors," Psychometrica, IIK, March 1938.
3. WAPNER, SEYMOUR, and WERNER, HEINZ, "Sensory-tonic field theory of perception," *J. Pers.*, *18*, 88-107, 1949.
4. WERNER, H., and WAPNER, S.: "Toward a general theory of perception," *Psychol. Rev.*, *59*, 324-338, 1952.

Chapter 4

Instruction

ONE of the more obvious types of sensory information available involves explicit directions. The manner in which the performer organizes this kind of information, the placement of the information relative to task performance, the manner in which the directions are given, as well as the quantity of information available, are all influential of the performance and of the learning of motor skills.

From the beginning of time men have guided the learning efforts of other men. Skills needed for survival were transmitted from generation to generation before the dawn of recorded history. During the past five hundred years, the writings of educators have reflected their keen interest in the influence of teaching methods upon learning. More recently, scientists of human behavior have conducted carefully controlled experiments to determine more exactly the influence of instruction upon learning efficiency.

It has been suggested that three types of instruction are operative in any learning situation: (1) those tendered by another individual, (2) those the learner gives to himself, and (3) instructions which seem to be elicited by the nature of the task itself. In this context, *however, instruction refers to guidance extended from a source external to the learner in a somewhat deliberate manner.*

The learning of a motor task does not necessarily depend upon another's instructions. With regard to process of acquisition, skills may be ranged upon a continuum. At one end are those which might be learned most efficiently through continual guidance, correction, and instruction. At the other may be grouped tasks which are mastered though a trial-and-error process. Most skills, however, lie somewhere within the central portion of the scale. Because man's complex sensory-motor apparatus facilitates interpersonal communication, most skills are more quickly acquired by attending to an external source of information than through internal adjustments to successes and failures.

The relationships between learning efficiency and instruction are extremely complex. In addition to the dichotomy based upon the relative emphasis upon instruction vs. trial-and-error learning, the problem may be considered from three other viewpoints: (1) in a time dimension, including consideration of instruction most appropriate for various stages in the learning process, (2) the extent to which instruction is designed to effect or to utilize various sensory end-organs, and (3) instruction from external sources, those elicited by the situation and those voiced internally by the learner.

In a temporal consideration of instruction and motor learning, three stages emerge: (1) *Pre-performance instructions* include those giving the learner advanced knowledge concerning the extent or difficulty of the problem, or perhaps a description of the mechanical principles involved. During this initial stage an attempt is usually made to promote a "readiness to act" on the part of the learner, sometimes termed a positive mental "set." (2) Instructions during the second stage of learning, the actual *performance phase*, may include manual guidance, visual demonstration, verbal directions, or the like. (3) The *task-completion phase* generally contains instruction giving knowledge of the results. These three stages, it should be emphasized, are not usually independent but frequently overlap. For example, as an individual gains knowledge of his success on an initial phase, he is frequently in the process of completing a second movement. Performance in various serial-learning tasks exemplify this overlapping phenomenon.

Instruction may also be classified according to the type of sensory experience involved: (1) *verbal instruction* of various kinds, (2) *visual guidance*, demonstrations, film viewing, and the like, (3) motor practice, *manual guidance* offering kinesthetic feed-back of the movement to be acquired, and (4) various *combinations* of motor-visual, visual-verbal, motor-verbal, or motor-visual-verbal instruction. Numerous investigations have been concerned with the relative efficiency of one type of instruction as contrasted with another when learning motor skills.

Instruction may also be typed according to the degree to which it is designed to motivate the learner as opposed to merely extending him information. The instructor-student status relationship further complicates the picture and has been shown to influence performance of motor skills tests. In addition, consideration of directions must invariably include reference to the process of perception.

The type, nature, and quantity of instruction is one of the important variables influencing the learning and performance of motor skills. The purpose is generally to achieve greater flexibility of behavior, while aiding the learner to analyze the task at hand. Instruction is the attempt to aid in the quick elimination of "bad" work methods, to prevent incorrect habits from forming, while facilitating neuromuscular adjustments to the movement desired.

Instruction has been shown to aid most the intellectually able and to reduce individual performance differences caused by structure.[355] In some situations, the absence of instruction, with the subsequent lack of knowledge concerning results, will indeed *prevent* learning from taking place. It is felt that a comprehensive consideration of the influence of instruction upon learning is imperative if one wishes to gain greater understanding of the manner in which motor skill is acquired.

Initially, instruction will be discussed in a time dimension, since consideration is given to pre-performance, performance, and post-performance direction, respectively. Research concerning the sensory aspects of instruction, visual, verbal, manual guidance, and various combinations, will be reviewed, and studies demonstrating the influence of knowledge of results upon performance and learning will be presented.

THE PLACEMENT OF INSTRUCTIONS IN TIME

The initial type of instruction placed in a time dimension consists of directions which attempt to prepare an individual for learning and might be termed the *task-preparation phase*. Instruction at this stage generally has several purposes: (1) to provide a "warm-up" or readiness to learn the skill (this is sometimes referred to as creating the correct "mental set"), (2) to make the learner familiar with performance principles indigenous to the task, and (3) to give the individual information concerning the general severity, duration, or difficulty of the task (sometimes termed the "amount" set).

Verbal instructions seem most important during this initial stage of learning. However, their complexity should not exceed the comprehension limits of the learners. It seems best to keep verbal pre-training to a minimum, especially in learning tasks containing rapid movements. Slowing of the movement to keep with a memorized verbal formula, especially during the latter stages of learning, usually is not to be desired. Verbal and/or written directions can, however, effectively point to similarities between the task to be learned and the individual's past experiences. They may help to motivate the learner and can also transmit knowledge of mechanical principles and spatial relationships involved in performance.

A visual demonstration is often a helpful method of task preparation. The demonstration may be copied, however, only to the extent to which the learner is able to identify with the demonstrator and to see himself in the role of the performer. It should be noted that observation of a complex demonstration might have a detrimental effect.

Manual guidance during the pre-performance stage is also effective in transmitting knowledge of the spatial relationships, the speed of movements desired, or the force needed. Many times, however, movements which are too enthusiastically guided by an instructor may delay the learner's gaining the "feel" of the task. In some cases, because of inexpert guidance, muscles opposite to those which are to be used later in the task may be more forcefully brought into play.

During this pre-performance stage, therefore, one may apply any of the various kinds of instruction mentioned, visual, manual, or verbal. Reference to Fleishman's research dealing with the importance of "non-motor" factors, however, seems to indicate that such pre-task training should be mainly concerned with transmitting mechanical principles and knowledge of spatial relationships.[308,313] Research concerning the "amount" set and its influence upon performance and learning indicates that knowledge of the extent and complexity of the task is also important during this initial phase in the learning process.

The second time stage in the learning of a motor task, the actual performance, may be termed the *guidance phase*. It is during this period that corrections are made which enable the individual to mold his movements into increasingly exact patterns with perhaps a more precise application of force. Performance guidance may come from manually moving the limbs or body of the individual or from interpolated verbal or visual directions. It should be remembered, however, that a learner may be "over-coached" during this period. He may, for example, be working partially on a trial-and-error principle, and continual directions may impede self-correction. The learner may be attempting to concentrate upon the whole task. Too complex a correction with minute attention to detail may serve to obliterate a feeling of the whole movement. Sharply spoken verbal criticisms, for example, may obliterate the kinesthetic sensations being used to gain the "feel" of the movement.

During Performance

Instruction during performance not only may consist of visually presented demonstrations and materials, verbal directions, or the opportunity to engage in guided practice but also may be characterized by the general emphasis placed upon various aspects of performance. Instruction emphasizing speed vs. accuracy, correcting the wrong movement as opposed to emphasizing the correct way to move, or placing relative emphasis upon praise or reproof has varying effects upon learning during this intermediate phase.

A primary consideration during this performance phase seems to be determining the appropriate quantity of correction and guidance to be offered as well as deciding the quality involved. The instructor should be sensitive to the transition from cognitive aspects of the task to the more basic movement or motor aspects.[714] Individuals should not be preoccupied or made overly concerned with analysis of the task during the performance phase, as such an academic approach may actually impede acquisition. It would seem best to place emphasis upon moving rapidly and accurately and upon the vigorous and/or accurate utilization of force during the performance phase. Recent research by McGuigan has indicated that motor activity may interfere with verbal information if both impose upon the individual during task performance. Thus it seems best to reserve extensive analysis to the preliminary phases.[641]

Post-Task

At the final stage of learning, "knowledge of results" is of vital importance to the later improvement of skill. Such knowledge may come from internal movement cues or from various types of external instruction. The instructor should be sensitive to information the learner has been able to obtain from internal cues, as well as the nature of the activity and the opportunity afforded to obtain knowledge of results. For example, when learning to swim, little visual information is obtained by the learner, since his face is usually submerged during a large portion of the practice period. Basketball free-throw shooting, on the other hand, is accompanied by continual verification of success or failure; the learner is able to see the accuracy achieved by each effort. Most learning has been found to be greatly facilitated by immediate knowledge of results. This is true also of gross motor activities.

TYPES OF SENSORY INPUT

As seen from the preceding analyses, instruction may be considered in a time dimension, the review of research will be organized in categories primarily based upon the relative emphasis the instructor places upon various types of sensory information. In the following section, the relative importance, most effective place within the learning process, the type of task most facilitated by visual, verbal, and motor guidance, or combinations of these three categories will be discussed. Research dealing with "knowledge of results" is accorded a separate section at the end of the chapter.

Verbal Instructions

As has been noted, the most effective placement of verbal instruction seems to be during the pre-performance phase and during the initial stages of task performance. This assertion is based upon the need for mechanical principles and for knowledge of spatial relations important during the initial stages of learning. Research also indicates that it is important to communicate a knowledge of the amount of the task to be accomplished during the initial stage of learning.

Most research indicates that verbal rehearsal of the task is most effective in paired-association skills, including the pairing of numbers with letters, colored lights with movement responses, and in nonsense syllables. However, Sackett also found that the learning of a serial-type task (a maze) was facilitated by verbal rehearsal of the complexities of the pathway.[778]

The instruction can have various degrees of relevancy to the task. As McAllister[624] and others have pointed out, increasing the specificity of instructions produces marked performance increments. Generally, such rehearsal of task elements is considered to offer a "warm-up" period and seems more effective as time devoted to it is increased.[615] Extensive pre-practice verbalization also seems to help an individual gain more initial proficiency when the task is one with which the learner has had little experience.

5

Mechanical Principles. A second reason which has been proposed for verbal pre-training is to transmit mechanical principles of the task. If such instruction facilitates performance, it might be assumed that some general "ability to analyze the task" factor underlies performance. The early study of Judd[508] substantiated this contention. As boys were instructed in the principles of light refraction and then asked to hit an underwater target with a bow and arrow, their accuracy was little affected when the depth of the water was suddenly changed. A second group, receiving no such instructions, had difficulty adjusting to the changed conditions.

Hendrickson and Schroeder,[439] in 1941, duplicating Judd's conditions, attempted to determine the role of "insightful" motor learning. These later investigators, however, felt that, in addition to transfer resulting from a knowledge of the principles involved, other factors were also important when the conditions were changed. Individual fluidity of behavior (willingness to change response patterns), ability to formulate the principles for himself, the manner in which the principles are presented, and habits of verifying self-judgments were also felt to be important when using the knowledge of principles to learn a motor skill.

Studies subsequent to these seem to disagree upon the extent to which knowledge of principles affects learning. Daugherty,[235] in 1945, found that the teaching of kinesiological principles positively affected the accuracy and force applied to sports skills. Coville,[183] on the other hand, found that a detailed knowledge of principles underlying ball bouncing, a combined tennis and badminton skill, and archery practice did not seem to facilitate performance. This latter study suggests that, while one may be aware of mechanical principles underlying a task, he may not possess the ability to apply them during actual performance and learning.

Again, consideration of the research does not offer absolute answers. The nature of the task, the ability of the learner to understand and to apply basic performance principles seem to determine the extent of their effect upon learning efficiency. The manner in which the principle is presented also seems to be an important variable.

Amount-Set. Advance knowledge of the amount and/or complexity of the task has also been shown to influence learning efficiency. Several investigations concerning the influence of the amount-set upon learning have been published during the past thirty years. The initial studies, usually dealing with arithmetic tasks, found that, when the amount of work with which the learner is faced encourages initial slow performance, a "pacing" effect occurs.[83] Later investigators studied the effect of the amount-set on motor activities. Usually, when individuals were faced with a given number of strength efforts, the amount of force exerted on the initial trials decreased with the number of pulls, indicating the same "pacing" effect as seen in the performance of "mental" tasks.[90,700]

The subtle influence upon performance of the *exact* knowledge of the extent of the task was clearly illustrated in Katz's study of 1949. Individuals, when asked to "run to that post" (180 yards away), ran the first 60 yards in 10.8 seconds. A second group, informed of the exact distance of the post, ran the initial 60 yards in 10.2 seconds. Katz[509] concluded that the duration of the work and the output of the individual are conditioned by the nature of the task and the material into which it fits as a part. Advance knowledge of task complexity would also seem to affect the initial effort and create a pacing effect. Investigations illustrating this principle, however, seem to be lacking. The factor is probably operative, although unidentified, prior to the performance of many motor skills in the experimental laboratory and in life.

Speed vs. Accuracy. Few researchers have been concerned about the relative influence of emphasizing speed vs. accuracy when teaching motor skills. Solley[843] studying gross motor skills, found that probably speed should be emphasized from the initial stages of learning and that accuracy gained at slow *speeds* was generally lost when a more rapid movement was required. When speed was a predominant factor in the performance of skill, it was concluded, early emphasis upon speed was best. Solley also felt that both speed and accuracy were important; equal emphasis upon both probably produced the best results.

In one sense, such principles relate to the whole vs. part question. When concentrating upon speed, the individual must generally attend to the whole movement, rather than become concerned with components of the movement pattern. Thus, as has been previously recommended, acquiring as much of the whole as can be perceived under conditions similar to that surrounding the final type of performance desired generally produces the best learning. Limits, however, certainly must exist. If practice of a movement at full speed so obliterates its components and/or presents too much of the whole for a learner to comprehend, slowing down initial practice would seem desirable. Following a knowledge of spatial relationships, a rapid movement cannot be said to be learned until it may be performed at full speed. This is generally accomplished with more facility if initial practice is carried out at full speed.

Negative vs. Positive Directions. During actual performance of the task and during the learning process, correction of the learner's movements may be either positive or negative. Emphasis may be placed upon what *to* do or what *not* to do. Basically, the traditional question of positive or negative reward is involved.

The findings of experimentations with rats have been verified in later studies with human beings. Wang[921] and Silleck and Lapha,[816] for example, found that positive instructions were better than merely extending the individual information concerning his inaccuracies when performing a maze task. It also was found that having subjects name the error after it was identified was beneficial and that verbal information during initial portions of the task was most helpful. Langfeld[557] also found that, when the subjects were moving a stylus down a groove, being told to "go down the center of the groove" had a more beneficial effect upon performance than being requested to "avoid the sides of the pathway."

These researchers, however, usually qualified their findings. It is suggested, for example, that the *tester* may be more important than the type of information given or whether praise or blame was extended.[557] It is also suggested that the relative spacing of negative or positive instruction may prove an important factor when assessing their effectiveness.[921]

Little attention seems to have been given to the nature of the task or the type of learner and positive or negative instruction. Those individuals who are unsure of themselves when facing a new task, or those lacking rapport with the instructor, might be more affected by blame and more encouraged by praise.

Manual Guidance

In addition to attending to verbal instruction, individuals may be guided manually when performing a task. The purpose is generally to mold movements into the desired forms through the manual correction of movements. Both Koch[537] and Lundgate[604] found that manual guidance was beneficial (as opposed to trial and error) when learning small maze tasks. Generally, it is found that manual guidance is more effective during the early stages of learning before incorrect habits are formed. If introduced too soon, however, the individual may not have the opportunity to explore the general nature of the task. If guidance is given too late in the learning process, on the other hand, habits may become fixed, and the learner may become confused. The effectiveness of guided practice has been found to be largely dependent upon the task and the criterion of learning efficiency established. Guidance during the initial part of the learning process, however, generally results in quicker learning.

Combinations of Instruction

Verbal vs. Manual. Chase,[154] in 1934 compared the relative effectiveness of verbal instruction and manual guidance in the learning of a small stylus maze task. It was found that, while manual guidance seemed to facilitate early learning, no real advantage was seen in final achievement. Chase felt that the learning of a spatial pattern becomes a discerning process as practice is continued and that continued reliance upon kinesthetic feed-back might prove detrimental during the later stages of learning.

Visual-Verbal-Manual. Generally, when visual demonstration has been studied as an aid to learning, it has been combined with manual guidance or with verbal instruction to determine their relative effectiveness. Studies of the effectiveness of filmed demonstrations seem concerned solely with the effectiveness of visual instruction upon learning. Here again comparison is usually made with verbal instruction (*i.e.*, the manner in which sound dubbed into the film aids in the effectiveness of the presentation). The pace and speed of words accompanying the film is also important. For example, Zuckerman found[999] that sound leading a filmed demonstration was more helpful than sound following it.

Films offer the learner an opportunity to engage in *delayed* imitation of the motor skill. They must usually be supplemented by verbal instruction. Their effectiveness may depend upon the extent to which an individual has an immediate opportunity to duplicate the filmed movements.

Karlin and Mortimer[512] recently compared the relative effectiveness of visual vs. verbal cues upon the learning of a crank turning task (to be turned at exactly 99 r.p.m.). Visual cues, since the subject was permitted to consult a monitor, proved superior to verbal information offered by the experimenter on retention over a 24-hour period.

Visual-Motor. Numerous studies have compared the relative effectiveness of visual cues and motor cues obtained from manual guidance on the opportunity to practice a movement. The tasks utilized have usually been fine motor skills, finger mazes, pursuit rotors, and the like. There seems to be a dearth of studies utilizing human subjects in gross motor tasks which compare the relative effectiveness of visual cues to kinesthetic or movement cues upon learning and performance.

One of the first studies illustrating the superiority of visual guidance over nonvisual guidance of movement was carried out in 1882 by Bowditch and Southard.[101] They found that a finger-aiming task with the subjects blindfolded, was performed more accurately when the subjects were given prior visual inspections of the target than when, without vision, their fingers were manually directed to the target center. Although Ammons[15] found no difference between pursuit-rotor performance following visual inspection of the task and moving through the task blindfolded, most experimenters found that vision provides important information in learning a motor task. As Miles[660] states, "No delays in action are occasioned by vision. It does not get in the way or occupy valuable space, it does all its coaching from the sidelines."

Many different amounts and variations of visual guidance have been attempted in experimental situations. Summarized by Miles,[660] these have included: (1) full-normal vision during all trials, (2) interrupted or fragmentary visual control, (3) blurred visual control, caused by aging, drugs, and similar conditions, and (4) distorted visual control, using mirrors or other refracting surfaces causing disagreement between visual and tactile impressions, or indirect visual control which involves the fixation of a point removed from that to which manual manipulation is applied.

In general, the accuracy of visual practice over manual or kinesthetic feed-back has been supported in numerous studies with stylus or finger mazes[144,660] and with pursuit rotors[585] and by Smith and Harrison,[834] using a three-hole stylus punch board. Not only has the research shown that visual inspection has a greater effectiveness than manual guidance in determining spatial relationship during the initial stages of learning but also that judgments of roughness, length, or curvature may actually suffer distortion if learned kinesthetically.[760] Thus, it would seem that whenever possible visual cues in the form of films, demonstration, or the like are superior to movement cues when learning skills. Attempts to teach a skill by first blindfolding the learner have not seemed as effective as permitting the individual simultaneously to attend to visual cues which may be present.

It is unfortunate that more research is not available dealing with the performance of athletic skills and the relative effectiveness of various kinds of sensory cues. Most of the literature deals with relatively fine motor skills, pursuit rotors, small maze tasks of various types, and the like. Thus, generalizations may be made only tentatively and are defensible only until more research is forthcoming.

It seems that manual guidance and verbal instructions prove most effective during the *early* stages of learning. The learner best receives an awareness of the mechanical principles involved (verbal) and a knowledge of the spatial relationships and task complexities involved in the performance of the task through verbal and manual guidance. Moreover, it appears that instruction of all kinds is most effective during the initial stages of the task and may interfere with speed and force of movements during the later stages of learning.

Spaced correction in the form of manual guidance and verbal instruction and demonstrations should be most effective during the *latter* stages of learning. Thus, the relative dependence upon trial-and-error learning and closely instructed practice would seem to shift during the various stages of learning. More instruction is desirable during the initial stages to correct movements and to prevent the adoption of incorrect habits. More trial-and-error learning seems beneficial as the learner approaches his psychophysical limits during the latter stages, although with correct instruction early in the learning process, fewer errors should be evidenced during these latter stages.

Wherever possible, visual demonstration should be utilized and is superior, when gaining accuracy of movement, to manual guidance and to kinesthetic practice without vision.

INSTRUCTIONS TO RETAIN

As individuals begin to perform and to learn a motor skill they may have various conceptions relative to the necessity to repeat the performance at a later time. They might assume that the immediate performance efforts will be their only exposure to the skill. On the other hand they may be aware that they most re-perform the skill at another time in the future. Information relative to the necessity to retain a skill might be offered either before, during, or at the completion of a learning program.

Relatively few investigations have attempted to ascertain the influence of instructions to retain upon retention. It seems, however, that if this kind of information is tendered prior to the beginning of the learning schedule, greater retention will result. Lavery,[567] in two investigations incorporating a target throwing task, found that instructions given *prior* to practice that a task's retention would be evaluated aided retention, while no difference in retention was forthcoming if these instructions were given at the completion of the learning schedule. Sanderson[780] also came to similar conclusions in an earlier investigation in which a maze task was used. It would thus seem that individuals learn differently when they are aware of the need for retention than when they feel their exposure to the task is to be of rather short duration.

KNOWLEDGE OF RESULTS

Knowledge of results may come in the nature of verbal information, visual confirmation of accuracy, speed, or some other success criterion, or through the feel of a successfully completed movement. The effect of knowledge of results may be considered from several standpoints: (1) the relative spacing of this knowledge and the effects of spacing upon learning efficiency, (2) the relation of knowledge of success upon the performance of various kinds of tasks, strength efforts, athletic skills, or laboratory tasks, including mazes, and (3) the effect of delay of knowledge of results on learning efficiency. Seashore and Brevales[795] point out that the extent to which knowledge of results is effective also may depend upon the alertness of the learner in supplying his own information concerning success. Therefore, the factor influencing the knowledge of results involves the little studied "self-estimation" factor. To what extent is the individual able to predict prior to attempting a task and able to determine at the completion of a task how well he will do, or has done, without the benefit of an external source of information?

An early study by Arps,[30] using a strength task (a finger ergograph), indicated a trend seen in subsequent research. It was found that the amount of work and the rate of work was positively influenced when the individual was constantly informed of how hard he pulled upon the ergograph. Muscular efficiency was increased, it was hypothesized, because knowledge of results operated to facilitate changes in the nervous system, as well as to help the learner maintain attention upon the task.[84] Howell[473] confirmed these findings in a later study which found that the use of graphs indicating force and speed of limb movements proved effective when learning the sprinting start. A masked group unable to see clearly the results of their efforts following each attempt did not enjoy the same success.

Spencer and Judd,[846] however, utilizing a perceptual-motor skill involving drawing dots which were the extension of lines, found that improvement seemed to take place when knowledge of results was lacking. While at a loss to explain this phenomenon, they hypothesized that improvement was possibly due to the subject's general familiarity with the nature of the task. They concluded that with subsequent practice a plateau would probably be reached.

Crafts and Gilbert[187] found that *nonspecific* knowledge of accuracy in a stylus maze *did not* produce greater learning. Subjects were informed when they were "below average" in performance, and no comment was made when they were average or exceeded the mean. Crafts attributed this finding to the fact that the college students' exact knowledge of results proves to be of no help as they generally are aware of how well they are doing in most tasks. In the absence of any extrinsic rewards or punishments, motivation was not greatly affected when some of the students found they were not doing well. Kneeland's[535] research on self-estimation seems to corroborate Craft's findings.

Greenspoon and Foreman,[394] using a line drawing task, found that, as students attempted to draw a line exactly 3 inches long their learning efficiency was directly affected as knowledge of their accuracy was increasingly delayed for periods of nineteen, twenty, and thirty seconds. The most effective learners were those who obtained *immediate* knowledge of results. If knowledge of results is offered too quickly after the completion of a skill or sub-skill, the individual may not be as favorably affected as if this information is delayed for several seconds. In general it seems that about a five- to ten-second delay produces the best improvement, permitting the feel of the skill to "set in," prior to asking the performer to interpret some kind of external information relative to the quality of his efforts.[568]

Bilodeau and Bilodeau,[86] studying the effect of spacing knowledge of results, found that learning to move a large lever a given distance was facilitated by the number of times knowledge of accuracy was obtained and not by the various ways in which this knowledge was spaced throughout a series of trials. They also found, as did Greenspoon et al.,[394]

Arps,[30] and others, that learning *did not* occur when knowledge of results was lacking.

At the same time the complexity of the task influences whether any positive benefit is derived from knowledge of performance level achieved. Chapanis, for example, found that knowledge of results produced no significant change in tasks which were simple repetitive exercises (button pressing to a light cue).[153]

It thus seems that the effectiveness of knowledge of results is dependent upon the form in which this knowledge arrives, the complexity of the learner and of the task, as well as the immediacy with which the knowledge is received. Retention is often best if knowledge of performance levels is received a few seconds after the task is completed; and at the same time spaced knowledge of results from an external source is sometimes more effective than continual feedback, as the performer receives information relative to his accuracy from various components of his visual-motor feedback system.

SUMMARY

Although instruction may be self administered or arise from the nature of the task, within this chapter the type of instructions discussed were those deliberately tendered by another individual to the learner. Within a temporal framework three stages emerge: (1) *pre-performance* instructions, those contributing to the general learning set and including amount and/or intensity of the task, its general nature, and similar information, (2) instructions tendered during *actual performance,* and (3) the *task-completion* phase, referring primarily to information giving the learner the knowledge of his success or failure to accomplish the task. Instructions may also be classified according to the type of sensory experience involved: verbal instructions; visual guidance, including demonstrations, the viewing of films, and the like; and manual guidance. In addition, various combinations of these have been researched.

In many cases the available literature offers only tentative clues relating instruction to skilled performance. It is believed that the following statements are presently valid ones.

1. Pre-task instructions should be primarily concerned with the transmission of task principles and of the spatial components inherent in the task. These kinds of instructions may be in the form of a visual demonstration of written or verbal information and should be compatible with the ability of the learner to comprehend.

2. Instructions during the task should not interfere with the learner's focus upon the movement patterns called for but should supplement performance. They might better be in the form of visual demonstration or of a minimal amount of manual guidance.

3. Instructions following performance are concerned with giving the learner knowledge of his success or failure or degrees thereof. The immediacy and clarity of this post-performance information seems to exert a direct and positive influence upon the success of subsequent attempts.

4. Advanced information concerning the amount, duration, and intensity of the task, if exact, leads to more vigorous performance on the part of the learner than incomplete, incorrect, or no information concerning the "amount-set." The pacing effect will nearly always be evident as an individual performs a series of tasks, with the effect more pronounced if no knowledge concerning the exact task limits is obtained beforehand.

5. Early emphasis on speed seems important, if speed is a vital part of the task. However, emphasis upon speed to the exclusion of spatial accuracy during the initial stages of learning may only prove an impediment during the latter stages of learning.

6. Directions emphasizing what *to do* vs. what *not to do* seem to facilitate quicker learning of a motor skill.

7. In general, the most accurate type of sensory input when learning a motor task is visual inspection. However, for effective learning, manual guidance, visual demonstration, verbal description, as well as practice, are best combined.

8. If an individual is given information prior to a learning program that he must retain the task, retention will be greater than if this information is extended to him at the completion of the learning process, or is omitted entirely.

Student References

Articles

1. BILODEAU, EDWARD A. and BILODEAU, INA McD.: "Variable frequency of knowledge of results and the learning of a simple skill," *J. Exper. Psych.*, 55, 379-383, 1958.
2. DAUGHTREY, GRAYSON: "The effects of kinesiological teaching on the performance of junior high school boys," *Res. Quart.*, 16, 26-33, 1945.
3. GREENSPOON, JOEL and FOREMAN, SALLY: "Effect of delay of knowledge of results on learning a motor task," *J. Exper. Psych.*, 51, 226-228, 1956.
4. KANTZ, D.: "Gestalt laws of mental work," *Brit. J. Psych.*, 39, 175-183, 1949.
5. SACKETT, R. S.: "The relationship between amount of symbolic rehearsal and retention of a maze habit," *J. Gen. Psych.*, 13, 113-128, 1935.
6. SOLLEY, WILLIAM H.: "The effect of verbal instruction of speed and accuracy upon the learning of a motor skill," *Res. Quart.*, 23, 231-240, 1952.

Chapter 5

Perception of the Self and of Near Space

THE manner in which elements within an individual's personal "space capsule" are structured may be considered from several standpoints. For example, spatial perception may be studied through analyses of the capacities of sensory receptors to deal quantitatively and qualitatively with various stimuli. Within such a framework, spatial and visual perception are often considered to be synonymous processes, and the focus is upon mechanical-physiological functioning of the visual apparatus. A broader view conceives of space perception as a dynamic relationship between the perceiver and various spatial elements, involving continual intersensory integration. Research dealing with the sensory-tonic theory discussed previously supports the importance of general postural tensions in the perception of spatial relationships. A third approach to space perception concentrates upon the nature of space itself and involves study of the stable cues within two- and three-dimensional space. Ittelson's transactional theory is based upon research of this type.

Three levels of emphasis may be placed upon the involvement of human movement in the perception of space. Some research findings support the overwhelming role of vision in spatial perception. Vision is viewed as the primary means through which the most accurate information is gathered. Literature pointing to the interdependence of movement and vision in the formation of spatial concepts suggests a second type of emphasis. Movement and vision are represented as interacting modalities. The dominant role may be assumed by either, depending upon the nature of the event or object, the developmental level or prior experience of the observer, or perhaps the stage in the learning process under consideration.

Research in growth and development often suggests that movement capacities are of paramount importance when learning about space. It is held that the developing infant gains initial knowledge of his restricted world primarily through manual exploration and that, as the organism matures, perceptions of extended space are formed largely through reference to previous and direct movement experiences with distantly seen objects.

The perception of space may be approached by taking a "proximal-distal" view of the problem. Essentially such a viewpoint rests upon the assumption that to form accurate conceptions about space, one must first learn about his own body, its structure and movement capacities. Secondly, one must perceive objects immediately adjacent, objects which can be touched or manipulated and with which direct experience may be gained, to form the individual's space capsule. The proximal-distal reference system terminates with the perception of distant objects within extended space. Such a conceptual framework begins as the individual forms a "body-platform" from which he then constructs immediate and extended perceptions of spatial objects and events.

The fact that the chapter is entitled "Perception of the Self and of Near Space" rather than "The *Visual* Perception of . . . etc." underscores the present approach. Emphasis is placed upon the interaction of various sensory modalities contributing to spatial perception and upon the totality of man's action system. Specifically, however, information is placed into the previously outlined "proximal-distal" framework. Initially, research is reviewed that explains the manner in which spatial concepts are learned relative to one's own body and how changing concepts about the objective functioning "self" influence and modify spatial perception. Next, the manner in which an individual's immediate "space-capsule" is constructed is discussed. This concept is based upon research indicating that an exact awareness of proximally located objects and events is gained through the coordination of visual and manipulative behavior. This awareness, in turn, is believed to establish the location and nature of environmental objects and events further removed.

CONSTRUCTING THE SELF-PLATFORM

Gaining accurate knowledge about the *self* may include information pertaining to its form and shape, the location of various extremities and plane surfaces, and the potential for movement. Such knowledge forms an essential beginning to the accurate perception of events and objects in space.

Research completed in 1957 by Werner and Wapner emphasizes the importance of the formation of an objective and stable self as the immature organism strives to form initial perceptual judgments.[955] In relating aspects of the sensory-tonic theory to developmental concepts, it was found that perceptions reported by younger subjects (six to nine years) were directly related to the manner in which their postures had been artificially modified. Older children, on the other hand, showed ability to separate experimentally produced internal tensions and judgments of various spatial configurations. These investigators concluded that during early stages of development perception of the world depends upon an egocentric personal reference system; if the young child is tilted to the right, he tends to perceive an upright rod tilted to the same side. Older children, in contrast, showed increasing independence from postural tensions and attributes attached to objects in their space field.

Gesell, studying the development of vision in the child, presented evidence also supporting the gradual emancipation of the personal self from perceptual judgments. Not until the eighth year does the child seem to realize that objects may be viewed differently by another person. Prior to that time spatial judgments are made only within a personal reference system.[352]

Thus, literature supporting perceptual theory, as well as systematic reports of child behavior, points to the important role of the structured, objective *self* upon which concepts and judgments about spatial events may be based. Within the following pages consideration will be directed toward the *means* by which the objective self is formed, the *how* of self-structuring, as well as *what* is learned about the body.

Factors which initially influence the formulation of judgments about the self rest upon the anthropological evolvement of various bodily structures. Bipedal locomotion, the subsequent freeing of the upper limbs to engage in manipulative behavior, and the proximal alignment of the visual apparatus in the frontal plane are important aspects of human development which influence the manner in which we learn about ourselves. For example, the placement of hand and eyes has resulted in these two action systems becoming intimately related and seems to provide an important means through which initial self perceptions are formed.

EVALUATING THE BODY-IMAGE

There are several types of research instruments available which purport to evaluate the body-image. Some of these depend upon the manner in which the child or adult projects himself into various pictures,[235] ink blots,[798] or similar configurations. The draw-a-person test is also used as a measure of body image.[5]

Some of these tests derive scores dependent upon the accuracy with which an individual can touch his body parts, and those of a picture of a man with which he is confronted.[72] A recently developed tool attempts to meet the criticism of the previous tests and avoids the necessity for verbal mediators by asking the child to imitate the gestures of the experimenter.[76] This latter instrument incorporates gestures made both with the arms and with the hands.

Dillon[249] devised a test to evaluate the accuracy of an individual's perceptions of his body size. Using ropes attached to a wooden frame, the subject is asked to adjust the components of the frame to duplicate his perceived height and width. Using this device Fisher[296] found that males who were committed to the idea of male superiority, and who had high aspirations relative to personal power, consistently overestimated their height.[296]

Many of these devices may be criticized because of their subjectivity, or because they really seem to measure attributes more obvious than the body-image (*i.e.* vocabulary or the ability to copy a visually presented demonstration). The less exact measures are usually employed in conjunction with other clinical devices in order to obtain a clearer picture of the total personality of the child or adult. Distortions in the responses using these kinds of measures are usually elicited from the severely disturbed adult and child, or among the immature.

The more exact measuring devices, incorporating verbal responses to requests for body-part identification are employed in well-controlled experimental studies, and have, particularly among the retarded, been found to be highly correlated to various measures of motor ability.[209]

The Early Development of the Body Image

The importance of visual-manipulative interactions in structuring the *self* is brought into clear focus through reference to studies of growth and development by Gesell, Piaget, and others. Infants are seen to gain initial self-knowledge through a process of visual-motor inspection, first of space on either side of their bodies and then of space and objects at the midline.

Following an initial developmental stage during which only visual tracking movements are made by the infant, the fists become unclenched and the head is habitually held to one side, allowing visual inspection of the arm and hand in a characteristic tonic-neck-reflex position. As the baby sees the openings and closings of his hand, the first impressions are thus formed about his capacity for movement. He integrates kinesthetic sensations from the moving hand and from the visual musculature controlling eye movements with direct retinal stimulation. The grasping behavior of infants, as studied by Halverson,[410] further illustrates the close integration of vision and manipulation accompanying these beginning explorations.

The asymmetric tonic-neck-reflex position assumed by infants operates to aid in the establishment of "laterality" described by Kephart as "the initial awareness that two sides of the body exist, and their differences.[521] The early formation of this feeling on the part of the developing human organism governs the later formation of ideas relative to his personal location in space, to the location of objects both moving and stable which surround his body on various sides, and to the action of his limbs, moving together and independently.

Later the infant's head position tends to return to the midline, thus enabling him to watch both hands simultaneously and preparing him for bilateral manipulation of various objects placed within reach. During this latter stage, touching hand-to-hand enables the formation of perceptions relative to object shape and size and to the evolvement of basic perceptions of depth and distance within a limited visual field. At this time the infant learns that objects and events may be perceived as passing from one side, across the midline, to the other side, and the rudimentary concepts concerning "directionality" are formulated.

The maturing organism must learn to track objects crossing the body midline without interruption, as well as to integrate continuous movements of his limbs along the same pathway. The surrounding space is structured from an increasing awareness of left-to-right movements, up-down relationships toward and away from concepts, and similar aspects of directionality.

Numerous investigations, in which the normal visual field has been distorted in various ways, seem to support the contention that spatial perceptions are learned, rather than dependent upon innate neurological functioning. The subject in Snyder and Pronko's study,[842] for example, wearing a lens system which both inverted and reversed his visual field, was able to drive a car unaided along a crowded street by the twenty-sixth day of the experiment. As Kephart pointed out, the environment would be seen as ever changing and circular unless directional reference points were established rather early in the child's development.[521]

In addition to learning various aspects of directionality, enabling the formation of more extended perceptions, the maturing organism also must gain detailed impressions of various gross positions of his body. Perceptions relating to the back, due to the placement of the visual apparatus, seem to present a more difficult problem of organization than learning frontal directionality and laterality.

Tasks to Heighten Body Awareness

In addition to early visual-motor experiences and direct contact with the environment and with the bodies of other children, the growing infant and child may gain knowledge about his body from more structured kinds of experiences. Kephart,[529] Harmon,[415] Laban,[548] and others have proposed various exercises to strengthen self-concepts.

Observing that children frequently engage in pencil-scribbling activity, and indeed seem to need this type of motor-visual exercise as a learning experience, Kephart,[529] Harmon[415] and others[357] have devised various structured tasks involving blackboard drawing to achieve a heightened self-awareness from which more complex learning activities may be approached. Kephart suggested that an exercise involving the connecting of dots in various sequences may aid the child in forming more accurate awareness of laterality and directionality. It is first suggested that the child only join dots placed on one side of his body, and when accuracy in this is achieved, the dots might be placed so that movements would cross the body midline. It is also suggested that the dots be placed further and further apart during later stages to promote more accurate directioning of movements.

Trampolining has been suggested by Kephart as an activity through which the objective body image may be strengthened. As the body becomes weightless, rising above the trampoline, it is suggested that heightened awareness is obtained relative to the three axes around which the body may move. As the performer learns to drop on various parts of his body, he begins to locate better his body parts, as the front-drop, back-drop, seat-drop, and the like are executed. Finally, the difference between size and length of various body segments is more accurately realized as differences in the distances of falls are experienced, for example, between a simple bounce on the feet and a seat-drop. Little experimental evidence has been forthcoming supporting the assumptions made by Kephart relative to the importance of the body image to intellectual functioning, however.

The increasing tendency on the part of the maturing child to verbalize experience has suggested other activities which might contribute to the strengthening of the objective body image. Simple imitative games in which the child directs another's movement are examples. Games in which the child is required to name body parts, or perhaps to point to them as they are named by another, are other examples of activities in which verbal-motor integration strengthens body concepts.

In addition, games which require the child to lie on the floor and to assume various positions and to move his limbs in patterned movements contribute to the structuring of the self. His awareness of his body, its parts, and their location may be evaluated by noting the rapidity of response to requests, whether movements are smooth and accurate and whether a movement "over-flows" from one limb to another. In such situations, the kinesthetic feel of the movement and the direct contact with the floor combine to facilitate construction of an accurate body concept.

Gesell[351] presented systemized observations of child behavior in front of a mirror and illustrated another means through which the maturing organism becomes aware of self. In general, it is found that as the child becomes older, more excitability is evidenced and exploratory movements are increased and directed toward the mirror "brother."

Other scholars have suggested several basic techniques to heighten the awareness of space. Typical of these are various blackboard tracking activities using bilateral or unilateral movements with the aid of rounds, squares, and templates. Harmon[415] has used a number of such activities in the Winter Haven Program. They are designed to heighten spatial perceptions of figures and to aid body alignment. It is felt that these, in turn, are related to intellectual and visual functioning. Laban in a discussion of "Effort Training," also suggested that an awareness of "space exertions" is necessary for efficient movement.[548]

The programs espoused by Kephart,[529] Harmon,[415] and Getman[257] purport to improve the intellectual functioning as well as the motor development of neurologically handicapped and retarded children and youth. Experimentalists who have investigated these relationships have arrived at conflicting findings. When Oliver found that physical improvement positively affected mental functioning, he concluded that the effect could have been caused by the improvement of the children's self-concept. Corder attempted to replicate Oliver's study, utilizing fewer subjects, and found substantially the same results. A more definitive study by Pangle and Solomon concluded that although motor functioning can be improved by engaging in motor activity, intellectual functioning is largely independent of the motor domain.[522] Robbins similarly found that a program of basic motor activities had no significant effect upon intellectual or perceptual functioning.[756]

Perhaps in no other area can researchers competent in carrying out studies in perceptual-motor functioning make a more significant contribution. Proponents of various systems of perceptual-motor training continue to postulate various relationships between motor, perceptual, intellectual, and emotional functioning. The data supporting these contentions, however, frequently contradicts the supporters of these theories.

Self-Structuring in Adulthood

Structuring of the body percept is not confined to childhood but continues throughout life. Sometimes these self perceptions are modified by conditions which result in rapid changes, for example, amputation, viewing films of oneself, or experiencing difficulty when performing a previously mastered skill. More often, however, self-structuring during late childhood and adulthood involves more gradual change.

Harlow's[414] study of the character dynamics of body builders, and the manner in which they attempt to alter radically their body structure and reshape its form to stabilize their personality structure, points to the manner in which the body is a springboard for basic perceptual framework in later life. However, whether modifications imposed on the body through the gaining of muscle or the sudden loss of fatty tissue effect changes in perceptions of space seems to require further research.

Clifton and Smith[164] completed studies relating to changing the self-concept following the viewing of motion pictures by college men and women. It was found that variations in the direction of more positive self assessments were evident after the subjects were permitted to see themselves executing a throwing movement. Shifts in self-concepts were not evidenced, however, after viewing self in walking, jumping, and running activities. It is believed this study illustrates that perceptions of the performing self may undergo change well past childhood, as individuals are presented with vivid pictorial evidence of their performance.

Self-Estimation Studies

Studies which deal with the effect and ramifications of the "self-estimation" factor in motor learning are limited. In an investigation which I carried out, it was found that subjects could generally determine how well they had done in a large locomotor maze task despite a lack either of knowledge of their traversal times or of the opportunity to view the performance of others. The subjects were asked to determine whether they ranked in the upper, middle, or lower third of a group of 60 subjects. Correlating actual performance means with their estimation, a +.992 was recorded. Of course, with a more exact breakdown, into 10 categories, for example, a lower correlation probably would have resulted.[197]

It is interesting to speculate, however, what information served as a basis for the estimates. The task consisted of moving the body with accuracy through space. By the time individuals reach the college level, they have had extensive experience in various sports movements and generally know how they will rank when their performance is compared to that of their peers, despite the unfamiliarity and unique nature of the task. Implications for the importance of self-improvement as a motivator, as opposed to inter-individual competition at the upper secondary and college levels, seems obvious.

Kneeland[535] determined the extent to which individuals were able to predict both how they would score prior to performance and what they had achieved following performance in fine motor skills (e.g., knot tying). She found that, when improvement was slight, individuals tended to over estimate their performance, and when improvement was great, they under estimated performance. As it might be predicted, estimates were more accurate following performance than prior to performance. Kneeland concluded that a number of factors influence accuracy of self-estimation, including (1) the possibility of improvement, (2) the nature of the task, (3) the attitude of the subject toward the task, (4) his initial feeling about it, (5) prior familiarity with similar tasks, and (6) the accuracy of estimate required. The literature dealing with aspiration level and accuracy of self-estimation has proliferated within recent years and has been summarized by me in another text.[215] For example, Dearnally studied self-estimates of endurance under "risky" conditions (the threat of receiving an electric shock).[244] Cohen and Dearnally's study of the judgment of "footballers" when attempting to score goals represents a similar line of investigation.[166]

Individuals are frequently able to predict how they will do or have done in a motor task. It is probable, however, that the maturity of the individual and his past experience when performing motor skills are the most important factors influencing the accuracy of self-estimation of performance and learning.

Body Type, As Measured, and Personality Traits

It seems likely that an individual's personality might be influenced in part by the manner in which others react to his physical characteristics, including his body-build, its conformations and size. Several investigations have concentrated upon these body-type personality relationships. During recent years this research seems to have been largely stimulated by the work of Sheldon and his colleagues.[808]

Following publication of *The Varieties of Human Physique* in 1940, which presented classification techniques for categorizing the physical structures of men,[807] Sheldon further explored the relationship between personality and physique. This study resulted in his *The Varieties of Temperament* published two years later.[808] While philosophers historically have often referred to the "appearance-behavior" relationship, it remained for Sheldon to demonstrate objectively that personality and structure may be related. While Sheldon's "constitutional theory" is accorded respect in any discussion of personality theories, his concepts are especially amiable for inclusion in a text about motor performance directed toward physical educators. Teachers on the athletic field receive daily evidence of the physique-behavior relationship as they observe youngsters at play. The picture of the robust, active, outgoing, muscular boy, as contrasted to the slightly built, poorly performing, withdrawn child whose movements may exhibit excess tension are physique-behavior patterns familiar to most professional workers in the field.

Calling upon the "trait" concept as conceived by Allport, Sheldon isolated three "clusters" of personality qualities. These he termed *viscerotonia, somatotonia, and cerebrotonia.* The individual high in *somatotonia* was characterized as needing physical adventure and having a strong inclination for vigorous physical activity. Further research associated these characteristics with the *mesomorph* (muscular) physique. The sociable, gluttonous, affectionate characterization of the fat person (the *endomorph*) was found to be a true one. The rotund individual usually scored high on the *viscerotonia* scale. The third personality-physique complex identified was the withdrawn and restrained *cerebrotonic,* who also possessed a linear build (the *ectomorph*).

The relationships between physique and personality studies by Sheldon may be explained in several ways: (1) Individuals respond not only to their environment but also in terms of how their environment has previously reacted to their appearance (or to their apparent capacity for movement). (2) Physique and temperament are further linked in that commonly accepted stereotypes are fostered upon individuals: the fat-jolly, muscular-active, and thin-withdrawn are familiar dichotomies. (3) A third explanation is that environmental influences have molded both temperament and physique. Thus, the overprotective mother or athletic father are probably as influential in determining personality by manipulating the environment as they are in shaping the bodies of their offspring through the transmission of their genes.

Several scholars have questioned the scientific basis of somatotyping. Most statistical analyses of body-build measures produce scores which arrange themselves on a linear continuum, rather than clustering into the three-part classification hypothesized by Sheldon. There is no scientific basis for the assumption that fat, thin, and muscular physiques arise from the three primary germinal layers.

Subsequent research has often failed to establish the close relationships between physique and personality which Sheldon proposed. For example, Hood, after surveying physique-personality trait relationships of 10,000 subjects (using the MMPI), concluded that "any relationships between physique and personality throughout the entire population is of a very small magnitude indeed."[468] Similarly, Reiter found that body-build was not related to items on Edwards Personal Preference Scale.[747]

On the other hand, Davidson and McInnes[237] found a high relationship between personality traits and physical type in young children. Individuals generally behave as they view themselves capable of behaving. Domey,[251] for example, found high correlations between physique and occupational choice, while Cortes and Gatte[180] also found high relationships between physique and the *subjects' own ratings* of their temperament.

KINESTHESIS AND STRUCTURING PROXIMAL SPACE

One of the primary means through which infants and adults gather impressions of proximal space involves cues arising from finger movements, limb positionings, and bodily postures. Movements may facilitate perceptual judgments relatively independent of vision, of location, shape, weight, and force qualities, and of the speed of objects within the immediate environment. Gesell,[351] for example, noted that an otherwise normal infant, blind from birth, passed through relatively normal stages of development, while depending solely upon tactile-movement cues garnered from objects in his surrounding space.

Kinesthesis ("movement sensation") was treated by many of the classic philosophers. Within the past one hundred and fifty years varying degrees of experimental interest and emphasis have been paid to the study of these sensations. Kinesthesis must be considered in the plural, as it seems to consist of a number of distinct kinds of sensations related to several kinds of sensory receptors within muscles, joints, and tendons, forming the basis for numerous kinds of perceptual judgments.

There are several types of sense organs which collect movement sensations and indicate the force, speed, and extent of movements of body parts. These include (1) muscle spindles, (2) tendon organs, and (3) joint end-organs. The muscle spindles are scattered throughout the muscles and are spiral in shape. They are activated only when the muscle is stretched. The tendon end-organs are stimulated by contraction of the muscle and are spiral-shaped fibers around the tendons. The joint end-organs seem sensitive to deep pressure and are located at the joints. Controversy still reigns as to the exact function of these organs, but it is certain that skin receptors, as well as vestibular functioning, are intimately related to the sensations carried by the kinesthetic receptors.

Historical Look at Kinesthesis

According to Boring,[91] it was Vater in 1741 who first discovered the spindles in muscles, but they were described more fully by Paccini about one hundred years later in 1835. Tendon receptors were described in 1876, and were more fully analyzed by Golgi in 1880. These fibers subsequently have been referred to as Golgi spindles.

The importance of kinesthesis to the perception of space was noted as early as 1820, when Brown pointed out that "our muscular frame" forms a "distinct organ of sense, which enables perception of spatial extensions to take place."[97] More recent factorial studies by Thurston,[886] Roff,[729] and others have included a kinesthetic factor as important when forming accurate and rapid judgments about spatial configurations.[759]

The early psychophysicists used the reported perception of weight differences to establish several basic laws and to quantify measurement methods. Weber's law rests upon such experimentation, holding that the just noticeable difference between a held weight and one held previously usually required a $\frac{1}{40}$ increase.

Goldscheider[775] in 1880, completed classical research concerning the nature of the muscle sense by determining thresholds for passive movements in various parts of the body. Movements at the shoulder joint were reported as sensitive to from .2 to .4 degrees of displacement, as the limb was rotated at the rate of .3 degrees per second. The shoulder was also found to be the most sensitive in terms of speed of movement. Goldscheider was the first to classify kinesthesis into the several components of sensitivity of muscular action, of tendon displacement, and of articulatory surfaces.

Around the turn of the century, experimental studies of kinesthesis were numerous. Underscoring the popularity of research exploring various aspects of the muscle sense was the reference to "The Great God Kinesthesis" at a meeting of the Society of Experimental Psychologists held during the early part of the twentieth century.[97]

Learning and Kinesthesis

Early learning theorists, notably Gutherie,[404] suggested conceptual frameworks largely dependent upon the chaining of movement responses. Humans were believed to think primarily by remembering minute movements of the vocal apparatus in the formation of word symbols, to imagine through passively visualizing movements, and to perceive through establishing patterns in eye muscles. Among the studies lending support to these "learning through movement" theories was that by Carter in 1936.[145] He found that maze traversals resulted in quicker learning when unusual muscular tension was produced by springs embedded in the stylus than when these accompanying movement cues were absent.

The study of kinesthesis became less intense in the intervening years as new experimental approaches were undertaken and theoretical frameworks based upon more central concepts were devised to explain learning and perception. For example, in 1930 Honzik and others[467] refuted the importance of kinesthesis in learning upon finding that mice could find their way through maze pathways after nerves carrying movement sensations had been severed.

Contemporary Research

Recently, kinesthesis has been accorded more attention in the experimental literature. Contemporary research has included factorial analyses of a multiplicity of kinesthetic measures and further explorations of kinesthetic thresholds.

Laidlow and Hamilton in 1937[551] produced figures which, in general, agree with Goldscheider's earlier findings. Thresholds of joint movements were found to average between .2 and .7 degrees of displacement. The speed of movement threshold, however, was found by them to be much less than was believed earlier, on the order of 10 degrees per minute. In general, however, these latter researchers found, as did Goldscheider, that the hip and shoulder joints were most sensitive to movement, followed in turn by various other joints.

Several variables, however, have been found to influence the perception of kinesthetic thresholds. As early as 1909, Thorndike[880] pointed out that exact laws concerning threshold phenomena might be questioned, due to the fact that practice was demonstrated to alter the sensitivity both to perception of held weights and to length of arm movements. It was also pointed out by this scholar that experimental conditions (i.e., how the weight was held) might negate previously devised "laws."

Contemporary research by Holway and Hurvich[465] lends support to Thorndike's earlier contentions. It was found that the weight-lifting task used by Weber to determine laws explaining just noticeable differences depended substantially upon the manner in which the weight was held. Sensitivity to weight was found to be greatest when the shoulder was the fulcrum, intermediate when lifted from the elbow, and least when lifted from the wrist.

Although Slocum[827] found that kinesthetic sensitivity was not significantly altered by fatigue, Leuba[577] found that duration, load, and rate of arm movement influenced judgment of their extent. Cleghorn and Darcus[163] discovered that sensibility to movement at the elbow joint was more pronounced when the joint was extened than when flexed, while Comalli[169] found that muscular tension affected tactual kinesthetic judgments of size. Such research lends further support to Thorndike's earlier assertion that many measures of kinesthetic thresholds are relative and subjective.

A recent contribution to the evaluation of thresholds was made by Ronco.[761] A *kine* scale was developed with which to evaluate sensitivity, with *kine* defined as the subjective magnitude of movements, one inch in length, made by the arm. Ronco found that estimates of the magnitude of movement in the horizontal-medial plane were related exactly to the distance moved. He presented a precise mathematical formula objectifying this relationship.

The exact role that kinesthesis plays in the control of skilled movement is not always apparent. Chernikoff[155] points out that, although reaction time to passive dropping of the arm has been found to range from 120 to 130 milliseconds, it is not fast enough to permit voluntary control of movement solely through kinesthetic feed-back circuits. It was suggested that the higher brain centers select a response pattern, and any correction of the movement, once underway, is difficult. This is seen most clearly as one attempts to correct an initiated ballistic movement (*e.g.*, throwing or batting).

Kinesthesis is probably of greater importance in the control of slow movements. In addition, awareness of a limb's starting point prior to beginning a ballistic action is probably dependent upon kinesthetic feedback.

The "feel" of a movement after completion, whether awkward, smooth, or jerky, also probably is dependent upon kinesthetic sensitivity. Kinesthetic feedback from the eye muscles aids in the formation of perceptions of depth and movement within the visual field. In addition, the formation of an accurate body image also is related intimately to sensations received from the various kinesthetic receptors. It is probable, however, that learning a complex movement is not entirely dependent upon kinesthesis but is a product of total perceptual organization.

Factorial studies, carried out by physical educators at the University of Iowa, have resulted in the isolation of several general kinesthetic qualities, although rather low correlations are obtained between various tests of body positioning. Static and dynamic arm positioning, thigh-leg positioning, and various movements utilized in maintaining balance are among the best measures of kinesthesis identified after the scores of a large number of tests were analyzed.[502]

Kinesthesis and Human Engineering. Human factors engineers have become interested in the accuracy with which individuals can position and move their limbs without vision in recent years. Usually such basic knowledge is then applied to the location of instrument controls and similar man-machine problems.

In one of the classic studies in this area, Fitts and Crannell[301] placed 24 different targets perpendicular to a line extending from the subject's shoulder and 28 inches away. The hands were initially started from a position in front of the body and the task was to locate these various targets accurately. It was found that the most accurate movements occurred toward the front of the body and slightly below shoulder height, the most common errors involved reaching too low. Three variables are usually seen to contribute to accuracy in this kind of a task, the original position of the pointing hand, the reaching distance, and the location of the terminal point relative to the individual's body.

Kinesthesis and Athletic Skill. Kinesthetic test scores seem to differentiate broadly between proficient and average motor performers. Wiebe,[961] using 20 tests of kinesthesis, found significant differences in the scores of varsity college athletes and non-athletes. Slater-Hammel,[825] using as a kinesthetic measure the ability to repeat muscular tension levels as recorded on an electromyograph, found that the constant errors were less for physical education majors than for liberal arts students.

Kinesthetic After-Effects. In 1933, Gibson[361] noted that subjects wearing prisms reported that straight edges not only looked curved but also felt curved to the touch. This observation prompted him to carry out further research which found that manipulation of a curved surface would also produce sensations of opposite curvature to a flat plane. Gibson's research and subsequent work by Kohler and Dinnerstein in 1947 gave impetus to numerous investigations concerning the phenomenon termed kinesthetic after-effect.[542]

Wertheimer and Leventhal[957] found that, with a high degree of satiation (movement in an initial task), the residual after-effects persisted for as long as six months. Corah,[178] among others, found that the amount of attention given to the initial task seemed to influence the amount of after-effect experienced; while Bakan and Weiler[45] found that the extent to which the subject was actively (moving a body member vs. just holding an initial object) perceiving an object influenced the amount of after-effect produced. In general, therefore, the literature suggests that the state of the organism (alertness) and the amount and the nature of the satiation affect the magnitude of after-effects. Attempts to relate susceptibility to after-effects to other performance and personality measures have generally failed.

Kohler[542] has proposed that the after-effect phenomenon is caused by some alteration of cerebral electrotonus, which carries over to create subsequent perceptual distortion. The after-discharge, previously mentioned as a property of a nerve impulse, is an important consideration in this context.

Kinesthetic After-Effects from Gross Action Patterns. The majority of studies dealing with kinesthetic after-effects have utilized tactual-manipulative activity rather than tasks involving movements of the entire body and/or of large muscle groups. However, it is common in the gymnasium or on the athletic field to experience after-effects which arise from gross action patterns.

Trampoline jumping, for example, is usually followed by a perceived inability to jump well on the floor. The batter who repeatedly "hefts" a weighted bat prior to using one of regulation weight seems intent upon producing a favorable after-effect. The common parlor game of standing in a doorway, pressing the arms against both sides of the frame, and then stepping away to let them rise, seemingly of their own volition, is another instance of a gross kinesthetic after-effect (the Kohnstamm effect). Indeed, in all cases where some overload is applied in an effort to improve athletic performance (*i.e.,* to develop "strength"), the *immediate* effect of removing such an excess results in a kinesthetic illusion or after-effect.

In a study by Cratty and Hutton,[219] it was demonstrated that locomotor activity while blindfolded could produce after-effects. Sixty subjects were divided into two groups of 30: One group guided themselves 10 consecutive times through pathways sharply curved right, while the other 30 moved 10 times to the left. After-effects were evidenced by their reports of curvature opposite to the direction in which they had been satiated when they were immediately placed in a straight test pathway. A typical delay curve was recorded. Within recent years continued research concerned with kinesthetic after-effects using manual tasks, those involving limb activity as well as tasks in which the total body is in action led to the following conclusions:

1. The after-effect is maximal immediately after satiation with the initial task, and then disappears slowly, leaving a residual after-effect which may be temporary or permanent.

2. Magnitude of the after-effect generally increases as a function of the duration of the time the satiation task is engaged in, until an optimum point is reached.

3. When attention is distracted from the inspection task, the after-effect is reduced. Conversely when attention is heightened, as when movement is involved in the inspection task, the after-effect is increased.

Further research in this area should serve to produce findings which are of practical value to the physical educator, therapist, and others. Several important theoretical questions should also be answered when the findings of additional studies are available. For example, there is some question as to whether these after-effects are due to stimulation of the body-part involved, or are the result of some kind of organization of the incoming stimuli by the central nervous system.[138] Practical questions revolve around whether producing *feelings* which distort kinesthetic perceptions actually result in *performance changes* during the time the illusions are reported.

Needed Research in Kinesthesis. Research by Franklin Henry[278] underscores one of the many areas in which little is known concerning kinesthetic perception. An experiment was carried out in which two types of kinesthetic adjustment were studied. In the first, blindfolded subjects were requested to exert a constant pressure against a lever the resistance of which varied unpredictably due to the action of an irregular cam. In the second, the subjects signalled when a change in the pressure exerted by the lever was perceived. Although it was determined that a reasonably close correspondence occurred between average perception of pressure changes reported and ability to respond by maintaining a constant pressure, the slight adjustment made by the subjects under the latter conditions was so low as to be below the threshold for pressure adjustment, thus implying that a reflexive mechanism was operative.

The findings of Henry suggest further investigations to explore what kinds of kinesthetic perceptions and adjustments reflexively occur at relatively unconscious levels and what types of movement positioning are dependent upon relatively conscious awareness on the part of the individual. Is the fact that such measures are moving or rapid, or are confined to certain positions or parts of the body, the influencing factor? Further exploration of dynamic kinesthetic sensitivity to irregularly produced changes of pressure and position and to other types of stimulation seems needed.[440]

Another important area of investigation involves the question of whether general kinesthetic *patterns* are formed as a movement is rehearsed or whether kinesthetic sensations serve as discrete links in a chain as a complex serial action is practiced. Numerous maze studies, using both animals and humans, suggest that both alternatives may be operative, depending upon the type of evaluative instrument used, the nature and complexity of the subject's nervous system, and the kinds of cues available.

The manner in which kinesthetic sensations integrate with sensations arising from the viscera and from surface indices of pain, pressure, and temperature, as well as the relationship of kinesthetic measures to balance, seem worthy of further study. Kinesthetic cues are rarely the sole means through which the individual perceives his movements. In the following sections visual-kinesthetic and vestibular-kinesthetic relationships are briefly explored.

VESTIBULAR FUNCTIONING

Studies in the sensory-tonic theory of perception, research in balance and kinesthesis, and a knowledge of the neurological basis of movement, all point to the inseparability of kinesthetic sensations and sensations arising from the inner ear in giving information concerning the total body position in space.

Investigations of vestibular functioning were undertaken as early as 1820 by Purkinje.[47] His main contribution was the discovery of an aftereffect of rotation in an opposite direction if rotation in the original direction was slowed down or suddenly stopped. Florens,[315] another physiologist, at about the same time found that tampering with the semicircular canals of pigeons caused balance problems. In 1873 Mach[47] demonstrated that rotation subjected each canal of the inner ear to specific pressures, depending upon the plane in which the individual was rotated. Mach was one of the first to develop a device in which a human might be rotated about two axes. This device was the forerunner of many more complex mechanisms of the same type.

The Structure and Functioning of the Vestibular Apparatus

The vestibular apparatus basically consists of three clear tubes filled with a fluid (endolymph) and incased in a bony labyrinth. The canals lie in three planes, and each contains hair cells supporting calcium carbonate particles (termed otoliths) which act to transmit linear accelerations of the body to neural impulses. Thus, as the head is oriented in different positions relative to gravity, the differential strain upon the hair cells signals this displacement.

Two general kinds of sensitivity arise from the vestibular apparatus: (1) an awareness of tilt in various planes from the upright, and (2) an awareness of change in acceleration or turning of the body upon one of several of its axes. Within recent years, particularly with the advent of space travel, extensive research programs have been instituted to determine the exact manner in which these organs function and the precision of the information supplied.

In a study by Fleishman,[305] testing the accuracy of the perception of verticality without visual cues, blindfolded subjects were required to adjust a chair to the upright after it has been displaced. The findings indicated that greater accuracy was achieved when the head was held in a fixed position, and that greater accuracy was achieved when the subjects were displaced to the left rather than to the right. Additionally, it was found that the magnitude and speed of the displacement were both influential of precision of adjustment at various stages of practice. The subjects in this investigation showed a high degree of consistency with which they were able to return to the upright; however, the accuracy of their adjustments was highly specific (i.e., many could adjust after being tilted to the right with accuracy, and not after being tilted to the left).

In general, however, it is difficult to isolate perception of tilt from other pressure and kinesthetic sensations. The straps holding an individual on any of the various tilt-tables overpower vestibular sensations to become the dominant way in which information is received. In fact, studies of individuals who have had their otoliths removed, or otherwise injured, indicate that their sensitivity to the upright is nearly equal to that of those who have no such problem. Cues from the vestibular apparatus, as well as kinesthetic sensations from the neck muscles and from other portions of the body, seem to override vestibular functioning with vision removed. When vision is available to the subject, a severe alteration of his visual field is necessary to produce distortions in the upright (e.g., removal of all light except a tilted luminous rod).

In agreement with the original studies of Mach, Groen and Jongkees[397] found that minimum perception of angular acceleration for man is about .5 degrees per/second. Thresholds for tilt are less definitive and depend upon the experimental conditions.

The studies of Witkin and his associates[970-972] point with most clarity to the interaction of vision and postural cues when forming perceptual judgments about body verticality and about qualities of the visual field. Three primary tasks have been utilized in this research: (1) The tilting-room-tilting chair test; the apparatus consists of a small room surrounding a chair, both of which may be tilted laterally either by the experimenter or the subject seated in the chair. (2) The Rod-and-frame Test: This test measures the perception of position in the visual field, and consists of a luminous square frame and a luminous rod seen in a darkened room, each of which may be tilted independently. As a further variable, the subject's body may be tilted to either side when attempting to judge the position of the rod and/or frame. (3) This apparatus is similar to the tilt-room-tilting chair task, except that the entire room and chair may be rotated so that it is more difficult for the subject to utilize gravity cues acting upon his body when attempting to adjust himself or the room to the upright.

Although this apparatus has been used in a variety of studies, they all involve creating a conflict between visual and postural factors of perceived upright. Each therefore represents a problem of integrating conflicting sensory experiences and arriving at a single perceptual judgment. The results of these investigations suggest that there are wide individual differences in the type of cues (visual or postural) individuals utilize when constructing their perceptions of positions in space, and of their own bodies. Usually, however, the subjects will "go along with the field" to varying extents, and base their judgments of verticality (of themselves or of the rod within the frame) upon their surroundings (the tilted room or the luminous frame). In general the findings also indicated that individuals are remarkably consistent concerning the manner in which they arrived at their perceptual judgments in the several tasks.

In general, it appears that the vestibular apparatus operating independently is not greatly depended upon. Highly developed otolith organs are noted in the shark as he moves about in his comparatively weightless environment. The organs seem to assume less importance in man, however, as his visual apparatus and kinesthetic receptors seem to play more important roles than do vestibular sensations.

Although believed by some to constitute only a nuisance by causing seasickness, the vestibular apparatus operates in close cooperation with other systems (the kinesthetic receptors, visual apparatus, and other perceptual and motor systems) to contribute to the accuracy of total body movement. More research emphasis has been recently placed upon the functioning of tho vestibular apparatus in man as he seems intent upon entering weightless space.

VISUAL-TACTILE-KINESTHETIC STRUCTURING OF PROXIMAL SPACE

Research concerning kinesthetic visual relationships points to the conclusion that each sensation operating independently results in the formation of a different perception than that which results when several sensations are used together. For example, when objects may only be seen, they often assume a different character than when they also may be explored manually. On the other hand, when objects may only be manipulated, different qualities are often assigned to them than if the eyes see what the hands are doing.

In addition, Gibson[364] has pointed to the important difference in the perception formed by active touching on the part of the individual, vs. his being touched by the object.

The findings of two types of research support the interdependence of tactual-motor-visual cues when making qualitative judgments of objects in near space. Studies by Bartley,[53] Zigler[925] and others emphasize the importance of visual imagery in the formation of perceptions of manipulated objects when simultaneous visual inspection is prevented. Factorial studies by Thurston,[886] Guilford,[400] and others, point to the importance of kinesthetic imagery in "mentally manipulating" seen objects.

Gibson suggests that in some respects vision and touch register the same information and the same experience, when that experience is, of course, close to the body.[364]

Bartley[53] in 1953 tested the hypothesis that visual imagery is operative in perception, even when tactual-kinesthetic cues are the only ones available. In size judgment with vision, near objects are generally perceived as larger than those further away. Bartley felt that, if visual imagery was important to tactual-kinesthetic perception, square blocks which were manipulated without vision might be judged larger when placed close to the individual than when located further away. His findings supported the contention that factors operative relative to judgment of distance and size with vision also function when only tactual-kinesthetic cues are available.

Zigler and Barrett[996] in a similar study, found that individuals depend upon visual imagery to form accurate perceptions of forms pressed against portions of the arm and hand. Both researchers suggested that, since tactual-kinesthetic cues seem inadequate in themselves for the comprehensive judgment of qualities of objects in space, visual imagery becomes indispensable for the complete integration of tactual-kinesthetic cues.

If visual imagery is important to the tactual-kinesthetic perception of objects, the reverse also seems to be true. A kinesthetic factor consistently emerges as in factorial studies relating many tests of visual perception. Generally, this attribute refers to the ability to "mentally rearrange" or structure objects perceived in two-dimensional space, while imaginally moving them in a third dimension.

The "hands" test is heavily loaded with the kinesthetic factor. The problem is to determine quickly whether several hands pictured in a variety of positions are left or right hands. The "flags" test is another in the same category. The task is to determine which of several flags placed in various positions is identical to a standard flag. Such tasks, it is believed, involve kinesthetic imagination, as they require that objects in space be mentally manipulated to change their relationship to the perceiver or to similar objects. While generally no overt movement response is required on the part of those tested, the ability to achieve a high score in such measures is believed to depend upon their facility to accurately imagine movement. Gibson[364] further emphasized the similarity between tactual and visual perception as he outlined the properties of objects which are manipulated with the hands . . . their similarity to the traditional gestaltic principles gleaned from a consideration of visual perception is striking.

Objects when handled, transmit an impression of *rigidity;* an observer can distinguish between two surfaces on an object, one yielding the other rigid, independent of visual cues. A second quality is termed *unity* by Gibson, and is suggested by the fact that when an object is felt with two or more fingers the sensations form a unitary perception of form, even when various combinations of fingers are used and these combinations constantly change. *Stability* is another perceptual quality gleaned from manipulative activity; even as the hands and fingers move over the object, if it is fixed, it is perceived as stable in space. *Weight* is a fourth perceptual quality gained from manual-tactile activity. The whole neuromuscular feedback system, finger joints, wrist joints and arm joints contribute to the impression of relative and/or absolute weight of the handled object. Utilizing a task in which an individual had to match an unseen irregular object with one which was in view, it was determined that the final quality gained from manual activity was an extremely accurate concept of *shape.* Noting the similarity of these qualities with other perceptual qualities gained from "pure" visual sensations and auditory sensations Gibson proposed a theory of perception which holds that perception is relatively independent of sensation; that perceptual "permanence" underlying the ever-changing sensations which bombard the human organism is the crucial operation, not the separation of the sensory input, and their later integration (via the learning process) into perceptual judgments.

THE GEOMETRIC ORGANIZATION OF NEAR SPACE

Theorists have conceived of the human's near space as possessing specific geometric dimensions, which are structured by kinesthetic judgments of time and force and by visual-motor integration. Weber in 1927 suggested that immediate space may be conceived of as a structured kinesthetic field, regulated by properties of time and force. Weber concluded that space may be thought of as having specific geometric properties and that the primary constituents of this near space field are measures of force and time. Ideas are contained in the theory which further lend support to the belief that kinesthetic sensitivity is varied rather than fixed.[935]

It was hypothesized by Weber that perception of short movements under load (when weighted) is perceptually equivalent to moving a greater distance under less load and that a given interval of time under a heavy load is perceptually equal to a longer period of time under a lighter one. It is further stated that the load placed upon the limb affects the perception of area and of straight lines, thus body positions, space, and time are intimately related. Weber's kinesthetic field theory, while in many respects inadequate and incomplete, nevertheless represents one of the earliest attempts to quantify perceptions of near-space in geometric terms.[935]

Karl Smith,[831] a contemporary researcher, has also formulated a theory to explain visual-motor functioning in the sphere of "personal space." Based upon the findings of displaced vision experiments, "The Neurogeometric Theory" holds that movements within exact areas and planes surrounding the body are regulated by specific neurons within the nervous system, detecting and controlling the location and range through which action patterns of varying complexity and magnitude take place.

Underlying this theory are studies which have involved the placement of a TV camera, directed toward a task, at various angles and in several planes around the performer's field of vision. The task itself is covered, preventing direct inspection by the subject, who must view his actions through a monitor. Thus, in effect, the eyes are removed from the body and placed at various angles from the normal visual field. The effects of the resulting disruption of visual-motor integration are measured by tests of performance accuracy. It was found that specific angles of vision displacement at which movement breakdown occurs could be determined. In the case of simple tasks, relatively little, if any, disturbance was noted in narrow ranges, while, with more extreme angular displacement, most subjects showed little adaptation to the experimental situation.

Both the plane into which the subject's vision is projected as well as the complexity of the task proved to be variables limiting performance accuracy. For example, in the horizontal plane, the accuracy of a task involving arm movements broke down at about 60 degrees of visual-motor displacement, while writing movements began to deteriorate at about 30 degrees. Less disruption was seen as the camera was placed in the vertical plane, above and in front of the performer. In general, and in agreement with similar studies, it was noted that more pronounced movement breakdown occurred in fine movements than in larger ones, when the same amount of displacement was involved. It was found also that the further the task was artificially removed from the normal visual field the greater the performance distortion.

Basically, the theory suggests that movement accuracy is dependent not only upon the complexity of the task but also upon its displacement from and/or within the usual visual field. Accurate utilization of space immediately surrounding the body, it was held, is thus partly governed by specific geometric displacement demands (or upon "the perceptual stress," to use Smith's phrasing) inherent in the task.

SUMMARY

A vast number of visual-motor integrations combine to aid in the perception of objects and events in near space. Many of these interactions serve as springboards from which to perceive accurately various characteristics of extended space beyond the reach of the individual. Initial notions of depth, for example, are gained as it is noted that various visual cues of distance correspond to the necessity to reach far out for certain objects or to pick them up without extending the arm or walking toward them. Thus no rigid boundaries exist between an individual's proximal space world and extended space.

Various basic concepts are learned as the infant and adult construct perception of their near space. Piaget, for example, suggests that concepts of force are initially perceived by forcefully manipulating heavy objects or by pushing against immovable structures. Concepts of roundness are formed as the tactual-kinesthetic impressions gained from touching spheres and cylinders are coordinated with the visual cues of shading, texture, and the like.

Near space may be structured through visual-motor integrations of various types, while farther removed events and objects may only be accurately structured by hypothesizing what *probably* would be the characteristics of distant objects if they could be actually handled. Thus the accuracy of perceptions of objects in space far removed is based upon standards and qualitative relationships gained through the structuring of near space. As objects and events move beyond the reach of the individual, more dependence upon distance receptors, hearing and vision, is required. Thus, the third stage of the proximal-distal framework is ready for exploration, after accurately structuring the self and obtaining knowledge of spatial relationships within reach of our exploring hands.

Student References

Books

1. GESELL, ARNOLD. *Studies in Child Development,* New York, Harper & Bros., 1948.
2. GESELL, ARNOLD, and AMATRUDA, CATHERINE S.: *Developmental Diagnosis,* 2nd Ed., New York, Paul B. Hoeber, Inc., 1960.
3. HARMON, D. B.: *Winter Haven Study of Perceptual Learning,* Winter Haven Lions Research Foundation, Inc., Winter Haven Lions Club, Winter Haven, Florida, A Preliminary Report, October 1962.
4. KEPHART, NEWELL C.: *The Slower Learner in the Classroom,* Columbus, Ohio, Charles E. Merrill Books, Inc.
5. HOWARD, I. P. and TEMPLETON, B.: *Human Spatial Orientation,* New York, John Wiley & Sons, Inc., 1966.

Articles

1. FLEISHMAN, EDWIN A. and RICH, SIMON: "Role of kinesthetic and spatial-visual abilities in perceptual-motor learning," *J. Exp. Psych.* 1. 66 No. 1, 6-11, 1963.
2. HALVERSON, H. M.: "The acquisition of skill in infancy," *J. Gen. Psych.,* 43, 48, 1933.
3. HARLOW, ROBERT G.: "Masculine inadequacy and compensatory development of physique," *J. Pers.,* March 1951.

Chapter 6

Visual-Space Perception

EXTENDED space is not bound by rigid dimensions but flows continuously from perceptions of the self and of proximal objects. Moreover, with the aid of auditory cues, it sometimes terminates farther away than the eye can see. Extended space is thus considered to consist of that portion of the individual's world about which judgments are made without the opportunity or the apparent need for direct contact. Perceptions of this portion of the space field are dependent primarily upon visual and auditory information integrated with temporal judgments.

The area of investigation is an extremely complex one, requiring careful attention to detail for comprehensive understanding. Therefore, several classifications might be kept in mind when examining the complexities. Perceptions of extended space may be approached by studying cues which permit the structuring of two-dimensional or three-dimensional relationships; or by considering auditory-space and visual-space as complete and separate structures unaffected by other kinds of sensory information.

The real world presents complex patterns of moving objects, changing backgrounds, and fluctuating intensities. The closer an experimental design has attempted to approximate reality, the more difficult it becomes to identify accurately the variables contributing to the total perception. Thus it is with some apprehension that we attempt to do so here.

Initially in this chapter, various conditions and cues are examined which enable the structuring of *stable* elements in space. Secondly, signposts which help to form meanings about *dynamic* attributes of spatial events are dealt with. Research relating to individual differences in perceptual ability is then summarized. The chapter concludes by contrasting measures of perceptual accuracy to structured movement tasks.

THE PERCEPTION OF STABLE TWO-DIMENSIONAL SPACE

Most of the gestaltic "laws" of perception offer clues through which two-dimensional space is ordered. As more elaborate treatment of these basic principles may be found in texts specifically devoted to gestaltic doctrine, notably those by Koffka[538] and Kohler,[541] only passing references will be made to the most prominent ones at this time. Many of these cues and perceptual principles are operative only to material in two-dimensional space. Many, however, are also basic to similar principles, under different labels, which order events in three-dimensional space and aid in the formation of perceptions about object movements.

In the previous chapter, the figure-ground concept was mentioned as an important general factor of perception and was placed under the broad classification of perceptual selection. This same concept is more specifically related, however, to the perception of two-dimensional and three-dimensional space. Most figure-ground tests involve two-dimensional diagrams; therefore, these concepts properly belong in this section rather than in the one that follows. One of the basic tenents of the figure-ground concept relates to the fact that objects centrally perceived are more clear than the surrounding and usually more distant field. Such an idea relates to the "clearness" cue, a characteristic of the space field by which three-dimensionality is perceived.

A second important principle in the perception of two-dimensional space involves *proximity*. In general, it is held that objects which are adjacent and placed next to each other will generally be integrated into patterned wholes. The closer objects are placed, it is believed, the more likely they will be combined into a common meaning or figure.

The principle of *similarity* is also important when discussing the perception of two-dimensional space. Objects which are similar in color, shape, or intensity are generally more prone to be combined into a common perception than fragments which are not.

Closure, an important gestaltic principle previously mentioned as underlying *perceptual organization,* is also important when structuring perceptions in two-dimensional space. In general, continuation of the lines in incomplete figures are perceived as commonly known wholes. Thus words partly erased, or incomplete pictures of animals, or perhaps incomplete circles quickly presented via a tachistiscope are generally reported as the completed object.

Thus the interrelated concepts of closure, figure-ground, proximity, and similarity, while by no means forming a complete list, seem the most important when considering the manner in which humans perceive structures in two-dimensional space. These concepts have been the subject of considerable research during the past forty years. Detailed inspection of this work is left to the reader, however, as the present focus and limits of space preclude a more extensive review.

PERCEPTION IN STABLE THREE-DIMENSIONAL SPACE

Most spatial perceptions leading to movement behavior rely upon a three-dimensional world. With the exception of handwriting, the painting and drawing of pictures, and various man-machine tasks requiring reactions to moving objects on radar scopes, most large muscle activities utilize three dimensions. Brief consideration, therefore, will be given to the nature of cues which serve to organize perceptions in a space capsule containing depth, as well as height and breadth.

Many of these cues seem to have been first discovered by prehistoric artists to lend reality to their cave drawings; and in most cases validity seems obvious. A detailed examination of the research underlying these signposts, while extensive, will be omitted because the main focus of the text is upon movement rather than upon perception. The material presented in this section is meant only to provide a basic background from which to consider perceptual-movement relationships and is not intended to be a comprehensive coverage of space perception.

One of the most important cues used to structure stable three-dimensional space is dependent upon the fact that a near object overlaps and partly blocks out portions of objects farther away. This *interposition effect,* related directly to figure-ground principles, contributes to the accurate relative placement of more than one object within the visual field. It is one of the primary cues through which perceptions of depth are obtained and is not dependent upon the simultaneous use of two eyes, but may be considered by a single eye. Most of the cues which follow are also monocular rather than binocular in nature.

Objects or surfaces containing textures, a ploughed field, a cobblestone street, and the like, also give clues concerning the relative position of objects placed on them. *Texture cues* are related to the invariance principle which holds that smaller objects will be perceived as located farther away, while larger ones will be perceived as closer. Thus the near portion of the ploughed field will appear to contain larger chunks of dirt, while the irregularities grow less distinguishable as the field becomes more remote. As a result, objects on such a background may be located more exactly by pairing them with the size of the textured pattern they seem to be nearest. Recent research on the invariance principle suggests that the size-distance relationship is not so exact as was once believed. Epstein,[282] for example, suggests that size as perceived and as measured are often different; thus the invariance hypothesis does not deserve a central place in explanations of space perception. Adelson[11] also explains that size-distance relationships are not exact, and the "feelings" may influence either independent of the other.

Related to the invariance principle is the use of *known standards* to perceive objects in three-dimensional space. Research suggests that the exact name attached to an object by the perceiver is the main determiner of its distance and/or size. For example, if a plain white card is thought to be a postage stamp, it will be perceived as farther away, in the absence of other cues, than the same object labeled a playing card. Individuals seem to be continually comparing objects in extended space to objects and quantitative standards familiar to them. The known size cues used to structure three-dimensional space are related to Helson's principle[438] of *perceptual pooling,* previously discussed. This is the tendency to form judgments by continual reference to the average of past experiences about similar objects.

Linear perspective is another type of cue enabling the more accurate perception of three-dimensional space. The tendency of parallel lines to converge as they extend away from the observer offers depth cues upon which spatial judgments are based. The numerous studies by Ames[21] and others involving the use of distorted rooms which seem to shrink or enlarge objects placed in them when moved to various parts are based upon this principle. The sides and windows in such enclosures are changed, and the nature of the change concealed from the observer by a coat of paint which obliterates the usually seen converging lines of wall-floor-ceiling intersections. The naive observer thus habitually constructs a normal space field based upon his past experience in looking at such rooms and becomes confused when size-distance relationships are not as expected.

One of the primary cues afforded us when perceiving three-dimensional space is related to the placement of our visual apparatus, enabling the two eyes to converge upon a single object. These binocular depth cues are obtained partially from the "additional-roundness" as the two eyes see slightly different portions of the same object. The perceptual integration of these two images helps to produce the effect of depth.

The primary manner in which binocular vision operates to provide depth cues, however, is dependent upon the various angles at which the eyes must be fixed by their controlling muscles to intercept and focus upon objects at varying distances. Thus, kinesthetic sensations arising from eye-muscle tensions, monocular depth cues, and the actual size of the retinal image are combined to form accurate distance-shape judgments of objects in extended space. Most of the depth cues may rely upon sensations received from a single eye. Binocular cues, based upon the convergence of both eyes, however, seem to provide the most accurate clues about the spatial world.

THE PERCEPTION OF MOVEMENT IN TWO-DIMENSIONAL AND THREE-DIMENSIONAL SPACE

The space field is rarely a stable one. Movements of objects within two and three planes continually occur to influence perceptual judgment. Humans structure many of their gross movements in response to movements in space. The assembly line worker acts upon perceptions of conveyor belt movements and upon actions of his hands when manipulating the object passing before him. The radar operator tracks objects moving across his scope by manually operating dials controlling cross hairs. The athlete continually bases his actions upon perception of dynamic qualities in space: of balls coming toward him to be caught, hit, batted, or struck or of runners moving away from him, to be thrown to or to be dealt with otherwise.

The picture is further complicated when it is considered that usually more than one object is in motion within the real world. Two men run out for the pass; cars move in the background behind the tennis court; and the machinist must attend to the rotation of the lathe as well as movements of his tools.

Thus, consideration of movement in structuring perceptions of space seems imperative. Such percepts are often referred to, due to their complexity, as *"events,"* and several investigations have been devoted to the factors influencing *event perception.*

Temporal Perception

Perception of movement in two-dimensional and three-dimensional space involves the integration of a time dimension with some of the cues previously identified. In general, when movements in space are viewed, conscious or unconscious judgments must be made concerning the time which has elapsed as an object or groups of objects transverse distances within visual or auditory fields. A brief review of the types of variables affecting perception of time thus seems worthwhile. The purpose is to present information about temporal perception which is related to movement of objects in space; it is not proposed to cover comprehensively such an extensive area of knowledge. The student is referred to reviews of research on temporal perception by Dunlap[263] from 1911 to 1916, by Weber[934] in 1933, by Gilliland et al.[368] in 1946, and by Wallace and Robin[917] in 1960 for more complete information.

Temporal perception has been described as an essential characteristic of movement and is defined as comparative or absolute judgments of the amount of separation between two units.[368] Many kinds of factors have been shown to influence the estimation of time and, thus, to affect the perception of movements in space.

Motivation is one of the primary modifiers of temporal perception and relates to the attention or interest in activities occurring within estimated time intervals. According to research by Harton,[425] Elkine,[278] and others, interesting jobs have been found to make time pass more quickly. More monotonous tasks in which few difficult judgments are called for cause the same time interval to be estimated as longer.

In general, it has been demonstrated that various internal physiological states do not influence time perception, except when modified by unusual drugs or the like. Neither blood pressure, pulse rate, heart work, breathing rate, nor alpha rhythms of brain waves were found to be related to the ability to estimate time, according to Schafer and Gilliland.[783]

The developmental level of the perceiver, however, has been shown by Smyth and Goldstone,[839] Elkine,[278] and others to influence the accuracy of temporal judgment. The estimations of children are extremely inaccurate and variable until around the ages of fourteen to sixteen at which time they begin to approximate those of adults. The perception of time thus seems to parallel, but to occur somewhat later than the ability to structure accurately, the self image.

Estimations of time intervals have also been shown to be related to the type of sensation delineating the interval judged. For example, Goldstone *et al.* found that visual cues were judged consistently longer than auditory cues of the same duration.[839]

The culture in which the individual is raised also has been shown to influence perception of time. Whether estimations are influenced by unique group feelings about time within the culture or are influenced also by the climate in which the culture is located is open to question. However, as findings by Renzende[749] indicate, the prevailing temperature influences perceptual inferences of this nature.

In a study relating the intensity of large-muscle activity to time estimation, Kawasima[515] had subjects estimate time while moving their arms in 10 degree circles. Overestimation occurred when action was easy and underestimation when it was difficult.

Specifically related to time-space concepts are findings by Abbe,[2] who studied the effect of time judgment of a constant time interval established by blinking lights placed varying distances apart. It was found that the time interval judgments were positively related to the distance between lights.

The close relationship between perceptions of time and space is further emphasized by Weber,[935] who suggested that, if actual velocity of an object equaled the space through which it moved, divided by the time involved, the velocity of objects as *perceived* might also be computed by dividing perceived space by *perceived* time. Thus the perception of movements is intimately related not only to their patterning, direction, and complexity but also to the accuracy of time judgments concerning their extent.

Many theories have been advanced to explain variability in time estimation. A most reasonable one was advanced by Rosenzweig,[765] who suggests that the general level of tension or "need strain" within the individual during the time interval to be perceived is the vital factor in the formation of such a perception. Generally, it is believed that, if tension is produced by the need to complete the task and by other variables producing a high motivation state, time intervals are usually underestimated. Maze studies by Berman[79] produced findings which support this "need tension" theory.

The body contains no identifiable organ through which time may be estimated nor do any rhythmic physiological factors seem to influence the process. The accurate estimation of time seems mainly attributable to general qualities of the situation, psychological factors inherent in the type of activity engaged in during the time interval judged, the type of sensations delineating an interval, and/or the developmental level of the individual.

The Perception of Movement in Two-Dimensional Space

Principles governing the perception of movement in two-dimensional space are derived directly from those factors influencing judgments about static objects within a similar field. In many cases, upon examining the literature, only broad, obvious generalizations concerning perception of movement are presented without substantiating experimental research. For example, the concepts of closure may be utilized to explain the perception of rapidly presented sequences of scenes which result in the integrated "moving" picture, the "phi phenomenon." The figure-ground principle is operative to produce the *apparent* movement of the "auto-kinetic effect." (If a single stable light is presented as the only stimulus in an otherwise dark field, it seems to move.) The development of various visual-spatial abilities in human infants has been the subject of numerous investigations. The classic studies of Walk and Gibson, for example, explored the awareness of a variety of animals, as well as of human infants, on "visual cliffs" constructed from tables containing one-half clear plate glass. The subjects were started on the "solid" side and then encouraged to crawl toward the "cliff." Those who retracted, it was hypothesized, evidenced an awareness of depth perception. These investigators concluded that all animals, when locomotion was possible, gave some evidence of perceiving depth, even turtles. Depth perception, it was hypothesized, is largely innate, although it is aided at times by the presence of learned cues.[914]

Awareness of movement on the part of infants seems to occur at an extremely early age. Haith found that visual movement suppressed non-nutritive sucking movements in infants from twenty-four to forty-eight hours old![406] Other investigators report similar findings on the part of children in early infancy.[281] The recent investigation by Dayton and his colleagues, using electro oculography for recording both eye movement and eye position, presents findings which support the conclusion that innately newborns possess a more highly developed fixation reflex than was formerly realized.[243]

One of the primary factors influencing perception of movement is the inherent defensive mechanism built into the human organism. For example, perception of movement is more accurate in the peripheral portions of the eye than within the central visual field.[753] This is believed to be part of a mechanism to alert the organism to danger more quickly as objects approach from the sides.

Much of the early research in this area was concerned with establishing characteristics of thresholds to movement perception. For example, Brown found that lower thresholds to movement result when objects are dull. More recent research by Leibowitz and Lomont[646] substantiates these findings. Leibowitz[547] found that thresholds for the perception of movement were significantly lowered when gridlines were added to the visual field, enabling use of invariance cues. It was found in this study that thresholds to velocity were lowered by as much as 48 per cent by the addition of these cues.

Brown[120] found that larger objects are perceived as moving more slowly than smaller ones. There was a marked relationship between size and speed perception. For example, if an object was doubled in size, its velocity was perceived as being half as fast. And, conversely, to make the object which is doubled in size appear faster, the velocity had to be doubled. Speeds were also found to be perceived as faster in the vertical than in the horizontal direction.[119]

Aubert[35] and later students attempted to determine how slow a movement could be reproduced and still be perceived. A range of variability was noted. It was found that the movement-speed thresholds ranged from one to two minutes of arch per second to ten to twenty minutes of arch per second, depending upon the availability of various auxiliary cues.

Several researchers, notably Heider[433] in 1944, Michotte[658] in 1946 and 1950, and Johansson[107] in 1952, have investigated the perceptions of reasonably complex movements of more than one object interacting to form spatial patterns. Generally, these investigators concluded that total relationships are perceived. Also, when a change in speed or of other characteristics in one portion of the pattern takes place, completely different perceptions are reported.

Michotte[658] utilized a complex projection machine which produced two moving, intersecting dots along similar and parallel arcs that caused an apparent recoil as the pathway of one contacted the pathway of the second. His findings coincide with those of Piaget[728] insofar as perceptions of physical causality were consistently reported, as one dot recoiled from the second. The subjects said that they saw one dot "pushing" or "launching" the second as contact appeared to be made. In a second study using squares moving in relationship to each other, Michotte again found that the paired movements of the objects were interpreted in terms of the living behavior of organisms. One square was reported to be "mad" at the second or "afraid" of the other.

Heider[433] in 1944 produced findings which agree with Michotte's. When a black circle was caused to move in and out of a larger triangle, it was reported that the movements were perceived in terms of human motives and purposes. The smaller dot was reported as aggressively trying to move into the "house" (the triangle), for example. Most of the researchers in this field have concluded that perceptions of moving schematas seem to be made quickly, holistically, and somewhat superficially, rather than analytically. And in most cases, these perceptions seem to coincide with the immediate needs of the observer.

In 1952, the Swedish psychologist, Johannson,[493] reported upon one of the more comprehensive research programs studying the perception of movements in space. Johannson used a complex projection machine which flashed dots of light upon a screen. They could be caused to form various patterns, and the colors could be controlled. This device was capable of moving the spots independently to form regular geometric pathways or to produce various irregular combinations of movements. Johannson requested that his subjects describe qualitatively the various phenomena they observed in this moving kaleidoscope. Parallel studies in this same research program investigated the effect of fluctuating auditory and cutaneous stimuli which were caused to vary in intensity and to assume various movement patterns. These studies were described by Johannson as investigations of "event perception."

In general, Johannson's findings paralleled those of Michotte insofar as his subjects reported perceptions of patterned wholes rather than analytical descriptions of discrete parts. For example, when a pattern was presented in which the end lights were moved in opposite directions while a central light remained fixed, the subjects consistently reported that a stick seemed to be tipping back and forth. They seemed to "fill-in" the space between the lights with an imaginary rod, thus illustrating the "closure" effect noted as characteristic of stable elements in two-dimensional space.

Johannson suggested that, when the objects were presented simultaneously, their various relationships, rather than their actual speeds, exerted the most influence upon perception, although at times both factors seem operative. For example, when two spots of light moving at different speeds were presented at the same time, the slower one seemed to form the "ground" or field for the faster one.

In conclusion, Johannson hypothesized that the perceptions of total motion occupied a central position, rather than the intensity of the sounds, the speeds of the lights, or the force of the tactile stimulation (puffs of air) in the reported perceptions. Almost invariably, the subjects utilized temporal terms when discussing their judgments of these dynamic movements. More recent studies have further delineated factors underlying the ability to organize effectively movement in space. Gottsdanker,[390] for example, studied the ability to detect gradual acceleration in moving objects on the part of human subjects.

Gemelli presented findings in 1954 which suggested that movement left to right within the space field is perceived as faster than movement in the opposite direction.[348] Goldstein and Weiner[377] in a more definitive study, however, assert as a result of their findings that movement from left to right is perceived as accurately as movement of objects in the opposite direction. These latter researchers further concluded that when more than one object is moving at the same time: (*a*) as they cross they reach a "region of proximity" in which the objects' movements influence the observer's perceptions of both, and as the objects move farther from one another, perceptual distortions because of their mutual proximity are reduced; (b) movements higher in the space field are perceived as faster than simultaneously moving discs which are placed lower; (c) an object which starts earlier is perceived as moving faster than one which begins its movement second. These researchers also found that their subjects, when viewing movement in two dimensions, would frequently report an illusion that they were viewing the objects in a third dimension.

It is believed that the findings of these studies in "event perception" have important implications for the student of human movement. They point to the fact that all aspects of the dynamic situation contribute to judgments of movements in space. For example, when a tennis ball is struck and moves toward the perceiver, judgments of its absolute speed may be influenced by the speed and direction of other background movements, the pathway taken by the opponent after hitting the ball, or, perhaps, the direction and velocity of cars moving in back of the tennis court.

The Perception of Movement in Three-Dimensional Space

There are few studies examining phenomena related to the perception of movement in three-dimensional space. The complexity inherent in designing such studies seems at times insurmountable, since it is realized that not only may several objects move within various configurations in space but also the observer might be made to change position.

In general, the term *movement parallex* has been coined to refer to several kinds of cues utilized to judge movements in three-dimensional space. This refers to phenomena relating to the apparent differences in speed at which various objects, varying distances from the observer seem to be moving relative to him and to each other. It refers also to the change in an object's shape which seems to take place as an observer moves around to inspect a complex figure from several positions. A commonly noted effect is that objects closely placed seem to move faster and in a direction opposite to that of the observer, while the farther away an object is located, the slower it is judged to be moving. If two objects are moving in the same direction and at the same rate, the near object seems to move faster, or if two objects are judged to be the same size, the faster moving one seems to be closer, provided other cues are eliminated or held constant.

The movement parallex phenomenon is extremely complex, however, and is often influenced by various illusionary situations. For example, if an individual is in a fast-moving train, the near telephone poles seem to move rapidly in a direction opposite to that of the train and at a speed directly related to that of the speeding vehicle. However, when these near objects seem to move rapidly, distant hills are often perceived to move in the *same* direction as does the train. Gibson *et al.*[362] have conjectured that the movement parallax phenomenon involves two types of spatial experience, "empty depth" and "filled depth." The former experience involves the perception of one surface in front of a second, while in the latter a receding surface acts to achieve a heightened depth effect.

Accurate perceptual judgments under such complex conditions, of course, underlie the performance of many movement skills. For example, ball tracking facility on the part of the sports performer, as objects come toward him to be caught or struck, depends upon correct interpretations of various movement parallax cues within his visual field.

Tschermak[899] has presented an extensive list of situations giving rise to problems in movement parallax, when using one eye. Among these situations in differential angular velocity of moving objects are the following: (1) Circular movement: Equations for determining velocities of various objects placed at varying distances and moving around a stable observer, are computed or, upon knowing the angular velocities, distances are computed. (2) Movement parallel to the observer: The problem in this situation is to first determine whether the individual is attending to various objects. Objects also tend to pass into the peripheral field, thus further complicating the problem. (3) Moving head, stationary objects: Approximately the same formulas are valid, depending on whether the head is moving parallel to or around the stationary object.

Graham *et al.*[391] published research in 1948 reporting findings derived from using a device which evaluated various problems involving movement parallax cues. The task required the subject to look at two needles, one above the other, against a uniform background. Both needles moved at a constant rate in a plane perpendicular to the individual's line of sight. One needle was firmly fixed, while the other could be adjusted to an equal distance from the observer via a micrometer setting. Only one eye was utilized by the subject to make the judgments, thus the findings pertain primarily to monocular movement parallax.

Both Zeger[995] and Graham[391] found there was an increase in ability to match distance between the two moving needles when the movement rate was increased. However, if speed was increased past a certain point, judgments of relative distance became impossible. It was concluded that sensitivity to movement parallax cues is primarily based upon the individual's ability to perceive differences between angular displacements of the two objects (in this case, needles).

Although these findings primarily have indicated fruitful directions for more extensive research, the device developed by Graham and utilized by him and his co-workers to study movement parallax cues appears to be one of the few exact devices to have been employed to date. With such a device one might investigate the nature of movement parallax cues, thresholds, and the effect of various variables upon the perception of movement in three-dimensional space. It would seem that such a tool might be utilized in comparing perceptual efficiency to performance in various sports skills which depend upon the accuracy with which movement parallax cues are utilized.

With the exception of several studies carried out during World War II by Liebowitz and others relating to the particular needs of the Air Force, few recent investigations have been undertaken in this area.[574] Ittelson, one of the most prolific researchers in visual space perception, has conducted several exploratory studies recently from which the following generalizations were drawn:[484]

1. If the observer is aware of the real distance of a fixed object, as he moves, the object will appear to remain stationary.

2. If the observer is unaware of the exact location of an object because of some environmental or experimental distortion, as he moves, the object will appear to also change position.

3. If an object is moving, and again its correct distance is known by the observer, its velocity will be accurately perceived.

4. Conversely, if moving objects are incorrectly located, their judged velocities will be distorted. Such generalizations support and parallel Weber's[935] "Perceptual Velocity Equals Perceptual Speed Divided by Perceptual Time" formula previously reported.

Most effects of moving objects in three planes could be duplicated upon two planes, as, for example, dots might be gradually changed in size to give the illusion of approaching or departing from the observer. Through such effects, more exact information concerning movement in three-dimensional space could be gathered. However, research of this nature seems to be lacking.

While this exploratory research points to general characteristics of the movement parallax and the extent to which it is broadly operative in the perception of three-dimensional movement, a large question remains unanswered. How do humans quickly judge distance-time relationships as they and/or objects move in space? And even more astonishingly, how do they subsequently prove (or disprove) the accuracy of their perceptions by acting upon them through the interception or the striking of moving targets in space via a thrown missile?

Broadbent[116] has coined the term *perceptual anticipation* to refer to the ability to predict and to intercept the pathways of incoming and/or departing objects in the space field. Although Leibowitz[573,574] and others have demonstrated that the more cues available, for example the addition of converging lines, the more accurately one may deal with moving objects, additional basic research is needed.

THE ROLE OF AUDITORY PERCEPTION
IN STRUCTURING SPACE

Sounds integrated with visual impressions make possible a more accurate estimation of the nature of events in three-dimensional space. The sound of the ball hitting the catcher's mitt permits the pitcher to make better judgments of speed when paired with a visual impression of the ball's movement towards the plate. Sounds help us localize objects in space and provide important cues in forming perceptions of reality.

The importance of sounds in space perception is given new meaning when they are eliminated or when some visual-auditory distortion is introduced into an experimental situation. For example, isolation in a non-echoing soundproof room has been found to have quite a disturbing effect, since the individual is removed from the familiar sounds which formerly aided him to better localize himself and adjacent objects in space.

Further illustrating the marked dependence upon visual-auditory integration when forming perceptions about spatial events was Snyder and Pronko's[842] distorted-vision study, previously referred to. The subject repeatedly mentioned the disconcerting effect of hearing cars and other objects approaching from one direction, while seeing them converging from the other side during the initial days of the experiment. Until these diverse sensations were resolved, stable perceptions about movements in his distorted world could not be formulated.

The nature of "auditory-space" has been the focus of experimental concern to various degrees during the past one hundred and thirty years. Although initially psychologists doubted that sounds could provide knowledge about space, as sounds have no size, researchers began to perform experiments in sound localization which indicated the importance of auditory cues when structuring the individual's space field. As early as 1887, for example, Lord Rayleigh[745] performed simple experiments in sound localization. First, he found that he could locate and identify his various assistants as they spoke in a circle around him with more accuracy than he could describe the location of tuning forks placed in the same manner. Rayleigh also discovered, in agreement with later researchers, that the location of sounds could be made with more accuracy when they were reproduced at the front of the body than when they were located at the sides.

Several researchers around the turn of the century, including Matsumoto[622] and Scripture[790] at Yale in 1887 and Pierce[730] in 1901, constructed "sound-cages" to surround their subjects. These were designed to pinpoint various localizing phenomena and to test popular theories of auditory-space perception. Some of these researchers argued that intensity rather than location was the most important variable when identifying objects in space. Others suggested that functioning of the balancing mechanism in the middle ear integrated with auditory impressions to form perceptions about auditory-space.

More recently, Wallach[918] has shown that the kinesthetic sensation produced by head movements integrates with auditory sensations to provide perceptions of auditory-space. It was found that, if the head is permitted to move when sounds are produced, a more accurate judgment of their location is made than if the head is immobilized. It was also found that freedom of head movements aided long distance perception of the location of sounds.

The most accepted theory concerning sound-localization involves the concept of *dichoticity,* or the near simultaneous stimulation of the two ears by different kinds of sound qualities within the left-right space field. Thus, it is felt that a mechanism operates which is similar to binocular vision. A comprehensive explanation, however, would have to include reference to the integration of auditory-kinesthetic sensations, and, when the eyes are used, to various visual factors.

FACTORS IN VISUAL-SPACE PERCEPTION

In recent years increased emphasis has been placed upon the isolation of basic factors of space perception. Typical of these efforts are factorial studies by Thurstone,[886] Guilford,[400] Roff,[759] and others. At times, these investigations have been carried out to add to man's basic knowledge about himself. In other instances, they have been pointed toward the identification of qualities desirable within certain kinds of situations. An example of investigations within the latter category are those to determine the perceptual capacities and characteristics most desirable in Air Force pilots.[401]

The factors isolated in such studies are diverse. Generally, they seem to depend upon the nature of the measurements obtained, the general focus of the research, the background and biases of the investigators, as well as upon more subtle circumstances. Even the number of factors has been questioned; some investigators argue that there are three basic factors; others, two. Some investigators find that various nonvisual factors, psychomotor coordination, verbalization, perseverance, and the like, are important to structuring spatial relationships.

Guilford[400] and Zimmerman,[997] for example, suggest that two main factors relative to space perception exist. Guilford identifies these as an awareness of objects in space and their imaginary manipulation. Zimmerman holds that one factor is *spatialization,* the observer orients and makes his judgments by projecting himself into the situation, and the second is *visualization,* believed to be more cognitive and involving the mental *manipulation* of objects in space.

The majority of the factorial investigations hold that three or more factors are important to the perception of space. Army researchers[401] in 1952, for example, following an analysis of items in the General

Classification Test, found that three factors emerged: skill in manipulating parts of a configuration in relation to each other; skill in manipulating objects in relation to the subject in and out of planes of the paper, and various non-spatial factors including speed, and the ability to apply sustained effort.

Thurstone,[886] one of the pioneers in the factorial analysis of spatial signposts, found in 1950 that two factors are involved in passive types of judgments (termed S_1 and S_2): the judgment of objects as viewed from various angles and when moved. A third factor included spatial relationships in which the observer's bodily orientations formed an essential role, or *kinesthetic imagery*. Although Zimmerman[997] has suggested that S_1 and S_2 are merely differences upon a difficulty continuum, Thurstone's factors have also been identified by other investigators.

Studies attempting to isolate factors important to airplane pilots generally find that various nonvisual competencies are important to the total process of space perception. Frequent factors identified include psychomotor coordination as well as verbal ability.

Upon reviewing these factorial studies, it can be seen that there are some differences of opinion as to the central factors of space perception. Perhaps these factors depend upon the distance from the observer an object is perceived, as suggested by Nishi[699] or perhaps they are dependent upon whether the objects are moving or stable. In any case, four factors of space perception seem to emerge consistently: (1) the ability to imagine movements of objects in two-dimensional space and at times to imagine them passing through three dimensions; (2) the ability to remain unconfused, to adopt new perspectives as the position of a spatial figure is changed, and to predict the shape and appearance of an object viewed from different angles; (3) kinesthetic imagery, or the ability to project oneself into the pattern and to manipulate objects mentally; and (4) the ability to compare various objects with each other in two-dimensional and three-dimensional space, usually involving the accuracy of depth perception.

It is noted, however, that test batteries including tasks which relate to perception in three-dimensional space are lacking. One omission is the usually included measure of depth perception; another, tasks which evaluate the accuracy and speed with which judgments are made concerning real movements in space and the facility with which various movement parallax cues are dealt.

In the following section, in which perceptual-motor relationships are described, the tests of space perception without exception involve tasks evaluating the facility to manipulate static figures in two-dimensional space. That even moderate relationships have been shown to exist between these measures and movement in three dimensions seems truly remarkable. The moderate relationships found point clearly to the importance of general and specific perceptual factors to accurate movement.

RELATIONSHIPS BETWEEN MEASURES OF PERCEPTION IN EXTENDED SPACE AND PERFORMANCE IN STRUCTURED MOVEMENT TASKS

Throughout the previous chapters dealing with the general perceptual process and the structuring of proximal events, it was brought out that the ability to form correct meanings about near space contributes directly to efficient movement. The number of studies demonstrating such a direct relationship between perceptual and motor functioning in extended space, however, is limited. Motor performance seems to have been viewed by many researchers as an independent phenomenon unrelated to perceptual causality. Numerous others have studied the process of perception while disregarding motor output.

Investigations which have compared perceptual-motor integration fall into two main categories: (1) those using perceptual measures involving two-dimensional cues, and (2) those which incorporate measures of three-dimensional depth cues. Studies in this area may also be classified according to whether they deal specifically with relationships of visual perception and movement accuracy or whether they involve a wider range of perceptual measures, including tasks of motor manipulation, balance, and the like. The McCloy Blocks Test was represented as a perceptual measure in one such study which evaluated general perceptual speed and efficiency. This task, however, involves the speed with which one can manipulate blocks in sequence by using rapidly presented color cues.

Research contrasting the ability to deal with moving objects in two-dimensional and three-dimensional space and motor task performance are notably lacking. Generally, investigations are carried out which compare perceptual-motor activities having highly dissimilar input qualities. For example, a test of *static* depth perception, involving the slow and deliberate alignment of rods within a tube, is often compared to fencing, basketball, or baseball skill, activities which require the rapid response to moving objects in space. The task of contemporary researchers, it seems, is to produce standardized measures of dynamic event perception which more closely approximate the real world of moving objects. Comparisons between scores achieved in such tasks to motor performance measures should produce higher perceptual-motor correlations than have thus far been obtained.

In general, most investigations comparing perceptual-motor functioning have found that efficient visual-space perception differentiates between broad categories of motor performers. Olsen,[708] for example, found that athletes scored higher in measures of reaction time, depth perception, and visual apprehension than did non-athletes.* Winograd[969]

---

*Visual apprehension was evaluated by measuring the capacity of individuals to deal with several objects, letters or words within a single span of attention. The actual task utilized included the quick presentation via a tatistiscope of several squares in sequence, each containing from 4 to 13 small dots. The subject's score depended upon his ability to make a quick estimation of the number of dots presented.

also reports findings which imply that perceptual tests may aid in broadly classifying motor performers, but that perceptual-movement measures are not related within more fine limits. Differences were found between varsity baseball players and non-athletes in several tests of visual efficiency, including binocular depth perception. This same investigator, however, failed to obtain significant correlations between perceptual tests and specific performance measures (batting averages, runs batted in, and the like). Montebello,[671] as reported by Miller,[662] also found that baseball players had greater sensitivity to depth cues than non-players, while finding no significant correlations between batting averages and perceptual functioning.

However, Graybiel,[392] reviewing research carried out during the 1952 Olympics, found that perceptual tests not only differentiated between performers and nonperformers but also permitted finer discriminations between athletes to be made. Moderate correlations were found between performance in tennis, football, and other sports and depth perception.

Bannister and Blackburn[49] reported in 1931 that athletes (Rugby football players) had significantly larger distances between their eyes (interpupillary distances) than did non-players. He felt that such an arrangement, facilitating the establishment of binocular depth cues, contributed to their superior playing ability. Although these findings remain unsubstantiated, studies clarifying the relationships between anthropometric measures, eye functioning, and physical performance are otherwise absent in the research.

Peripheral vision or the ability to perceive objects within a large angular span, usually on the horizontal plane, has been found to be an important factor relating to motor skill performance. The basic measure usually obtained is the span of vision encompassed as the head is held immobile within the medial plane. Graybiel,[392] for example, reported that when peripheral vision is eliminated more difficulty in motor task performance is experienced than when central vision is eliminated. Although McCain[398] found only slight differences between the peripheral vision of high school athletes and non-athletes, Stroup,[864] studying basketball players, found that significant differences did exist between these measures of visual sensitivity. In this latter study, peripheral vision was evaluated by a test which involves the perception of two rotating targets placed in two extreme edges of the visual field and moved through a range of 220 degrees. Thus, evaluation was made of "the-field-of-motion" perception, and probably a greater range was found than if only the sighting of static objects was used.

Several researchers have taken motion pictures of the eyes and heads of sports performers in an effort to determine over-all visual behavior when tracking objects in space. Mott,[677] exploring the relationships between eye movements evaluated in this way and performance during the beginning stages of four experimental motor skills, found that individuals performed better whose eye movements were smoother, as contrasted to movements which were jerky and abruptly changing from object to object involving many fixations. Hubbard and Senge,[475] using a similar approach to inspect the tracking movements of baseball batters, also found that smoother eye movements were related to superior performance.

These researchers also determined that head movements were kept to a minimum when tracking fast-moving objects coming toward the observer. It was noted that little head movement accompanied the visual tracking of incoming balls pitched at from 50 to 90 miles per hour. It is believed that evaluation of tracking ability through the use of an eye movement camera holds greater promise in the future. Such a device, by projecting a beam of light into the cornea and gathering the subsequent reflection in a camera which simultaneously photographs the subject's visual field, is able to produce a film of the visual field with a spot of light indicating where the individual is looking. The advantage to the use of such an instrument over the cinetomographical analyses described above is obvious.

Two studies indicate that visual-motor integration breaks down when objects approaching or departing from the observer exceed certain speeds. Hubbard and Senge,[475] for example, found that baseball batters were unable to track speeding baseballs thrown toward them when these balls were from 8 to 15 feet from the plate. It was suggested that further visual tracking was not only impossible, but impractical, as the movement (the bat swing) designed to intercept the object had already been initiated and could not be stopped, even if perceptions of the ball's course *were* modified.

An unpublished study by Stull, reported by Miller,[662] suggested that the speed with which an object *departs* from the perceiver may be a factor influencing the efficiency of perception. It was hypothesized that a basketball shot by an individual in the usual manner leaves him too rapidly for efficient binocular convergence to occur. It was suggested, therefore, that basketball shooting accuracy primarily must be due to the use of monocular, rather than to binocular, depth cues.

Two studies of a more general nature illustrate the manner in which several kinds of tests are utilized to determine the contribution of general perceptual factors to accurate movements in space. Kreiger[544] found that a moderate correlation existed between scores in a standard test of figure-ground perception and the ability to adjust a tennis racket to incoming balls thrown from various angles by a mechanical device. Thus figure-ground perception seems related in this case to perceptual anticipation, since it was found that about a 25 per cent common variance existed between the two scores.

One of the most comprehensive perceptual-motor comparisons was completed in 1960 by Donna Mae Miller.[664] One hundred and sixty-two subjects, consisting of both men and women recognized as champions, near-champions, or low skilled performers in volleyball, basketball, fencing, swimming-diving, and gymnastics, were used. The battery of perceptual measures included those evaluating speed, orientation in space, spatial visualization, tests of closure, the McCloy Blocks test previously described, and two tests of static balance. The main differences found by Miller between outstanding sports performers and low-skilled persons were balance, depth perception, closure, and the Block tests. Little difference was found between champions and near-champions on these same tests. Men scored significantly higher than did women on tests of spatial visualization, a factor which correlates with the findings of other researchers.

The significant correlation found between depth perception and balance confirmed the findings of previous investigators who held that vision is an important factor in maintaining balance. The importance of balance in performance was indicated, since the balance scores were found to provide the most valid indication for distinguishing between differing levels of sports ability. Miller concluded that champions in the various sports included evidenced measurable (although in most cases slight) differences in visual perception and were consistently superior to the intermediate performers. Marked differences were found when comparing high-level to low-level sports performers.

The research now available thus suggests that the ability to judge accurately spatial events differentiates only within broad limits between athletes and non-athletes, or between those able to move accurately and those who cannot. Relatively few investigations have attempted to delineate procedures with which visual-space perception might be improved. Several of these have been concerned with lowering recognition time of balls traveling in space. Haskins,[428] for example, found that the use of training films was beneficial in shortening the time necessary to perceive accurately the direction of a tennis ball.

Smith[836] found that using photographically portrayed targets her subjects habitually underthrew distance targets and overthrew near ones. Furthermore she found that throwing at visually presented space fields which were affixed to the eyes of the subjects was helpful in studying some of the variables of the situation and that the motor responses of her subjects seemed to combine with visual perceptual cues to afford an accurate judgment of distance.

SUMMARY

Extended space is defined as that portion of the individual's world about which judgments are made without the opportunity or apparent need for direct contact. Perceptions of this portion of the space field are primarily dependent upon visual and auditory information integrated with temporal judgments. Perception of stable, two-dimensional space depends upon gestaltic concepts of closure, figure-ground, proximity, and similarity, while the principles of known standards, linear perspective, texture, and interposition, become important when forming perceptions of stable three-dimensional space.

The study of movement in two-dimensional and three-dimensional space has been referred to as *event perception,* and perceptions of this nature are interlinked with the judgment of time. The perception of movement in space is a function of the size of the objects and their luminescence, as well as their speed and other cues available. When two or more objects move within the same space field, they are generally interpreted as assuming some human function (*i.e.,* one may be perceived as pushing another, or one may be reported as being a house with another trying to get in). In general, when complex movements of several objects are initiated within the space field, the total field is perceived as a dynamic whole, with relationships between the objects rather than their discrete functioning being most often reported. Judgments of velocities in three-dimensional space depend upon the position and movement of the observer, the perceived distance of the object from the observer, as well as the perceived size of the object in motion.

In general, four factors of space perception seem to emerge: (1) the ability to imagine movements of objects in two-dimensional and three-dimensional space; (2) the ability to remain unconfused, adopting new perspectives as the position of a spatial figure is changed and to predict an object's shape and appearance when viewed from different angles; (3) kinesthetic imagery, the ability to project oneself into a pattern, to manipulate objects mentally; and (4) the ability to compare various objects with each other in two-dimensional and three-dimensional space.

Perceptual differences are found between athletes and non-athletes. Slight to moderate differences in peripheral vision, ability to track moving objects, depth perception, and figure-ground acuity have been found, generally favoring the athlete over the non-athlete.

Student References

Books

1. GIBSON, JAMES J.: *The Perception of the Visual World,* Houghton Mifflin Co., Boston, 1950.
2. ITTELSON, W. H.: *Visual Space Perception,* New York, Springer Publishing Co., Inc., 1960.
3. VERNON, M. D.: *A Further Study of Visual Perception,* New York, Cambridge University Press, 1954.

Articles

1. GRAYBIEL, ASHTON, JOKEL, ERNST, and TRAPP, CLAUDE: "Russian studies of vision in relation to physical activity and sports," *Res. Quart. Am. Assoc. Hlth., Phys. Ed. & Rec., 26,* 480-485, December 1955.
2. JOHANNSON, GUNNAR: "Configurations in event perception," Uppsala, 1950.

SECTION III

THE PERFORMER

Chapter 7

Maturation

A CHAPTER entitled "Motor Characteristics" is usually found in texts describing the development of the infant, child, or adolescent. These surveys leave little doubt that maturation plays an important role in forming many of the movement patterns evidenced by human beings. Since this book's primary focus is upon motor performance, a chapter is devoted to describing the role of maturation in the formation of movement attributes.

The meanings various writers have attached to the terms *growth, development, maturation,* and *aging* often have differed considerably. The definitions offered here represent a rough consensus and, it is hoped, form a stable basis for discussion.

Growth refers to quantitative change, measurable variations of body size and proportion. *Development* is a far more general concept and may refer to quantitative structural changes as well as to a variety of other bio-psycho-social attributes. Reference, therefore, may be made to social development, mental development, personality development, motor development, and to various other behavioral attributes.

Maturation refers to changes taking place throughout the lifespan in the *anatomical and physiological complexity* of the organism. It is an ongoing process which is evidenced during the formative years by an increasing potential to perform a variety of tasks. Within the present context *aging* is simply considered to be the terminal portion of the maturational process. It is believed that maturation, as a concept, lies somewhere between the narrower term, growth, and the all-inclusive word, development. Further differentiation between these terms may be made by considering the manner in which each is assessed. *Growth* may be measured rather directly by using anthropometric techniques. Maturation level is usually assessed through the consideration of several indices of structural and/or physiological changes occurring as the individual grow from infancy to adulthood and later to old age. *Development,* on the other hand, may be evaluated in a variety of ways depending upon the orientation of the scientist using the term.

In general, the relative influence of maturation, as contrasted to learning and other factors, upon movement behavior is dependent upon both age and the type of task involved. For example, maturational factors are most influential during the initial and final stages of the human lifespan. Gross motor activities seem more dependent upon maturation, while fine manual skills, after infancy, tend to inscribe gradual acquisition curves primarily determined by learned experience. In addition, the evolvement of perceptual factors influences movement behavior as the individual ages. For example, older children become less variable in their judgments of depth.[427] Gilinsky[367] has demonstrated that with advancing age, there is an increased ability to organize distant space.

In addition, as children mature variations occur with regard to their figure-ground dependence when making perceptual judgments. Witkins et al.[975] found that from the ages of eight to ten children were dependent more upon the object's context, from the ages of ten to thirteen they make judgments relatively independent of the central figure's surroundings; while from the ages of thirteen to seventeen there was a slight return to dependency upon the context.

The relationship between maturation and movement behavior has been written about in several areas of the literature. Studies of infant and child behavior usually relate general and specific movement characteristics observed as typical of various age groups. Other studies have focused primarily upon the task and have traced developmental stages by noting changes in movement characteristics manifested as maturation occurs. Throwing, jumping, and tumbling stunts have been treated within the latter classification system.

A two-part discussion is presented here. After an initial section describing the manner in which maturation and performance are related during infancy and childhood, the emergence of maturational characteristics in three types of tasks will be discussed. The chapter will conclude with a discussion of movement characteristics that emerge during adolescence, adulthood, and old age. Reference also will be made to the manner in which structural changes directly modify performance and the way in which bodily fluctuations caused by maturation may change movement attributes indirectly through readjustments in the individual's self-concept. The manner in which changing cultural expectations may modify motor performance as the individual matures into adolescence is also examined.

THE IDENTIFICATION OF MATURATIONAL SIGNPOSTS

The manner in which maturation best may be assessed depends upon the portion of the lifespan under scrutiny. During early infancy, most investigators have simply relied upon chronological age in months. During and just prior to adolescence, various characteristics indicative of sexual maturity are often used. In adulthood various anatomical and physiological factors, as well as performance measures, have been used. Further complicating the picture is evidence that various parts of the body mature at different rates.

Gesell and Amatrude[354] have proposed that a Development Quotient be applied when assessing infant and child development. Similar in concept to the Intelligence Quotient, the Development Quotient would identify the proportion of normal development that is present at a given age and predict the portion of normal development still to take place. The formula suggested is:

$$D.Q = \frac{\text{Maturity Age}}{\text{Chronological Age}} \times 100$$

The formula and concept are flexible. It is suggested that, in addition to separate ratings for motor, adaptive, language, and personal social development, specific motor functions such as prehension, locomotion, and manipulation also may be identified by using the formula. *Maturational age* is computed by comparing the kinds of tasks (*e.g.*, locomotor, manipulative) that the child can actually accomplish with normal behavior for his age group Researchers Gesell and Amatrude warn, however, that such a quotient is a beginning, not an end, for understanding maturation and suggest that "a single summative numerical value cannot do justice to the complexity and variability of infant development."[354]

Thus, during infancy, maturational level may be identified by the manner in which children perform, by observations, and by collecting home records of behavior. In addition, Walker[915] has reported the use of Sheldon's classification of body-build for two- and three-year-olds. More exact measures of maturational assessment await further research and more sophisticated measuring devices.

During infancy, height, weight, and other body-build indices become increasingly depended upon to identify maturation levels. Pryor's[728] weight-width index, for example, has proved a useful means of evaluating general maturational channels through which the growing child might pass in his way to adulthood. Based upon ratios comparing bony structure (measured by chest and hip width) to body weight, norms have been formulated to indicate desirable "bulk" to be carried on skeletal frameworks of various sizes.

Another scaling system was developed by Wetzel in 1943. Wetzel's technique is based upon the measurement and interpretation of physique, developmental level, and nutritional status, and places the individual child within discrete developmental channels which may be diagrammed on a chart to indicate a longitudinal pattern of growth. It is thus possible, according to this physician, to separate or combine the effects of different attributes and to form a graphic picture of physical progress or of the interruption of normal development.[958]

As late childhood and early adolescence approach, other indices are often utilized. In some cases, the onset of the menarche in the case of girls or the first ejaculation in the case of boys is used, and maturation is determined by the number of months which have followed such concrete evidences of sexual maturity. However, chronological age and body-build formulas continue to be employed to evaluate the maturation of adolescents. These indices (except at extremes) are not too helpful when attempting to predict performance, nor do they often correlate with other physiological measures of maturity.

A measure of skeletal maturity, based upon long bone growth, has been found to be one of the most valid measures of maturation during adolescence. The long bones of the body consist of a shaft containing the marrow and a wider portion at either end termed the *epiphysis*. During infancy and childhood, both the epiphysis and shaft gradually become ossified, except for a strip of cartilage situated at their junction known as the *epiphysial cartilage*. At this juncture and under the control of various hormones, all longitudinal growth of the bone continues to take place until the middle twenties. With the aid of a fluoroscope or x-ray picture, a rather exact indication of skeletal age may be determined by comparing an individual's epiphysial development to established norms. From this maturational sign, final adult height can be predicted rather accurately. In addition, skeletal age has been found to be moderately correlated with other indices of sexual maturity, as well as with certain physical performance measures.[799]

The identification of indices of aging becomes more tenuous as the individual matures. Experience and declining physiological capacities exert opposite influences upon performance to render previously used measures less valid as indices of maturation. Various organs and systems of the body seem to age at varying rates. As the individual gets older, he becomes increasingly reluctant to extend himself in all-out performance. These factors combine to create sampling problems when selecting subjects for experiment in the older age groups. In general, maturation may be best measured by a comprehensive assessment of performance as well as by inspection of anatomical-physiological attributes forming the total pattern.

The Assessment of Movement Characteristics in Infancy and Childhood

Studies of the movement characteristics of infants have often depended upon systematized observations, coupled with home diaries. These observations have been sometimes carried out with the aid of motion picture cameras, and norms with regard to motor maturation have been evolved through longitudinal studies involving individuals or groups of children. During the initial weeks of life, observations are collected relative to general posturing, regarding, and positioning movements of the trunk, arms, and head. In later months, the ability to manipulate various environmental objects, such as blocks[410] and wheeled vehicles,[505] has been studied. Further difficulties may be encountered when attempting to assess the motor ability of children because of the differences in reactions they exhibit when performing in front of other people as well as differences in experience. Daval[236] and others have suggested that when children are observed, they may be at various points on a practice curve, and thus the differences recorded may be attributable to differences in the amount of practice rather than simply to level of motor development.

Experimentally, two main approaches have been taken to the study of the motor performance of children. Some investigators have analyzed a single task, such as the hurdle jump,[425] throwing,[405,449] and beam walking.[224,793] Other researchers have constructed extensive batteries containing several tasks. Some of these batteries contain a preponderance of tasks requiring basic qualities of strength, speed, and power or agility, while others have constructed groups of tests which purport to evaluate general body coordination.[104,494,709]

The Johnson Battery, for example, consists of a series of separate tasks performed on rectangular tumbling mats marked for the purpose with lines and squares along their length. These 10 motor problems include front and back rolls, full and half jump turns down the mat, and simpler movements resembling "hopscotch." The individual is given a 10 score for perfect performance in each task. Points are deducted if the subject fails to turn in the correct direction, if a landing is not accomplished in the correct square, or if both feet do not reach the mat simultaneously on a landing so prescribed. Johnson found that although no significant correlations were found between total score and I.Q. when testing children, a slight correlation of .49 was found between motor performance as measured in her tests and the intelligence of collegians.

Modifications of the Brace Test also have been utilized to evaluate the motor performance of children. The original battery consisted of 20 items which included single stunt-type skills scored on a pass-fail basis. Examples include jumping to the side, touching one foot to the other and landing, folding the arms, squatting to the knees, and rising, and the like. Vickers et al.,[912] among others, have utilized the Brace Test with younger age groups (5 to 9), employing a modified scoring system and omitting some of the more difficult items.

Three other scales purporting to measure general motor ability have been developed in Europe, the most used published by a Russian, N. Oseretsky. The Oseretsky Scale was constructed for age levels from 4 to 16. There were originally 6 sub-tests at each level which were to evaluate general static coordination, dynamic manual coordination, general dynamic coordination, motor speed, simultaneous voluntary movements, and asynkinesia (lack of precision of movement or of surplus movement). Two other test batteries included one developed by A. Marmolemko, also a Russian, which emphasizes "life's essential movements," walking, grasping, and the like. A third was developed by Maria

J. A. Van der Lugt in 1939 and translated into English in 1944. It is primarily a manual ability test with different forms for adults and children.[907]

The Oseretsky Scale was translated into English in 1946 by Edgar Doll, and over the intervening years it has been shortened and made more practical.[709] Sloan,[826] for example, reduced the number of items from 85 to 36 in 1955. Although many of the items on the Oseretsky Scale include manipulative tasks, it also incorporates gross movements such as rope jumping, jumping and touching the heels with the hands, standing on one foot, walking backward (heel to toe), (tennis) ball throw for accuracy, and the like.

Researchers using these batteries have established norms for various age groups and identified sex differences in motor performance. They have generally failed, however, to identify a single test which evaluates over-all motor ability. Except when contrasting gross observational measures of movement patterns evidenced by the very young, the isolation of a general factor which might be termed "coordination" has proved difficult. Millard[661] and others have attributed the lack of intercorrelations between motor performance measures to the fact that such comparisons involve tasks performed at various points in the learning process. Thus, even at early ages, experience may overshadow inherent motor qualities.

A third attempt of researchers interested in the motor ability of infants and children has been to relate mental ability to movement accuracy and motor maturation. Here again they usually have failed to demonstrate significant relationships between motor ability measures or indices of early motor maturation and later mental ability.[62]

Nature or Nurture, and Co-Twin Control

In addition to studies based upon observations and statistical analyses of group and individual performance data, the relative effect of environment and heredity upon the acquisition of motor skill has been investigated. These studies usually have attempted to determine whether motor skills taught to one of two identical twins significantly affected performance levels attained or whether the untaught twin seemed to acquire motor acts relatively independent of environmental support in the form of specific instruction.

Although the several variables present in such studies are difficult to control, for example the twins must be kept apart or they will teach each other, the general approach is an interesting one. The advantage of using identical twins, of course, is that their hereditary characteristics are alike, and thus changes in performance may be primarily attributed to variables experimentally introduced.

In general, findings point to the importance of inherent qualities in the formation of locomotor and manipulative activities during the early years of life. Hilgard,[452] for example, compared two twins, one trained in ring tossing, walking board skill, and paper cutting. It was found that performance differences on all tests were as similar to each other at the end of a training period as they were at the beginning. In another study, reported by Gesell,[354] the stair-climbing ability of twins remained remarkably alike despite instruction afforded one twin. Training in cube behavior and in language skills has also failed to produce marked differences in later testing.

Contrary evidence, however, has been presented by McGraw,[640] who found that her experimental twin, Johnny, learned to swim at ten months, to dive at thirteen months, and to skate at sixteen months. However, the preponderance of findings emanating from co-twin investigations emphasizes the overriding importance of maturation and inherent qualities in the formation of motor skills during the early years of life.

The method of co-twin control has merit only if uniovular twins are used and their training period is preceded by a measurement period during which initial differences are carefully noted. In addition, the training period should be carefully controlled, and the final measurements recorded exactly. With these kinds of precautions, studies of this type can provide additional insight concerning the roles of maturation vs. learning in the formation of movement behavior.

VOLUNTARY MOVEMENT IN EARLY AND LATE INFANCY

Voluntary movements begin before birth with early traces recorded about 17 weeks after conception.[737] These fetal movements have been classified into two main types: (1) *allokinetic* movements, including passive movements caused by exterior forces, primarily reflexive in nature, and (2) *autokinetic* movements, or those which are believed to be initiated in the cortex and are voluntary. Many reflexive patterns identified before birth persist and mark the beginnings of movements which permit the infant to explore his gradually emerging world. The tonic-neck reflex is an example of one which leads toward visual-motor integration as the head is turned toward flexed arm on the same side. Research by Walters suggests that the duration and vigor of prenatal movements correlate positively with postnatal motor ability. During each of the last three months fetal activity is indicative of motor development, according to this researcher. Thus, the infant seems to begin his propensity to move prior to birth and literally seems to begin exercising in the womb![920]

The movements noted soon after birth, however, are largely undifferentiated and inaccurate and resemble the squirmings of babies of any mammalian species. The development of the capacity to move accurately is believed to be related to the maturation of the nerve sheath (myelin). It is conjectured, however, whether the inclination to move hastens this development, or movement accuracy is controlled by nerve sheath development (the myelination process). In any case, movement accuracy and the maturation of the myelin sheath roughly parallel each other. The newborn infant evidences innumerable reflexive patterns, some of which blend later into voluntary movements; others disappear, while a few are retained throughout life. Most infantile reflexes, however, disappear only to be elicited if a pathological loss of the inhibitory higher centers occurs.[72]

Some of these reflexes are independent of gravity. The Moro reflex, for example, is seen if certain stresses are imposed upon the newborn. This reflex consists of extension of the arms, and is opposite to the startle or fright reflex which elicits a flexion movement.

Several kinds of reflexes of the limbs are evidenced when the head moves or is moved to various positions. These tonic-neck reflexes may be either asymmetrical, in which the limbs on the side toward which the head is turned extend, or symmetrical, when the reverse occurs. The asymmetrical tonic neck reflex has been postulated by some to be indicative of some kind of pathological condition if it continues beyond the first week or so of life.

The infant's palms and feet both exhibit a reflexive flexion when they are lightly touched. While many newborn can exhibit this reflex so strongly that they can support their weight with their hands, it disappears in the normal infant by between the sixth and twelfth month of life.[812] The absence of these grasping reflexes at birth is usually indicative of some kind of neural malfunction.

Several reflexes present at birth result in the infant's unconscious effort to right himself if his head is placed in any position other than upright. These body-righting reflexes are elicited if the head is held back or forward or to either side, if the body is otherwise held upright. Conversely a group of movements termed the labyrinthine righting reflexes result in the infant's head flexing to conform to the upright, if his body alignment is disturbed relative to gravity.

The body-righting and labyrinthine reflexes chain together to enable the child to begin to assume the upright position as he prepares to crawl and later to walk. Aiding these reflexes are the supporting reflexes evidenced in infants at about the eighth to tenth month. An example of these latter reflexes is seen as the infant reaches out with his hands as he approaches a surface upon which he may support himself.

The pullup reaction of the infant appears after several months. This is evidenced if the child's hands are held and the body is angled to the sides, to the front or back. As the body is placed "off balance" the arms will flex and the child will pull on his supports, attempting to regain the upright position.

A complex reflex pattern seen in infants resembles the voluntary walking movement which appears a year or so later. These stepping and ascending movements[721] are elicited in newborn children by placing them in an upright position and inclining them slightly forward. As their feet touch the ground a series of motions resembling walking are elicited. This reflex may be triggered whether the child is upright or held in an inverted position, thus suggesting that it is independent of rudimentary labryinthine functions. Crawling movements in a horizontal plane may also be elicited by putting slight pressure alternately on the soles of the infant's feet as he lies stomach down on a table. Similarly if a newborn is placed in water, coordinated extension and flexion movements of the arms and legs resembling swimming occur. This latter reflex is often claimed to be a voluntary and learned pattern by those "instructors" who purport to be "teaching" infants to swim.

These reflexive movements listed above lead to more or less coordinated movements of the extremities, but have "no temporal connection with the later appearance of independent locomotion."[721] No two children will move in exactly the same way when attempting to acquire a gait pattern involving upright locomotion, although most will pass through creeping, crawling, and sliding on the buttocks prior to engaging in free and erect gait. Upright gait has to be learned; however, the three other gait patterns do not necessarily have to precede it.[721]

However, many of these basic reflex patterns have been noted to persist and to interact to varying degrees with voluntary movements at maturity. For example, general flexion and extension patterns are seen supporting or inhibiting jumping movements as well as other more complex skills; it is easier to jump when the arms are vigorously extended at the shoulders; similarly it is easier to extend the right arm vigorously in shot-putting when the head is jerked to the left. The research by Hellebrandt and her colleagues, for example, attests to the role of various neck reflexes in the shaping of a variety of voluntary trunk and limb movements.[436]

The movements of the infant have been subjected to several classification systems which have attempted to list, step-by-step, the kinds of movement occurring during various periods of infancy. The California Infant Scale of Motor Development is typical. This scale consists of 76 items listed in order of difficulty, and an infant is checked to determine which ones he is capable of performing. Other systems and scales presented by Thompson[879] and Shirley[812] are similar in nature. In general, voluntary infantile movements fall into the following categories: (1) postural control, including movement of the entire trunk and random postural activity, (2) active efforts at locomotion, including turning, stretching, and attempts at crawling, (3) beginning walking movements, and (4) anticipatory and selective visual-motor regard, using the hands and upper limbs, including prehension, approaching, grasping, and releasing objects. The appearance of movement behavior in these categories overlaps considerably and occasionally occurs simultaneously. Locomotion and prehension, for example, are frequently seen at the same time.

Muscular strength and control proceed rapidly during the early months. By four months of age most babies can lift the head and neck from a prone position and about a month later can sit with some support. Control of the body proceeds from total bodily adjustments to finer movements, with development generally proceeding from the head to the feet (cephalo-caudal) and from the midpoint to the extremities.

Motor and mental abilities during the first fifteen months are inseparable,[62] but after this time test scores seem to diverge. However, Piaget[728] suggests that children's concepts of time, space, and force continue to be based upon initial manipulatory experiences.

With regard to the use of objects, Gesell and Thompson[356] have suggested that several behavioral attributes appear in a predictable sequence: more regard of the object, grasping it (prehension), manipulation, and finally exploitation as the object is placed in various relationships and used in various ways. The objects which have been utilized in systematic studies of manual behavior have included spoons, cubes, bells, pellets, cups, and the like.

Following the acquisition of the ability to walk, variations of gross body locomotion become possible. Hopping, skipping, and standing on one leg soon follow. Gutteridge[405] reported that about 42 per cent of the children she studied were jumping well at three years of age, at four and one-half, 72 per cent were successful, while at five years, 81 per cent showed proficiency. Children are closer to six before they can hop skillfully. Galloping is not usually seen in three-year-olds but is engaged in proficiently by four- and five-year-olds, according to Breckenridge and Vincent.[107] The ability to skip is acquired after the child learns to gallop, at about the age of five and one-half to six.

Although there is some disagreement among researchers, hand dominance appears very early, during the first three or four months of age. This is evidenced and reflected in movements of the total musculature including head turning, leg use, body rotation, and the like.[366] Marked individual differences in the extent to which lateral dominance is manifested becomes apparent. Some individuals are totally left- or right-handed, while others evidence unilateral control. Jenkins,[492] for example, found that only 3.3 per cent of the subjects tested at five years of age were both left-handed and left-footed, while about 7.7 per cent were left-handed and *right*-footed. In general, the dominant hand influences early skill acquisition, while the nondominant hand is used frequently for supporting or stabilizing the body while the other is in use.

After the age of two, more differentiation between tasks occurs, and the rapid growth patterns tend to slow. Motor abilities, which had been more closely related during infancy, tend to become more specific, a trend which continued into adulthood.[62]

Several experimenters have undertaken the task of measuring the manner in which three- and four-year-olds grow up with various kinds of structured movement patterns. Wellman,[947] for example, studied "motor coordination" by using a tracing board. The task was drawing a line accurately within a groove which gradually narrowed. Wellman found that the task was a helpful one to explore various principles of perceptual organization relative to vertical, horizontal, and lateral movement patterns.

Jones[505] studied the development of the motor skills of two-, three-, and four-year-olds as they became proficient in the use of various wheeled toys. After numerous systematized observations of the use made of trucks, bicycles, tricycles, and the like, it was found that, while basic performance seemed to depend upon maturation, the development of skill was more attributable to practice. Higher skill and more self-reliant play when using this kind of equipment was attributed to prior experience with older playmates, previous availability of play materials, and previous participation in an outdoor play area.

It would seem that at a rather early age environmental supports markedly affect maturation in determining the quality of motor activity participated in. In addition, sex differences begin to be evidenced at about the ages of two and three. Both Goodenough and Brian[382] and Hicks[449] reported that boys are superior to girls in ball-throwing tasks at this age.

The effect of physique also begins to be asserted in the motor performance of nursery-school age children. Cunningham,[229] for example, using several kinds of gross motor tasks, found that performance was more dependent upon body-build than upon instruction or verbal ability. Walker[915] found that relationships existed between Sheldon's classifications of body-type and various kinds of behavior, at the ages of two, three, and four. Positive correlations were obtained between mesomorphy and observational ratings of "energetic," "good gross motor coordination," "competitive," and the like. On the other hand, a negative correlation was obtained between mesomorphy and fine coordination in this age group. Walker also found that other physique types showed the expected results as their behavior was observed and recorded. The thin ectomorph tended to have "poor gross coordination" and, in general, evidenced other attributes in contrast to that of the mesomorph. The infant endomorph was found to be self-assertive, revengeful, easily angered, and competitive. No significant correlations were found relating motor behavior to endomorphy as has sometimes been found in the studies of older children.

MOVEMENT IN CHILDHOOD

Movement behavior in childhood (ages five to ten) becomes stable as growth decelerates. More exact movement patterns become possible, and the child from five to ten seems to enjoy the acquisition of skill for its own sake and to experience joy in movement much as does a young animal. The years of childhood mark a transition from early developmental patterns which included postural adjustment and the unfolding of manipulative behavior to the adolescent skill in specific sports. It is during this period that major emphasis upon basic activities, throwing, running, jumping, and the like, should occur, so that a smooth progression is made into the movement behaviors socially desirable in adolescence.

Sexual differences continue to emerge during childhood, with the boys showing superiority in activities requiring power. In general, children at this age exhibit more stable performance techniques. For example, they are not as likely to vary their characteristic throwing methods suddenly as are younger children.

Carpenter,[143] Seils,[799] and Jenkins,[492] among others, have formulated test batteries to evaluate performance characteristics of primary age children (ages five, six, and seven). Hartman using the hurdle jump and Wild using throwing have attempted to evaluate performance with specific kinds of tasks.

Latchaw,[565] Cumbee et al.,[227] and Glassow et al.[372] have studied the motor abilities of individuals in later childhood (ages seven to ten) by using test batteries, while Cron and Pronko[224] and Seashore[793] have reported research evaluating the balancing ability of children from the ages of seven to twelve.

Frequently, the tester imposes test batteries designed to evaluate the motor ability of children, and attempts to assess the performance of rather basic movements, running, stand and running broad jumps, throwing for accuracy and distance, speed of running and such activities. Jenkins,[492] Seils,[799] and Carpenter[143] report that no significant correlation was obtained between height, weight, and performance of this kind of task. Most researchers, however, report that performance in most of the tasks improves from grade to grade. As Carpenter[143] states: ". . . some kind of maturation is an important factor in molding performance of these movements."

Using a more refined measure of maturity than did earlier investigators, Seils[799] found that relationships did exist between skeletal maturity and gross motor performance items, including throwing and catching by both boys and girls and jumping by girls. Seils' findings pointed to two main trends which emerge during this period of life, the growing importance of body-build (a negative relationship between weight and jumping ability) and the growing specificity of motor skill performance.

Carpenter[143] found that mean scores were consistently higher for boys than for girls. Jenkins[492] also found that, although sex differences were less marked at seven than at the younger ages, boys were superior in both standing and running broad jump, as well as in the baseball throw. Only in the jump reach test were there greater age differences than sex differences. Underscoring the importance of learning upon motor ability scores, even during childhood, was Jenkin's finding that the girls were superior to the boys in a task closely resembling hopscotch, a favorite pastime of the feminine members of his sample.

Numerous researchers, using batteries and single performance measures, have attempted to analyze and isolate basic factors of motor performance during the primary years. McCaskell and Wellman[627] used a multi-item battery. Vickers et al.[867] employed a modified Brace Test, Hartman[425] studied ability in the hurdle jump in relation to other gross measures of performance, and Carpenter[143] and Cumbee et al.[227] constructed batteries consisting of tasks assessing balancing ability, speed, strength, and the like. Their search for a single general performance measure proved unsuccessful. Hartman, for example, found that the hurdle jump score was no better than a number of other tests in predicting over-all score in a battery which included throw for distance, 35-yard dash, and similar tests. Hartman also found that sex differences became more pronounced after five years of age, while item intercorrelations ranged from .4 to .66 when comparing the jump reach and dash scores with performance on the hurdle jump.[420]

Vickers, using a form of the Brace Test, modified the pass-fail scoring suggested by the originator into a 5 point scale and found that higher over-all ability scores were associated with abdominal strength and high I.Q., while performance was inversely related to obesity. Vickers was surprised to note that younger children consistently indicated their ignorance of the names of various parts of the body, a deficiency which was discovered as the experimenter attempted to instruct the subjects concerning the performance of the stunt-type tasks.[912]

Both Carpenter and Cumbee utilized factorial techniques in an attempt to isolate basic motor performance qualities evidenced during primary years. Although they found marked specificity, both identified a factor related to the speed with which the subjects were able to move the total body. Carpenter isolated general factors of strength and ball handling (including scores on baseball and volleyball throws for distance and catching ability). Cumbee also identified factors relating to arm and hand velocity, as well as balance of the total body and facility in balancing objects.

In summary, studies dealing with motor performance during early childhood (ages five to eight) indicate that specific abilities become more pronounced as children mature and that sex differences become evident in performance scores particularly after the age of five, as boys gain superiority. It is also found that skeletal maturity is a better index of motor performance potential than chronological age and that obesity begins to inhibit performance in tasks which require over-all agility and jumping.

Latchaw[565] studied the motor performance of girls and boys in later primary years and essentially confirmed the findings of studies with the younger age groups. Using tests of various basic movements, including running, jumping, throwing, catching, striking, and kicking, it was found that experience and maturation were more important than age in predicting mean scores. In addition, the average scores recorded for boys were higher than those for girls. It also was found that lower relationships between scores were recorded when comparing body-build indices of girls to performance tests than was recorded as the same comparison was made for boys.

MATURATIONAL ANALYSES OF SELECTED MOTOR TASKS COMMON TO CHILDHOOD EXPERIENCE

Several investigators have traced the acquisition of specific kinds of movements during childhood and in early adolescence. Among the most frequently studied movements have been balance, studied by Seashore,[793] Cron and Pronko,[224] and others; agility and tumbling ability as reported by Johnson,[494] Millard,[661] and others; and throwing, investigated by many, including Goodenough and Brian,[382] Hicks,[449] Gutteridge,[405] and Gesell and Thompson.[356] These investigations trace the beginnings of skill acquisition, including the effects of maturation during the earlier ages, the growing importance of imitation and learning during the intermediate years of childhood, and the irregular performance curves attributed to motivational changes or to fluctuating cultural demands in adolescence.

Balance

In general, the balance ability of children has been studied using dynamic measures of moving (dynamic) balance, rather than static measures which involve balancing on a fixed point. A rather complex quality is evaluated which includes the use of vision to establish equilibrium, vestibular functioning, and posturing and use of the limbs to maintain positions. Seashore[793] and Cron and Pronko[224] used walking tasks on beams of various widths. Scores were obtained by noting the distance or the number of steps which could be taken. Seashore found that two trials made scoring most reliable.

Both investigators indicated that the peak of balance performance was reached at about the age of eleven, after which plateauing occurred. Cron and his associate[221] found that girls were superior prior to the age of eight, after which the boys excelled. Seils[799] also found that boys showed steady increase in balance scores after that age, while Seashore[793] found that the girls did not. Height and weight are more highly correlated with balance during the ages of five to twelve than during the later years of thirteen to eighteen. Seashore also found that age and balance correlated higher during the early years (five to twelve) than during those which immediately followed.

If, as numerous investigators feel, balance is a basic factor in perceptual motor ability, further investigation of the development of this quality is imperative. It seems that balance ability may plateau earlier in life than do other basic qualities (strength, speed, and the like).

Tumbling Agility

Researchers, using the Johnson test composed of tumbling items, have found that gradual improvement occurs with age.[494] McCloy,[629] using the Brace Test, also found that performance and age were positively related. In a study of a single tumbling stunt, the front roll, Millard[661] reported that a gradual gain was evidenced, followed by uneven performance between the ages five and one-half to fourteen.

Similar to the acquisition of balancing ability, there is relatively large gain in this agility stunt during early years of childhood, as learning and maturation combine to produce better performance. In later childhood, as rapid growth changes occur and motivational and practice conditions vary more, less regularity is noted.

The learning curve is presented below. It is based upon the per cent of children who were successful at the various age levels.

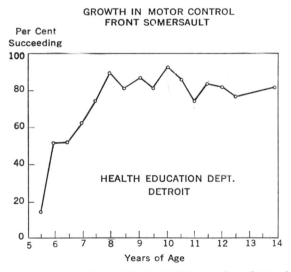

FIG. 3. Single-cycle motor skill. (Millard, *Child Growth and Development in the Elementary School Years,* courtesy of D. C. Heath and Co.)

Throwing

A lack of throwing proficiency during childhood can cause problems in peer relations, since it is one of the basic movements required in sports skills. Its beginning can be traced to the needs of prehistoric man for protection and for obtaining food.

In infancy, it is unclear whether the first throwing attempts come as the result of simply moving the arm in a rapid arc and the subsequent loosening of objects which happen to be in the hand at the time or whether inherent throwing patterns are manifested. In any case, throwing behavior becomes evident rather early. Gesell,[356] for example, notes its emergence as early as the fortieth week.

It has been stated that throwing is a kind of "kinesthetic release" which takes a large variety of patterns.[356] Some children lift and toss the ball, others simply roll it out of a supinated palm, while still others hurl objects in a rapid ballistic movement. Usually this latter pattern is made with a downward motion, causing the thrown missile to bounce, a phenomenon which usually delights the infant. Marked variations in throwing behavior both in the same individual and among children are noted during the early months. This may be due in part to individual differences and variability in visual perception or to immature neuromuscular "programs."

Most batteries designed to measure general motor ability have included a throwing task. Oseretsky[709] included "shot-putting" a tennis ball for accuracy, while others include throwing for distance. The latter, of course, requires more power and strength components, while the former involves accurate visual-motor perception for successful performance. In any case, gradual improvement in both distance and accuracy throughout the early years of life are recorded by investigators.

Both Wild[965] and Hicks[449] carried out studies specifically directed toward throwing behavior. Hicks scrutinized methods used by 60 children from the ages of three to six when throwing at a large circular target which moved down a track. Wild incorporated cinematographical techniques to study the stages through which throwing behavior passes during early childhood. Hicks found that when three- and four-year-olds attempt to throw for accuracy, a typical method was difficult to identify and individual variations were noted. The performance gains evidenced by the predominantly right-handed subjects were due to maturation rather than to practice, for when instruction was introduced it could account for little improvement. Even for this early age, however, Hicks had difficulty separating the effects of practice from maturation in the formation of throwing skill. Upon finding that the boys excelled the girls, it was conjectured that the adults may have manipulated the environment in favor of boys.[449]

Gutteridge,[405] using subjective ratings of throwing ability, found that two- and three-year-olds were unable to play ball (including catching) "well." However, improvement was marked during the next years as 74 per cent of the children from five to five and one-half were rated as proficient, while most of the six-year-olds attained an acceptable level of ability. It was also noted that the children showed a wide range of ball-throwing ability, from "extreme awkwardness" to "excellent."

Dusenbery[265] also found that maturation and throwing were related, since correlations of .7 for boys and .62 for girls were found when comparing age and throwing distance.

Wild[965] studied general throwing characteristics of children from the ages of two to six and one-half and also found that during the early ages, maturation is more important than learning, while practice becomes a more important modifier of performance after the age of six. Four stages were identified by Wild.

(1) Ages 2 to 3: Throwing is predominantly overhand or underhand in a vertical plane, with a decided elbow bend, accompanied by little or no body movement.

(2) Ages 3½ to 5: Movement of the arm begins, occurring in a horizontal plane while the arm follows through more, and the body begins to orient to the direction of the throw.

(3) Ages 5 to 6: Stepping, by the right foot, begins (for right handers); a weight shift occurs.

(4) Ages 6½ and over: Trunk rotation begins; total motion summates forces to provide for more power and accuracy; a step is now taken with the leg opposite to the throwing arm.

Wild suggested that major trends in learning to throw involve moving from a nonsupport leg change to the opposite foot forward movement and from a shorter time of the hand on the ball to a longer period which provides for more acceleration. In addition, the arm initially moves in a vertical plane to later a horizontal one. The ability to throw side-arm as well as over or underhand appears about the age of six or seven.

Goodenough and Brian[382] presented findings which differ somewhat from the conclusions reached by Hicks. It was found that throwing rings for accuracy, on the part of four-year-olds, was improved with practice. They also noted, however, that extreme variability occurred and that boys were superior to girls in this skill. It also was found that behavior which contributed to inaccuracy included: the lack of attention, elation due to success (produced overthrowing on the following trial), and incorrect focusing of attention (looking at the arm instead of at the target).

ADOLESCENCE

As adolescence (ages ten to eighteen) is reached, three interrelated forces combine to alter movement attributes. (1) A growth spurt occurs, which, accompanied by hormonal fluctuations, serves to change body shape and size and to alter performance potential. (2) These body-build changes tend to affect the individual's feelings about himself, which, in turn, affect performance. (3) Changing cultural demands are felt concerning the kinds of acceptable movement tasks to engage in (both as to type and intensity). Critical to the personality development of adolescent boys is whether they are early or late maturers. Studies by Mussen and Weatherly[687,932] point to the fact that late maturation handicaps personality development, while earlier maturers exhibit more stable personalities. Masculine interests in vigorous games correlate with masculine personality characteristics.[686] The same clear-cut relationships between onset of maturational indices and various personality attributes do not usually appear in studies when girls are utilized as subjects.

Among the important manifestations of physiological maturity is increased strength, and the resultant ability to utilize greater power in various movements. While this change is less marked in the case of girls, increases in strength differ only quantitatively between the sexes. In addition, structural modifications of the bony-level systems, with increased size and changes in body shape, serve to alter movement potentials. The sacro-femoral angle of the girls becomes less efficient in providing the straight-ahead drive needed for fast running. A wider male shoulder-girdle affects changes in muscular mechanics.

Failure to accept and adjust to bodily changes occurring during adolescence may have a marked psychological effect upon behavior. Increased awkwardness during this period of life may be not only the result of sudden spurts in long bone growth and the subsequent need for neuromuscular functioning to "catch up" but also attributable to emotional tensions related to alterations in the self-concept.[501,857]

Evidence of the effect of changing social expectations upon movement behavior may be obtained by consulting longitudinally obtained performance curves, as well as by reviewing sociological studies of the value systems within and surrounding the adolescent's world. In general, cultural demands exert equal and approximately opposite influences upon the movement of boys vs. girls. During adolescence the former are encouraged, threatened, and offered every cultural sanction to participate in and, above all, to excell in athletic skills. Girls, on the other hand, are often discouraged from placing too much emphasis upon athletic participation. Jones,[501] for example, found that approval was generally given to girls having a moderate interest in tennis, golf, and swimming within higher socio-economic groups. Care had to be taken, however, that participation by the girl did not occur at too high a competitive level. Thus, during adolescence, both the male and female are introduced more precisely to what the American culture considers to be appropriate adult feminine and masculine behavior, including the intensity and type of athletic skills in which they may participate.

Measurable Motor Performance of Adolescents

Reports of longitudinal studies of motor performance of adolescents include: (1) More marked differences appear between the performances of boys and girls, making their association in vigorous activities justifiable primarily from a social standpoint. (2) Greater specificity is noted with respect to motor skill development. (3) Indices of physiological maturation become more valid predictors of boys' performance than that of girls. (4) Adolescence signals the plateauing of the motor performance of girls, whereas the boys continue to improve.

Jones[500] and Nelson and Henry[693] indicate that strength, movement speed, and reaction time improve during adolescence. While this is more marked in the case of the boys, these increases roughly correspond to various physiological indices of maturity. Typical of the curves in basic physical measures is the evidence of grip-strength improvement in a longitudinal study which attempted to relate performance measures to growth and maturation. Over 180 children were tested over a six-year period. The grip strength of boys usually is seen to double from the ages of ten to fifteen.

In 1940, Espenschade[284] studied the motor performance of adolescents using a variety of tests such as throwing for distance, jumping, standing broad jump, jump and reach, the Brace Test, and agility run. Her findings, as well as those previously reported by Jones, emphasized the growing divergency of performance manifested by girls and boys during this period of life. Espenschade found positive relationships between physical maturity and performance among the boys, while the relationship was not demonstrated when the same indices were compared for girls. It was further found that strength and performance of boys was related, while the same measures were unrelated on the feminine side of the ledger. Taken together, these findings seem to indicate that as adolescence is reached, the girls fail to perform to their potential, while the boys utilize their fullest capacities to do well in motor skills.

Further emphasizing sexual differences during adolescence, Espenschade found that the mean performances of boys evidenced increases in all events during adolescence, while girls reached maximum performance levels at about fourteen, which then gradually declined. This trend was true whether age was determined chronologically or through evaluation of skeletal maturity. It would appear that during this period, cultural influences begin to override absolute capacity to perform, to make the validity of data questionable when taken at·face value, and explainable only by referring to the cultural pattern in which the performance occurs.

In 1962 an investigation was published which had been sponsored by the Office of Naval Research[311] involving the physical fitness testing of 20,000 boys and girls between the ages of twelve to eighteen years.

Utilizing tests evaluating flexibility, throwing ability, strength, agility, trunk strength and the like. This investigation represents one of the most extensive testing programs evaluating motor performance ever carried out with the nations' youth under reasonably controlled conditions.

The findings of this investigation indicated the following general trends when the data were plotted for each task by age. Most of the curves for boys showed negative acceleration; improvement was noted to a "critical" age, after which little improvement is noted. Exceptions occurred on tests of grip which presented a linear relationship to age; on a test of abdominal strength (hold one-half sit-up) showing no increase from the age of fourteen to eighteen; while a test of dynamic flexibility showed a decrease up to the age of sixteen.

The curves plotted, based upon the girls' scores indicated the following trends (1) decreases in running speed up to age fifteen, some improvement through age seventeen, then a decrease in performance to age eighteen. (2) In the softball throw and broad jump there is relatively little improvement up to the age of sixteen or seventeen, after which some improvement is evidenced. It was felt by the investigator that the number of tasks in which little or no improvement was evidenced during these years in the case of the girls was a reflection both of maturational phases of female development, as well as a waning of interest and participation in athletics on the part of the female subjects during these years of their life.

The performance curves in this investigation for the boys and girls did not overlap (an exception is extent flexibility where boys tend to become more flexible while girls get less flexible). In the running tasks the boys and girls were not much different at age thirteen but tended to become increasingly different thereafter. In general, the investigation pointed out that the performance differences between boys and girls increase markedly through the adolescent years.

Social Effectors of Movement During Adolescence

To determine the effects of culture upon behavior, one must examine the present values. A helpful study, *The Adolescent Society* by sociologist James Coleman,[168] makes frequent reference to the influence of cultural demands upon movement attributes. The book summarizes findings concerning adolescent values, parental values which influence adolescents, and teacher-administrator expectations which surround the adolescent. Numerous interviews and questionnaires were collected from pupils in ten high schools in a variety of socio-economic settings.

Coleman found that almost half of the boys wished to be remembered after high school as athletes, rather than as leaders in activities, brilliant scholars, or most popular. Male membership in the leading school social groups was mainly attributed to participation in athletics. Other qualities, such as appearance, common sense, and sense of humor, took a back seat to movement skills. Only within schools located in an extremely high socio-economic settings did the athlete-scholar outweigh the athlete in popularity, but in no case did the outstanding male scholar seriously threaten the athlete's popularity.

Adolescent girls, on the other hand, could succeed socially by being attractive, dressing well, and by coming from a family with above-average cultural advantages (e.g., a college-educated father). But even the girls could enhance their prestige through association with some aspect of the male athletic program, such as cheer leading.

Coleman points out that both parents and colleges sustain the image of athletics as the road to success. While the parents do not whole-heartedly support their offsprings' values, they contribute to their social goals by encouraging participation in athletics. Coleman found, in one school surveyed, that, while six high school athletes were offered college scholarships, the outstanding male scholar had been ignored by recruiters in higher education.

In addition to contributing to group approval, the adolescent's feelings of worth are decidedly affected by the extent to which he achieves success in athletics. Jones discovered that, among boys lowest in strength, most tended toward social introversion, felt a lack of status, and evidenced feelings of inferiority. On the other hand, males scoring in the upper extremes in strength seemed to experience no such negative feelings about themselves and, on the whole, evidenced favorable personality traits, reflected in healthy aggressiveness and the attainment of leadership roles.[499] A follow-up to this study was carried out twenty-seven years later, using the same subjects. The remarkable consistency found in the personality trait scores of the subjects points to the importance of early maturation and physical ability in the formation of rather stable systems of behavioral characteristics.[503]

ADULTHOOD

It is during the adult period (over twenty), when youthful maturation processes are completed and the degenerative effects of aging have not yet been felt, that experience exerts the most pronounced effects upon motor performance. It is during this period that the most efficient performance of both manual and gross motor skill may be manifested, if the individual continues to participate in and continues to benefit from past experience. Welford[943] has presented a chart which diagrams the relative influences of learning and physiological capacities upon skill performance during adulthood. It indicates that, during adulthood, experiences and capacity exert equal and sometimes opposite effects upon performance, with the performance measure obtained a resultant of these two forces.

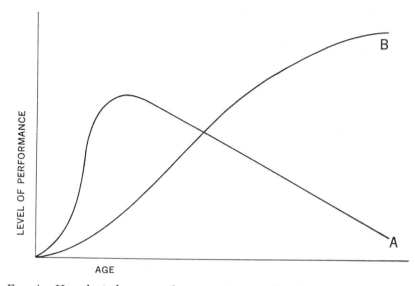

Fig. 4.   Hypothetical curves relating performance based on organic capacities (A) and experience (B) with age. (Welford, *Aging and Human Skill,* courtesy of Oxford University Press.)

"A" represents absolute organic capacities while "B" represents experience. These two curves, of course, are also dependent upon the nature or the task as well as individual differences in strength, endurance, and similar qualities.

Thus, performance and the capacity to learn physical skills becomes stabilized during adulthood and is not subjected to the intergroup variability evidenced during childhood and later in old age. The peaks of strength and endurance are reached during the early twenties, and skilled performance becomes largely dependent upon practice and experience. Bachman,[38] for example, found that no significant differences were evidenced by various age groups from twenty-five to forty-nine, when measuring the ability to learn two gross motor tasks; one a balancing task, the other a ladder-climbing task. Studies such as these lend further support to the premise that performance becomes relatively stable during adulthood.

During later adulthood, motivational factors impinge upon the individual and affect his willingness and inclination to perform. The adult, after the age of forty, becomes less inclined to learn new skills and, it has been found, tends to use recreational skills learned during childhood and adolescence. Having passed through the years during which all-out achievement, both physical and mental, was stressed, the individual enters his later years attempting to obtain maximal satisfaction and gratifications out of what has been termed "the prime of life."[889]

Few studies have been directed toward adult capacities in motor performance; those available have been primarily directed toward comparing adult to old-age performance. Most of the studies, of course, have utilized college-age youth, since students were most readily available to the investigator. Exceptions are studied by Pierson[432] and Mendryk,[049] both of whom utilized movement and reaction tasks as performance criteria. Mendryk found that college-age subjects evidenced significantly better reaction and movement times than did twelve-year-old boys and forty-eight-year-old men. Pierson found that correlations between movement time and reaction time increased in the older age ranges. Nobel et al.,[701] and Shepard et al.[809] carried out studies which compared the performance of individuals from the ages of eight to eighty-seven years on two complex coordination tasks. In common with findings on similar studies carried out by other investigators it was found that improvement occurred until about the age of sixteen years on the part of females, and to the age of twenty by males, after which a decline in performance was noted. The middle years of life are usually productive of the best performance on complex coordination tasks, with the males usually superior to the females.[809]

Success in skilled movements during adulthood is largely attributable to opportunities the individual has had to practice, and it is during this period of life that the best scores in manual skills are recorded. Proficiency in gross movement tasks, however, tends to decline slightly, especially during the latter years of adulthood, although the ability to acquire new skills remains rather stable until the fifties are reached.

FIFTY AND OVER

There are no distinct signposts to indicate when an individual should be termed *old*. Entry into this period of life may be measured in a variety of ways, both through the evaluation of performance and by assessing biological functioning. It is a common experience to observe individuals in their sixties performing intellectually and physically in a manner superior to individuals twenty years their junior.

In contrast to the scarcity of investigations carried out with emphasis upon the physical attributes of adulthood, several programs have been carried out inspecting the skill of the aged. These programs usually have been designed to identify the attributes of the elderly in industry. Various types of studies have been conducted which are concerned with the physical performance of the aged. Examples are investigations which have attempted to establish norms for work output, those which contrast the performance of younger to older individuals, and studies in industry and in the experimental laboratory.

Difficulties arise, however, when attempting to obtain a fair sampling of subjects when testing the older age ranges. Mortality, occupational influences, motivation, and similar variables often confound the findings.

When evaluating work output in an industrial plant, for example, it is frequently found that older workers who were not performing well have been removed from the job, so that all who remain are well above average in ability. Despite these difficulties, however, it is possible to obtain relatively valid findings from such investigations. In the main, they have pointed out that, just as during infancy and childhood performance of the aged becomes more variable, since the effects of experience and a lowering of physical capacities seem to influence individuals to varying degrees.

Differences in movement speed have been identified in the aged. A lowering of reaction time seems to be caused by a lessening of the ability to integrate input to output within the central nervous system, rather than to movement capacities at the peripheral level.[530] Older subjects evidence less endurance, particularly in the performance of large muscle tasks. Changes in task complexity more markedly lower performance of the aged than of younger performers. The learning of new tasks becomes more difficult, particularly within the oldest age ranges; and the capacity to retain information on a short-term basis also seems to suffer in old age.

Perceptual changes occur, which are relatively independent of the lowering of visual acuity. Perceptually, the older subject appears less flexible. Increased visual-motor integration seems to be needed as the older individual performs tasks which are performed by the younger subject relatively independent of close visual guidance. The older individual thus appears to become less "plastic" with regard to perceptual-motor performance, as well as in measures of muscle elasticity. Szafran[873] suggests that in old age a "blurring" of visual-motor perceptions occurs.

Older adults also tend to be more disturbed by various stressful conditions associated with performance. Studies indicate that elderly workers tend to withdraw from assembly line tasks which involve strict pacing, particularly if the rate is determined by younger workers' outputs.[943]

Research has been carried out to determine the reasons for the slowing down of perceptual-motor performance during old age. Although Miles[659] first suggested in the 1930's that slowing was due to a decreasing capacity of the neuromuscular system at the peripheral level, more recent research findings seem contradictory. Singleton[822] and others believe that the slowing of performance, particularly those "loaded" with perceptual judgments, is primarily attributable to a lowering of integrative capacity within the central nervous system. Older people seem able to "program" their movements for only a short sequence and within a relatively short time period and are forced to hesitate between movements within a complex series.

Age and Motor Learning. Three important characteristics are manifested with regard to learning motor skills as old age approaches: (1) Older people seem to require and to seek more information about a task, many times facts irrelevant to actual performance. (2) Long-term retention is less affected by old age than is short-term memory of immediately needed performance elements. (3) The learning of new tasks becomes more difficult, while performance in tasks which have been practiced over long periods of time does not seem to suffer.

There seems to be a need for stronger "input" cues on the part of the older learner. Younger individuals engaged in a chain-throwing task, for example, found little need for extraneous cues, while older subjects went about carefully acquiring all possible information.[871,943]

It is common observation that older people recall incidents out of the *distant* past with some facility. However, experimental evidence by Brown,[943] using a grid-plotting task, suggested that the inability of the older subjects to remember short-term directions probably lowered their performance and learning rate. It was felt that the material had been presented too rapidly for full comprehension, since the older subjects seemed ignorant of important directions.

One of the pressing questions needing further research is determining how much of the slowness to learn is attributable to an increased "carefulness" on the part of the older subjects and how much to decreasing *capacities* to integrate and move.

Student References

Books

1. AUSUBEL, D. P.:   *Theory and Problems of Adolescent Development*, New York, Grune & Stratton, 1954.
2. GESELL, ARNOLD and AMATRUDA, CATHERINE S.:   *Developmental Diagnosis*, 2nd Ed. New York, Paul B. Hoeber, Inc., 1960.
3. JONES, HAROLD E.:   *Motor Performance and Growth*, A Developmental Study of Static Dynamometric Strength, San Francisco, University of California Press, 1949.
4. PIAGET, JEAN: *The Construction of Reality in the Child*, New York, Basic Books, Inc., 1954.
5. WELFORD, A. T.:   *Aging and Human Skill*, New York, Oxford University Press, 1958.
6. PEIPER, ALBRECHT: *Cerebral Function in Infancy and Childhood*. New York: Consultants Bureau, 1963.

Articles

1. ESPENSCHADE, ANNA: "Motor performance in adolescence," Society for Research in Child Development, v. 5, Serial No. 24, No. 1, National Research Council, Washington, D.C., 1940.
2. FLEISHMAN, EDWIN A.:   "The dimensions of physical fitness—the nationwide normative and developmental study of basic tests," Technical Report #4, Office of Naval Research, August 1962.
3. RAGSDALE, C. E.:   "How children learn the motor types of activities," *49th Yearbook*, Chicago, University of Chicago Press, 1952.
4. SEILS, LEROY: "The relationships between measures of physical growth and gross motor performance of primary grade school children," *Res. Quart.*, 22, 244-260, 1951.
5. WALKER, RICHARD N.:   "Body-build and behavior in young children," I. Body-build and nursery school teacher's rating, Gesell Institute of Child Development, Monograph of the Society for Research in Child Development, Serial No. 84, Vol. 27, No. 3, 1952.
6. WILD, MONICA R.:   "The behavior pattern of throwing and some observations concerning its course of development in the child," *Res. Quart.*, 9, 20-24, 1938.

10

Chapter 8

Motivation

THE terms *motivation* and *motive* are used in many contexts. The criminologist constantly searches for the motives believed to be the roots of asocial behavior. Worker incentives are studied in the effort to increase production. To create a realistic drama, the playwright must attempt to construct a believable interplay of his characters' motivations.

Throughout history, the why's of man's behavior have provoked philosophical and scientific speculation. The early Greeks suggested that actions could be attributed simply to the seeking of pleasure or to the avoidance of pain. Contemporary research also reflects a similar, although at times more complex, interest in motivation. About one-third of the experimental work in the behavioral sciences deals with the elusive concept of motivation. Drive, need, motive or some similar construct has been utilized to explain fluctuations in learning curves, to account for individual performance and/or perceptual differences, and to describe more clearly the total personality complex.

The word motivation is a broad term, referring to a general level of arousal to action. It is derived from the latin *movere,* meaning literally *to move.* The term *motive,* on the other hand, is usually considered a specific condition contributing to performance and to the general motivational level. The words *drive* and *need* also assume many varied and subtle meanings, depending upon the type of evidence utilized for their objectification. In general, the term *need* refers to a rather internalized deficiency, something the organism *lacks.* The concept of *drive,* on the other hand, involves the positive concept of *the impetus to action.* In some cases the two terms may be independent of one another, for example, an individual may require (need) some chemical addition to his system in the form of a dietary supplement but lacks the drive to acquire a vitamin preparation which might remedy the situation. Drives consist of variables which impel the organism to action. They are usually thought of as existing in varying degrees within the organism at all times, and only when various theoretical and/or experimental thresholds are exceeded do they become identifiable. Motives are theoretical constructs which attempt to explain the reason individuals select certain behavior and activities in which to engage, the reason people engage in tasks for extended durations of time, and/or the reason an activity is performed with varying degrees of intensity.[405]

Within many theoretical frameworks, however, differentiation among the terms drive, need, and motive is quite difficult. In any case, a drive may be conceived of as an initiator of action, while a motive refers more to the direction the action may take. A need is construed as an organismic deficiency, either psychological or physiological, which may or may not lead to action.

In a broader sense, however, the concepts of drive and motive are usually expanded to refer not only to factors which initiate some facet of behavior but also to conditions which sustain and direct actions once they have been started. Thus *motives and drives are factors which underlie and support the general motivational level of the individual by initiating, molding, and sustaining specific action patterns.*

THEORIES OF MOTIVATION

The effects of the general motivational level and of specific motives seem to permeate the total performance situation. They influence the initial attitude of the individual, his preparatory "set," and his state of readiness for action. A motive may also be thought of as an intervening variable interposed between perceptual-input and motor-output. In addition, motivation plays an important part in the evaluation of an action once it has been completed. Was the experience satisfying and worthy of repetition? Or was it unpleasant and to be avoided in the future? A thorough consideration of the role of motivation must include an examination of factors which affect events within the total behavioral chain, as well as conditions which simply trigger and mold performance.

The concept of motivation, therefore, is an important one to the scientist and philosopher attempting to gain a comprehensive understanding of human functioning. Speculation about the subject has led to many obtuse questions which have been treated within various theoretical frameworks.* Are motives innate or learned or both? Is it valid to consider unconscious motivations? Are motives physiological, psychological, or socially determined, or do their origins emanate from all three sources? Is there a general drive state, or are motives to action specific in nature? Is motivation merely the avoidance of pain and the seeking of pleasure, or are more complex factors operative? What is the relationship of motivation to learning, to perception, and to personality theory?

Despite the limited scope of the present discussion of motivation, certain of these questions will be dealt with briefly. The final portions

*Madsen,[610] Bindra,[91] and Young[988] have discussed motivational theory as related to learning and perception. Berg and Bass[75] have published a text concerning the role of social motives. Rethlingshafer[75] has related motivation to personality theory, while Berlyne[78] has examined the role of curiosity, exploration and manipulation as related to motivation.

of the chapter are concerned with general conditions which contribute to the motivated state, and with the kinds of actions which in themselves seem to constitute motivating experiences (play, exploration, and manipulation).

Instinct, Drive, and Learned Behavior

Around the turn of the century, it was hypothesized that man's behavior was largely governed by unlearned action patterns, or *instincts*, which enabled him to survive by dealing more effectively with his environment. For example, fighting was believed to be the manifestation of the aggressive instinct. Such activities as working and playing were also believed to be instinctive.

In more recent years, instinctual theories of motivation have lost favor since the reasoning seems circular. "People behave as they do because they have built-in mechanisms compelling them to act as they do," seemed to constitute an unsatisfactory explanation for the many varied and seemingly self-directed activities in which human beings are observed to participate. A second main criticism of the instinctual theory was that is assumed that activity was either occurring or was not occurring. This was questioned, when following the development and use of the electroencephalograph, neural activity seemed present even during trance-like states.

Need-Primacy Theories

A second view of human motivation was proposed by theorists who hypothesized that human behavior could be attributed to four or more primary drives. All human actions, it was suggested, could be traced finally to activities which satisfied physiological deficiencies, such as hunger, thirst, elimination, and sexual appetite. The primary exponents of drive theory, Hull and Freud, differed primarily in the emphasis placed upon conscious and measurable drives vs. unconscious drive mechanisms and the degree to which they felt the sex motive was an instigator of human behavior.

Again, however, such a mechanistic approach to motivated behavior found many critics. The general human tendency to seek activity and to master a task for its own sake was noted. To play, to manipulate, and to explore seemed unrelated to any of the visceral needs which drive theorists suggested were basic. The drive theorists also seemed to view the human being as an inert machine, "turned-on" only when internal needs to survive were present.

Closely associated with the need-primacy or drive-reduction theories of Freud and Hull is the concept of homeostasis introduced by Cannon[139] in the 1920's. Homeostasis refers to the general and specific processes which enable the organism to maintain its physiological integrity through balancing internal adjustments with external and internal stresses. It is assumed that, as imbalances occur, built-in regulators act to return the organism to a state of equilibrium. Although such a doctrine would seem to support the drive-reduction concept, Cannon himself has suggested that organisms at times seem to seek imbalance by undertaking self-directed activities as stimulating kinds of undertakings.

Multi-Factor Theories of Motivation

In order to explain many of the complexities of human behavior, various theories were proposed which suggested that motives may be effective at various levels, that there were classes of factors which seemed to affect human performance. Tolman,[891] for example, speaks of *primary needs* (hunger, thirst, *etc.*), *secondary needs* (socially related, such as affiliation and dominance), and *tertiary needs* (learned behavior involving various kinds of goal-directed activity).

Murray[685] and McDougall[634] both produced systems of basic needs which were dependent upon the individual's social environment, rather than simply upon his physiological constitution. Murray's list included such factors as:

Affiliation: liking for people
Aggression: moving against people
Dominance: drive to dominate people
Cognizance: exploring, asking questions, and the like

McDougall's list of socially important motives included the exploring tendency, the aggressive tendency, the gregarious tendency, and the dominating or self-assertive tendency. Thus theoretical systems relatively independent of basic tissue needs began to be developed.

Theories of this nature generally rested upon "the functional-autonomy of drive" concept first outlined by Allport. In general, it was proposed that while activity initially might have a physiological basis, movement later becomes independent and self-sustaining as a motivator in its own right. The need to complete a task once started, the need to master a job for its own sake (rather than to establish a home for the possible sexual needs involved), and other such facets of human behavior seem more explainable in such liberalized theoretical frameworks than in the simpler need-reduction or instinctual theories of Hull and Freud.

Trends in Motivational Theory Construction

Several threads are discernible upon reviewing the literature dealing with theories of motivation. For example, one of the most popular approaches to motivation, as old as human thought, was the hedonistic theory. It suggested that the seeking of pleasure and the avoidance of pain are the mainsprings of human activity. Later experimentalists, unhappy with such a simple dichotomy when explaining human motivation, devised the complex classification systems previously reviewed.

Although it had long been noted that pain could be elicited by stimulating various portions of the brain electrically, more recently Miller[665,666] and others have found that through the use of finite deep-penetrating electrodes, animals can be stimulated so that they apparently receive pleasurable sensations. If it can be assumed that such stimulation produces generalized feelings of pleasure, as experimental findings seem to infer, the hedonistic theory again becomes more tenable. Langworthy and others have become concerned with the role of non-specific neurons, making up controlling mechanisms within the brain which modify arousal level, alertness, and emotionality. The reticular activating system has come in for more than its share of study in this respect.[558] Others have become interested in the influence of external bodily manifestations of emotion and general regulating systems within the nervous system. Gellhorn, for example, has been concerned with the role of bodily and facial contortions which influence emotional states by sending impulses to the posterior hypothalamus, thus influencing hypothalamic balance. Gellhorn suggests that muscular facial patterns arouse diffuse hypothalamic-cortical control systems, while the sensory-motor area in the cortex is excited via the specific afferent system from tactile and proprioceptive facial receptors.[347]

In general, however, the over-all trend seems to be in the production of more liberalized theoretical frameworks, expanding the list of human motives to include such activities as manipulation, exploration, and play. A longitudinal survey of the writings of single experimentalists also reflects this more accepting tendency. At the beginning of their careers, some scholars in the behavioral sciences reflect an exclusive dependence upon measurements obtained from animal experimentation. Later in their careers, however, these same researchers have seemed to acknowledge the existence of motives in kinds of observable behaviors more resistant to strict experimental treatment. It is believed that the final theory reviewed in this section reflects this latter trend.

Capacity-Primary Theory of Motivation

A theory in keeping with the diversity and complexity of man's movement behavior has been termed the capacity-primacy or behavioral-primacy theory by its proponent, Woodworth.[934] In general, it is hypothesized that the organism has a basic need to interact with his environment and that the manner in which this interaction takes place is determined by individual capacities for movement.

It is similar to a drive-system suggested by Goldstein,[358] which included the need to actualize one's capacities. However, the behavioral-primacy theory is more direct. Goldstein suggested that self-actualizing activities are based upon unconscious motives, whereas the capacity-primary theory implies that activities may be satisfying for their own sake.

Woodworth's theory[434] is a protest against the failure of the need-primacy theories to predict the activities, interests, and motives of human adults and, in particular, to explain the play activities of animals and children. It suggests that since men have hands to manipulate their environment, a need exists to handle objects, just as the bird with wings must fly and the web-footed duck must swim. However, in the simplicity of the theory lies its weakness. For, indeed, the reasoning seems somewhat circular. That "Man moves in complex and in unstructured ways because he possesses the musculature which encourages movement," does not constitute the most sophisticated explanation. In any case, it is believed that Woodworth's theory holds the most promise when explaining the diverse and sometimes unstructured forms of movement behavior engaged in by man.

An extension of the basic approach to understanding human motivation first proposed by Allport and Woodworth has been the recent interest in the measurement and influence of *achievement needs* upon human behavior. A recent factorial study of achievement needs identified two components of this general trait: *personal need for achievement* and *social need for achievement*. The latter component of achievement need suggests that the need for recognition, social reinforcement, and competition is somewhat independent of personal satisfactions when performing a task. (A treatment of Social Motives is found in Chapter 9.)

Further investigation of the "achievement need" carried out by Mingione suggested that need for achievement increases with age, and is stronger in individuals higher on the socio-economic scale than in those less favored culturally.[667]

THE MEASUREMENT OF MOTIVES

The assessment of human motives has proved to be difficult. Three general approaches have been used: (1) direct self-reports concerning statements about attitude, feelings of anxiety, and the like, (2) indirect means by use of the psychiatric interview or various projective tests, and (3) the behavioral approach, either by studying performance under various kinds of motivating conditions or by introducing various punishing variables, such as delaying the task.

Surwillow[868] has listed nine specific motivational conditions which are characteristically utilized in the laboratory situation. These include: (1) intrinsic interest of the task, (2) social incentives, (3) scores, which encourage improvement, (4) monetary rewards, (5) suggested importance of performance, *i.e.*, in determining norms, (6) social-competitive, performing the task with others, (7) rewarding for improvement, (8) threat of punishment, and (9) administration of punishment. Note is generally taken of the effect of these variables upon actual performance scores and upon resultant fluctuations in learning curves. Although seldom utilized, it is believed that another method may hold promise in the evaluation of motivational level. As the estimation of time seems related to the motivational state of the individual during the time period to be judged, a time-estimation task, in connection with various other tasks, might prove to be a valid measure of motives and/or of general motivational level.

Atkinson[33] has presented several criteria by which motivational measures might be judged: (1) The measure should reflect sensitively the presence or the absence of a motive or its variation in strength. (2) The measure of a motive should reflect variations only in that motive. (3) the measure should be valid and related to similar methods purporting to evaluate the same motive. Atkinson and others have reported, with regard to this last criterion, that observations, self-reports, and other measures of motivation generally fail to correlate, further indicating the difficulty of obtaining a valid measure of motivation.

One of the first, and certainly the most ambitious, research programs designed to evaluate adult motives was carried out by Thorndike[881] and published in *The Psychology of Wants, Interests and Attitudes* in 1935. Thorndike used various kinds of cognitive tasks, interpolated and accompanied by motivating conditions, to study what was termed the "Law of Effect." Innumerable situations in which various kinds of social approval or disapproval, various negative rewards such as electric shocks, and money rewards were used in order to investigate their effect upon the performance of a number of mental tasks. In general, it was found that adult motives could be molded by various kinds of external conditions. Typical is the experiment in which subjects' opinions concerning the artistic merit of Christmas cards were changed after a training period in which choices of the best cards were given approval when they corresponded to those previously selected by a group of art critics (Experiment 62). Much of the more recent work concerning the effect of various motivational states upon motor skills and physical performance measures has utilized Thorndike's general approach to measurement.

Questionnaires

Questionnaires with which to collect and tabulate self-reports of the motivational state of the individual also have been utilized in the past. Some require a yes-no choice, while others provide a five-point breakdown upon which the individual may indicate the degree to which he believes something to be true about himself and the way he feels. Obtaining reliable responses to questionnaires is often difficult, however, since an individual's constellation of values may shift between the first and second administration of these evaluative tools.

Indirect Methods

The various indirect measures of motivation seem to impose even more impressive difficulties. These assessments often occur within psychiatric interviews, since hidden meanings are searched for in the subject's use of words, verbal mistakes, or the manner in which the individual moves and expresses himself in general. Most of these methods require extensive clinical experience before interpretations become valid and reliable. Examples are the Rorschach ink-blot test, the Thematic Apperception Test, and similar devices which require the individual to place his own interpretation upon relatively vague and generalized forms and/or situations.

Perhaps the most accurate method of evaluating motivation lies in the interposition of various motivational conditions in the performance situation and then measuring performance fluctuations. Most often, these variables include differing kinds of instruction, the imposition of various stressors, such as interrupting the task, or the introduction of varying social conditions in the experimental situation. Performance fluctuations are generally studied as a function of the nature and degree of the motivational variable introduced.

Hypnotism and Motivation

Hypnotism has been used as a direct and indirect technique to determine motivation performance relationships. Hypnotic suggestions have been used in attempts to induce superior performance beyond the individual's "normal" capacities. In most cases, when such a variable has been introduced, marked variations in the individual's usual motor output have been induced. Two primary types of changes are involved: those specifically suggested by the hypnotist, including traditional alterations of reaction time and muscular tonus; and movement changes which seem to occur spontaneously.

Several investigations have been carried out concerning the effect of hypnosis upon muscular strength. Wells,[948] using a hand dynamometer as a measuring device, found that he could induce increased or decreased strength as desired. It was found, however, that it was more efficient and reliable to suggest a decrease in strength than an increase. Hatfield[429] substantiated Wells' findings with regard to strength increase as the result of hypnotic suggestion. Johnson and Kramer,[495] have produced findings which state that a hypnotic suggestion of failure was consistently more reliable in producing decrements in the ability to repeatedly press a dumbbell than were suggestions to increase performance.

As it appeared probable that continued pressure on some strength testing devices, i.e., a hand or arm dynamometer, causes pain, researchers have attempted to induce greater strength by suggestions of "no-pain" introduced during the hypnotic state. Marked increases in arm strength resulted from this kind of suggestion.

Work capacity has also been increased by hypnosis. In general, resistance to fatigue and work prolongation can be significantly effected by suggesting to the individual that he is less likely to feel the pain of tissue impairment during hard work. The usual task has been repetitive work with various kinds of dynamometers. Examples of studies in this area are those by Nicholson,[696] Williams[966] and Manzer.[616] Johnson, Massey, and Kramer,[496] however, found that no significant increases in performance were evidenced on a bicycle riding task under hypnotic suggestion.

In addition to investigations concerning the effect of hypnosis upon involuntary smooth muscle actions, several investigators have studied the effects of suggestion upon voluntary muscle control. Measures of steadiness have been studied the most frequently. Weitzenhoffer,[942] presenting a review of studies in this area by Eysenck and others, found that induced suggestions of "relaxation" improved steadiness measures more than direct suggestions to "be accurate." There seems to be a lack of investigation involving the effect of hypnosis upon the voluntary motor control in more complex tasks, perhaps due to measurement and safety problems.

Johnson et al.[496] utilized hypnosis in an ingenious way to assess the effectiveness of pre-performance warm-up. All subjects were placed under a hypnotic trance, and then half engaged in warm-up activities which were forgotten in the post-hypnotic state. Their findings indicated that warm-up may be a variable related to motivation, since it was discovered that no significant performance differences were noted between the two groups in a post-hypnotic performance test.

In general, the findings of such studies suggest that man is capable of much more in terms of physical performance than he actually exhibits. Inhibitory factors, which sometimes can be removed through hypnotic suggestion, seem to depress performance particularly during the adult years. It is believed that further investigations in this area might prove worthwhile in more complex movement tasks. It is felt that a more comprehensive understanding of human motivation might be gained through hypnosis, by gradually "peeling-back" performance blocks which have perhaps been built up throughout the individual's lifetime.

MOTIVES AND MOVEMENT

The general and specific conditions which modify movement performance will be explored next. In the initial section, factors which contribute to the general motivational level will be discussed, including the arousal-level concept, the "What is it?" reflex, and the formation of the pre-performance "set." The second section will deal with more specific motivating conditions, including the effects of restriction, fatigue, competition, reward vs. punishment, social facilitation, group interaction, and similar variables, as they affect motor performance.

Factors Contributing to the General Motivational Level

Arousal to Action. Basic to an understanding of the manner in which motives affect the individual is the concept of arousal. It is suggested that the general readiness of the individual to act may be placed upon a continuum, from a deep trance-like sleep to the hyperactivity characteristic of the mentally ill. Most individuals function in range somewhere near the midpoint, although fluctuations occur daily and hourly. Ryan and others[773] have found that an individual's basic level of arousal, measured by galvanic skin response, affects gross motor control.

The arousal curve is a more comprehensive construct than the previously discussed idea of tension level, although there is, of course, an overlapping of the two concepts. The tension level may be thought of as the upper portion of the arousal curve. Both curves when plotted in relationship to performance assume the same "U-shaped" pattern, indicating that there is an optimal level of arousal (or tension) within which the most efficient motor performance may occur. This optimum is generally dependent upon the nature of the task. The arousal level of an individual is a function of where he may be on several kinds of psycho-physiological cycles which impinge upon him at a given moment. These cycles are as short as a heart beat or as long as the menstrual cycle, and include the twenty-four-hour sleep cycle. Other cycles consist of annual fluctuations of various physiological indices which indicate the willingness or readiness to act.[32]

The extent to which motives may affect performance depends directly upon the point in the arousal curve at which the individual may be momentarily functioning. The higher his state of arousal, to a point, the more susceptible he is to various kinds of environmental conditions which may encourage him to move. A point is reached, however, at which the individual may be thought of as over-aroused (motivated), and to preserve his integrity he may either blot out environmental stimuli or be unable to move efficiently because of excess tension.

The "What Is it?" Reflex. As the individual has been motivated at least to notice some kind of motivating circumstances or stimuli, general skeletal musculature changes are noted. The head and total body orient to the direction of the object or event, the eyes become more adaptable to light, and previous movements are halted as general muscular tonus is raised. Pavlov[718] has termed this general pattern in animals the "What is it?" reflex to indicate bodily manifestations showing that the organism is ready to react to some portion of his environment. This state of attention is further characterized by changes in brain wave patterns, the slower waves present in lethargic states are replaced by the faster alpha waves. Visceral changes also prepare the organism for action.

Following these general and specific indices of readiness on the part of the skeletal-muscular systems, the sensory organs, and the central nervous system, a decision is made to act or not to act. This state of attention indicates that a motive to move has not gone unnoticed, the potential to move has been improved, and the probability for action has been enhanced.

The Performance "Set." Following the impingement of some event upon the attention of the organism, a specific readiness or "set" is produced. During this period, the human performer begins to adjust to the demands of the task, including self-instruction concerning his capabilities to perform the task, the amount or intensity of the impending task, as well as specifics related to task performance. (See Amount-Set, Chapter 4.)

In general, this prefocusing may be related to a short-term or long-term view of the task. Information in this area suggests that a mixed-set may be produced (*i.e.,* responding to one kind of stimuli and not responding to another). The research by Henry and his co-workers suggests that the more complex the task the individual is "set" for, the longer will be his reaction time.[442]

MOTIVES AFFECTING MOVEMENT

Restriction from Movement as a Motive to Move. It is a common observation that when children are required to sit still for long periods of time, as in the traditional classroom situation, they tend to evidence heightened activity needs when released from such restriction. Restraint thus has seemed to build up a backlog of action which needs an unusually large amount of expression.

Systematic studies by Shirley,[813] using animals, support the assumption that inactivity, induced by forcing the animals into small cages, results in an increase in activity upon release. Hill[460] produced similar findings; however, his data suggest that there is an optimal time of restriction which will produce the most post activity, and if exceeded, less activity will be the outcome.

There also seems to be an optimal or typical amount of time during which restriction may be tolerated by humans, and this seems related to maturational level. The time which an infant will tolerate restriction of his movements is relatively short, while an older child can be restrained longer without apparent frustration or discomfort.

However, I am not aware of research using human subjects which treats the relationship between restriction and the subsequent activity levels. While common observation indicates that the need for movement is increased by restrictions, there is little objective evidence as to the exact relationships involved. While hyperactivity certainly follows restriction and restraint has a physiological genesis, other factors also seem operative.

Fatigue as a Negative Motivation. The phenomenon of fatigue is a little understood parameter of human performance. Few deny its existence, yet at the same time most researchers are unable to agree upon a single definition. Bartley and Chute,[55] following an analysis of innumerable experimental viewpoints gleaned from psychological and physiological sources, suggest that fatigue may be regarded as a condition occurring to the whole person caused by a conflict situation in which the general attitude of the individual might be termed *aversion.*

In addition, these authors suggest that the term *impairment* be used to refer to actual tissue conditions which indicate the accumulation of waste products of activity, while *fatigue* be construed as an attempt to retreat or escape from the situation which has become too difficult to contend with. It is further suggested that impairment does not necessarily accompany fatigue, and that, indeed, inactivity can lead to fatiguing boredom, while moderate and changing activity is less likely to prove fatiguing.

Man seems to abhor doing nothing. Thus the concept of fatigue as aversion is important when studying motivation. While physiological impairment, if carried to individual limits, certainly curtails performance, boredom elicited by inactivity or sustained participation produces the same disinclination to move. There seems to be an optimal level of activity, more specifically of interesting complex activity, required to keep fatigue to a minimum. Anticipation of boring or repetitive work can be fatiguing or can produce a state of fatigue before the task is begun. Whereas anticipation of an interesting, though perhaps a somewhat taxing, task may produce an exhilaration which is antithetic to fatigue.

Thus fatigue may be evaluated by collecting subjective reports from the subjects pertaining to the monotony of the task, by noting performance decrements during sustained activity, as well as by various physiological indices signifying various kinds of tissue impairment due to prolonged periods of time at a task. The feelings people have about performance and their attitudes toward various components of physical endeavors influence their achievement in both direct and in subtle ways. For example, in a recent study by Smith and Bozymowski,[828] it was found that warm-up aided performance on an obstacle course only for those participants who expressed prior positive attitudes about the influence of warm-up on performance. On the other hand, individuals who expressed the opinion that warm-up would not aid performance failed to perform better after warming up.

Rewards, Punishment, and Movement. One of the most investigated phenomenon in educational literature concerned with motivation is the relative effect of rewards and punishment upon mental and motor performance. Much of this interest gained impetus from early studies by Thorndike dealing with motivation or his "Law of Effect." It was usually found that the effects of reward were far superior to those of punishment and that punishment with a reward following was more motivating than punishment alone. Innumerable findings have supported the influence of this "law of effect" upon performance and learning. For example, Locke[591] found a .42 correlation between pursuit rotor performance and a "liking" score.

Simple monetary reward will elicit more physical work on the part of human subjects than the absence of reward. Toppen in a recent series of studies, for example, found that more work was elicited when increased payments were made to college students engaged in a repetitive strength-endurance task. Similarly, payment by the "piece" was more effective in raising work output than was work paid for at an hourly rate.[893,894]

In general, when attempting to relate the effects of rewards and punishments to motor activity, many variables make the relationship difficult to investigate. Initially, the movement itself, if the behavior-primacy theory is accorded validity, may prove to be motivating for its own sake. The optimal tension level principle is also operative. Conditions which are rewarding to one individual and serve to raise tension to an optimum may cause a second individual to perform badly as the desirable level is exceeded.

Punishment, on the other hand, frequently elicits fear and anxiety. Thus, the relative value of punishing or giving approval when performing a motor task varies from individual to individual. In addition, the form of the reward, the individual offering verbal encouragement, and similar variables all affect the reward-punishment-performance relationship.

Suggested Task Failure as a Motive to Achieve. One of the most frequently manipulated variables is suggesting to the subject that he either is failing or exceeding accepted norms. This is referred to as "failure-stress" if the latter condition is introduced. Interesting findings utilizing this technique have been reported by Bayton and Conley.[64] Using a manipulation task, it was found that prior success or failure, before the introduction of suggested failure, determined the effect of such stress upon performance. It was found that after initial success (also manufactured by the experimenter), the introduction of suggested failure tended to spur performance to greater heights, since the individual seemed to attempt to sustain the feeling of status he had gained during prior trials. On the other hand, if failure was introduced during the early trials, later performance was impeded.

Leshman[575] has also presented findings which suggest that the aspiration level of the performer and his stated expectations determine performance decrement when some kind of failure stress is introduced. Using a pattern-form problem, it was found that muscular tension became greater when experimentally suggested failure followed stated expectations which were realistic than when expectations were unrealistic. It was also found that tension levels increased with failure and decreased with success.

MOTIVATING TYPES OF MOVEMENT BEHAVIOR

Some types of movement behavior seem, in themselves, to constitute motivating experiences. Of particular interest are actions which have been labeled play, manipulation, and exploration and which seem to be manifestations of a basic need of the organism to deal with his environment. Play, manipulation, and exploration are interrelated kinds of behavior. For example, play seems to result in the individual exploring his environment more fully, as various movement patterns are tried out which in another context might be imperative for survival. At the same time, exploration and manipulation appear so satisfying that they might be classified as play. In the following pages a discussion of these activities together with the forces which seem to mold them, of the various forms they seem to take, as well as theoretical frameworks which purport to explain their existence, is presented

Play

No one the least sensitive to the nature of children and animals can deny the existence of playful behavior. As Gavin Maxwell[623] states in a charming story outlining his friendships with several pets in the remote regions of England . . . "Otters are extremely bad at doing nothing." The same statement might be applied to most animals and certainly to most human children.

Play is a spontaneous activity motivating for its own sake. It is engaged in throughout the entire hierarchy of the animal kingdom in various forms. Playful behavior has been studied by the anthropologist, the naturalist, the psychologist, and by experts in child development. It may be observed as fish jump from the water, when monkeys swing from trees, and as puppies and children play chase in the backyard.

As Huizinga stated in "Homoludens" (Man the Player) . . .

> Play is older than culture, for culture, however inadequately defined, always presupposes human society, and animals have not waited for man to teach them their playing.[476]

Characteristics of Play. In general, it is found that the young of the species engage more in playful behavior than do older members. Welker,[946] for example, comparing exploratory and playful behavior of three young and three older chimpanzees, found that the younger ones played for more extended periods of time.

Playful activity contains elements of surprise and is usually marked by a distinct beginning and ending, as though tension has been alleviated.

Play generally takes place in a social context, since when playing one usually associates with another of the species, or occasionally with a member of another species.

Playful behavior seems to involve a wide degree of individual differences in both animals and man. Organisms differ both in the kinds of movements they manifest as well as in the specific forms they choose to express playful moods.

Theories of the Purpose for Play. As many reasons have been postulated for the existence of play as have been advanced to explain motivation in general. In close alignment with instinctual theories of motivation was the explanation advanced by Groos,[398] who in 1898 suggested in his text *The Play of Animals* that play is an instinctive act the purpose of which is to dispose of surplus energies. Many have attempted to justify exercise and physical education totally upon the same premise today (*i.e.*, that activity simply uses up energy which, in another form, might prove disruptive or destructive to society). Tolman[891] reemphasized this viewpoint in 1932 when he stated that animals and man seem to be trying to achieve a harmonious fatigue.

Several criticisms of this theory were forthcoming. For example, it was suggested that if play was meaningless as an educative device, why did play activities of children so resemble necessary kinds of motor behavior of the adult of the species? The young child pretends to drive a car, while the kitten's aimless pouncing upon a ball suggests later mice-catching skills needed for survival. To further weaken the "surplus energy" theory of play, scientific inquiry failed to identify structures within the human organism which might conceivably store up this "energy" and then release it in the form of play.

Another theory suggested that play is simply a joyful release. It was proposed that play was some kind of mystical expression on the part of the individual. Such an explanation, while satisfying to some, failed to suggest any kind of experimental verification and, indeed, seemed circular.

A utilitarian explanation has also been advanced for the existence of play-like behavior. It has been suggested by Beach[65] following a review of theories of play, that joyful movement serves a useful function. Since it is noted that the young of the species engage most in playful pursuits, it was assumed that the purpose of play was to build up a store of movements necessary to optimal functioning in later life.

It is my feeling that playful behavior might indeed fulfill a number of functions in addition to being the manifestation of a basic need for activity or of a general excitatory state of the organism. Play seems to provide for a release of tensions, and at the same time, its imitative quality seems to prepare the young for the adoption of adult responsibilities. In addition, playful behavior seems satisfying in and of itself, apart from more useful consequences. In summary, play is the manifestation of motive to move, to explore, and to manipulate the environment.

Exploration and Manipulation in Animals and Man

Just as a basic need for self-expression in play seems to be present in the animal and human organism, there also seems to be a basic curiosity drive which is expressed in manipulative and explorative activities. Exploration involves movement of the total organism, while manipulation usually involves limb and finger movements. The two types of behavior are thus similar and differ primarily with regard to the amount of space occupied during their expression.

Several basic factors seem to channel and to mold the type and quantity of exploratory and manipulatory behavior. Two of the most important of these are the *novelty* and the *complexity* of the situation or objects. In addition, as is true of play, younger people are usually seen to engage more frequently and for more extended periods of time in exploratory and manipulatory behavior than do older individuals.

Novelty. The role of novelty in establishing and encouraging exploratory behavior has been examined in some detail by Berlyne.[78] In general, this author suggested that there are several kinds of novel situations which may direct attention to an object: (1) *relative novelty,* when something is new as compared to a similar but different past experience, and (2) *absolute novelty,* when an object or situation is unique to the individual's entire range of past experiences. In addition, Berlyne speaks of short-term or long-term novelty, depending upon whether the newly encountered situation is similar to experiences occurring within the recent or the distant past.

Two hypotheses are presented by Berlyne to explain the motivating effect of novelty upon manipulatory and exploratory behavior: (1) the *habituation hypothesis,* which suggests that novel objects are motivating simply because they have not yet had a chance to lose intriguing qualities which all objects originally possess; and (2) a second theory which proposes that novelty represents a *conflict* within the individual, an imbalance or tension which may be alleviated only by exploring and manipulating the new situation.

Complexity. A second contributory factor in the initiating of exploratory and/or manipulatory behavior has to do with the complexity of the object or situation. In general, it seems that objects or situations that are too simple do not encourage exploratory behavior, while, on the other hand, an object or situation may be too complex to draw the organism's attention. In short, there seems to be an optimal level of complexity in the new situation that will encourage the organism to engage in a maximal amount of exploration and manipulation.

Illustrative of research focused upon manipulation and exploration are studies by Welker[946] using chimpanzees as subjects. Various shaped and colored blocks were presented to the primates and the following measures were recorded: (1) total responsiveness based upon the total number of five-second periods during which an animal touched any

11

object, (2) number of contacts, (3) shifts, the number of times touch shifted from one object to another, (4) withdrawals, the number of times the subjects withdrew from the experimental situation, and (5) a listing of the objects touched, the number of different objects touched and the length of contact, and the average length of contact with each object of a given classification.

Welker found that novelty, or the introduction of new or different blocks of a more complex nature, resulted in an increase in the total responsiveness score. On the other hand, a decrease in responsiveness measures was noted when the object presented was less complex than previous ones, i.e., not as colorful or as intricate in shape or form. In addition it was found that with repeated presentations of the same blocks a decrease in the various responsive measures was recorded, indicating that the principle of saturation was operative. A significant decrease in responsiveness, for example, was noted when comparing scores recorded on the first day (during the ten-minute experimental period) and scores collected on the third day of the nine-day experiment.

Welker also found that in addition to novelty and complexity, the *proximity* of the object to the animal seemed to be an effective variable. The blocks which were placed in the row nearest the chimpanzees were more frequently handled that were those in a row farther away. More recent research has elaborated upon the findings presented by Welker. Menzel in 1961 also found that, while at times primates may be initially fearful of complex stimuli, they handle them more than the simpler objects after their anxiety is dissipated. Menzel found that objects of a maximum size elicited the most manipulatory behavior on the part of primates; objects which were too big or too small, on the other hand, elicited only a moderate amount of inspection on the part of his subjects.[652]

Sackett found that early environment influences the tendency to manipulate objects. Jungle-reared monkeys manipulated most and handled more complex objects than did their cage reared cousins.[777]

Children are being utilized more in contemporary experiments dealing with the influence of novelty and complexity upon manipulatory behavior.[247] Similar to the findings of studies in which primates are used, it has been found that complexity elicits more activity than does simplicity.[797] Similarly novelty also encourages more interest than does the familiar.[422]

The personality of the child, as well as age and sex, influence his reaction to novel situations. Mendel[648] found that while the preference value of toys increased as a direct function of its novelty, younger children as well as those who were scored high in anxiety by their teachers preferred less novelty than did the older children and those with low anxiety scores. Similarly, the boys preferred more novelty than did the girls.[648]

The observations of Piaget,[729] Gesell,[351] and Halverson,[488] among others, confirm the extent to which the human infant seizes upon every opportunity to manipulate and to explore his environment. It is believed that no comprehensive theoretical explanation of human motivation may exclude this kind of persistent and universal human activity.

SUMMARY

Motivation is a broad term referring to a general level of arousal to action. Motives, on the other hand, are specific conditions which affect performance and contribute to the general motivational level.

Theories of motivation include those based upon concepts of instincts and basic drives, as well as those advocating the importance of physiological needs, psychological needs, and social needs. The capacity-primary theory of motivation suggests that the multiplicity of activities, interests, and movements engaged in by man need not be dependent upon innate physiological drives, but may depend upon innate capacities. The existence of play, manipulation, and exploratory behavior, it is believed, is best explained within such a theoretical framework.

A general condition contributing to the motivational state is the individual's state of arousal. Upon presentation of the task, the "What is it?" reflex is usually noted. General postural adjustments necessary to take in sensory information are indicated. This, in turn, produces a general readiness or "set" prior to task performance.

Specific motives to move, or not to move, include restriction from movement, fatigue (task-aversion, boredom), and specific rewards or punishments. Conditions which raise general tension level may affect the performance of different individuals in different ways, depending upon prior level of efficiency and general complex of personality traits.

Play, manipulation, and exploration are specific kinds of movement behavior which seem self-sustaining, motivating experiences in their own right. The intensity of these activities is dependent upon the age of the participants, as well as upon the complexity and novelty of the situation.

Student References

Books

1. Asch, Solomon: *Social Psychology*, Englewood Cliffs, N.J., Prentice-Hall, 1951.
2. Fowler, Harry: *Curiosity and Exploratory Behavior*, New York, The Macmillan Co., 1965.
3. Rethlingshafer, Dorothy: *Motivation as Related to Personality*, New York, McGraw-Hill Book Company, Inc., 1963.
4. Woodworth, R. S.: *Dynamics of Behavior*, New York, Henry Holt & Co., 1958.
5. Young, Paul T.: *Motivation and Emotion*, New York, John Wiley & Sons, Inc., 1961.

Articles

1. Gates, G.: The effect of an audience upon performance, *J. Abnormal & Social Psych.*, 18, 334-344, 1924.
2. Welker, W. I.: "Some determinants of play and exploration in chimpanzees," *J. Comp. & Physio. Psych.*, 49, 84-90, 1956.

Chapter 9

Social Motives

MEN are seldom oblivious of their social setting when performing motor tasks. Some of the most important variables affecting the physical performance of humans are other people. The more enlightened theoretical positions described in the previous chapter, attempting to explain human motivation, have incorporated social motives into their frameworks.

The intensity of a physical act, the length of time a task is engaged in, as well as the selection of the task itself are dependent more upon various factors within the social clime than upon more subtle variables, or upon basic physiological drives. After the first few days of life the behavior of human infants begins to be influenced in direct ways by their parents and by others with whom they come in contact. Throughout childhood and adolescence and into adulthood, individuals are influenced to varying degrees when performing a variety of tasks by the presence, the encouragement, or at times by the disapproval of others.

Social motives may be defined as variables molding human behavior which are an integral part of the social context in which the behavior is observed or measured. There are several dimensions to this type of impetus to action.

Initially one might consider the effect of various "unseen audiences" upon the performance of individuals or groups. These absent spectators include subcultures against which a person compares his performance; and perhaps parents and colleagues whom one knows might later judge the results of his efforts even though the activity might be undertaken in solitude. The subtle influence of broad socio-cultural variables is another example of a type of absent audience influential of performance.

A third classification includes social motives which may be identified in situations in which two or more people are performing the same or related tasks at approximately the same time. Research dealing with competition, cooperative behavior, group interaction, inter-personal communication, leadership, and group cohesion is concerned with information of this nature.

The number of investigations dealing with various socio-psychological variables has proliferated within recent years. Many of these studies in order to elicit exact performance measures have employed a variety of motor tasks, particularly when children have been used as subjects.

The following information is selective rather than an attempt to cover the vast amount of this kind of literature in a comprehensive manner. At the same time a consideration of the points raised within these pages, it is believed, will enable an educator to become more effective in his efforts to mold and to change the movement attributes of others.

The Effects of Observers upon Performance

A single observer or a group watching one or more individuals perform may evidence various kinds of behavior. The viewers may passively look on while a person performs, they may gesture or by their facial expressions express support or disapproval of his efforts, or they may verbally reinforce or "razz" individual or group efforts.

There is an increasing amount of literature which suggests that even passive, silent observation will elicit obvious or subtle performance changes on the part of individuals or groups. McBride and his colleagues found that the proximity of the experimenter to the subject would elicit measurable changes in the galvanic skin responses of the latter, a reasonably reliable measure of activation influential of a variety of motor attributes. Furthermore these same experimenters found that whether the experimenter was standing to the front, back, or side of the subjects also altered this electrophysiological measure.[625]

As early as 1897 Triplett reported that the presence of an audience caused both negative and positive performance fluctuations in a reel-winding task and in competitive bicycle riding[897] Gates in a more recent study also found that an audience influenced different individuals in different ways when they were attempting a test of manual dexterity. Gates varied the size of the audience from a single experimenter to a small group of six onlookers to a large group of about one hundred.[346]

The sex of the observer relative to the sex of the performer has been found to influence performance in a variety of tasks. Generally, individuals perform best and for more sustained periods of time when in the presence of the opposite sex. A number of investigations have explored this cross-sex effect, demonstrating important lessons for experimenters when collecting data from human subjects, as well as illustrating important principles for educators interested in changing the movement attributes of adults and children.

In a series of studies carried out from 1961-65 Hill and Stevenson,[456] found that skilled performance by adolescent girls improved in the presence of male experimenters who verbally reinforced their efforts. It was found that testing by a member of the opposite sex increased competitiveness and anxiety about the task, as well as the desire to please the experimenter. Stevenson suggested that this effect is more pronounced in female subjects tested by males. However, the research by Bendig[70] concluded that the reverse is true, stating that males seem to have higher needs for social approval.

Noer and Whittaker elicited this cross-sex effect in an indirect way.[702] Using a mirror-tracing skill, improvements were elicited in girls by suggesting that "girls do twice as well as boys in this task, but you did not," and suggesting the reverse to the male subjects in their experiment.

It might be hypothesized that this cross-sex effect is operative in a number of tasks and serves generally to activate the performer; thus perhaps it can be counted upon positively to influence simple tasks while at the same time proving detrimental to more complex ones. However, the number of studies dealing with this problem is small, and the kinds of tasks examined under these conditions are extremely limited.

This cross-sex effect is often noted by coaches and others concerned with optimum performance. The exact parameters of this phenomenon await further investigations. For example, there is no information relative to the effect of female onlookers upon the performance of males in a wide variety of tasks. Similarly there is little information relative to the number of onlookers of the opposite sex which can be counted upon to elicit the most performance improvement. One might also assume that less skilled performers might be hindered in their efforts by the presence of a member of the opposite sex, while the reverse might be true when more proficient individuals perform. I know of no experimental evidence, however, confirming or disproving these assumptions.

The effect of onlookers upon motor performance appears also to be a function of age. Stevenson, for example, suggests that with increased age children become more aware of various aspects of social reinforcers.[854] Missiuro fixes the age at six years, at which time children's motor performance becomes positively affected by onlookers. Improvement was noted in an endurance task by his subjects at this age; while prior to six the children were noted to be generally activated by the presence of an audience, they did not direct this heightened arousal into measurable performance improvement.[669]

The personality of the performer also influences his susceptibility to the audience effect. Bendig found that individuals high in achievement needs were most influenced by onlookers.[70] Cox[185] also found that when boys were asked to perform a marble-dropping task for sustained periods, those with low anxiety scores performed best in the presence of a number of types of spectators, including their parents, peers, teachers, and strangers. Those who scored high in measures of anxiety performed best when only the experimenter was present.[185]

Thus to predict the effects of a silent audience upon performance of skills one must take into consideration the age and personality of the performer, the nature of the task, the size and composition of the audience, as well as the sex of the onlookers as compared to the sex of the performers. Innumerable studies suggest themselves after a survey of the relatively scant literature available upon this and related subjects. For example, little information is forthcoming relative to the effects of experience upon physical performance while a person is performing with an audience present. A recent investigation by Singer comparing the performance of athletes and non-athletes in an experimental task suggests that experience in front of audiences might be specific to the task, and may not generalize to any great extent.[821]

Investigations also seem needed exploring the influence upon his efforts of the feelings an athlete has about the audience. Although Olgvie and Tutko have postulated that most superior athletes have negative feelings about all individuals who watch them; they have not, however, presented data elaborating upon the possible relationships between the intensity of these feelings and various facets of sports performance.[706]

When Observers Talk

Spectators may accompany their observations of the performers by verbal behavior denoting approval or disapproval of the efforts they are observing. Relatively few studies have been carried out in which negative verbal reinforcement was studied as effective of motor performance, although this frequently occurs in athletic stadia and on playfields. More numerous are investigations in which praise has been studied as influential of physical performance.

Earlier studies of these questions utilized relatively few subjects and were rather inexact. Laird, for example, found that the performance of seven fraternity "pledges" were severely disrupted when they were "razzed" for their efforts by seniors.[552] A study by Latane and Arrowood established that verbal harassment during the performance of physical skills tended to depress scores on complex activities (pushing buttons to light cues), while serving to facilitate performance in simpler tasks.[564]

Several investigations have compared the effects of negative and positive verbal reinforcers upon motor performance. It is usually found that verbal "punishment" elicits a heightened state of arousal resulting in more rapid or more intense efforts.[564] At the same time negative verbal exhortation tends to disrupt complex performance. The effect of praise is heightened if the subjects have high needs for social approval,[583] or are between the ages of five and six.[583] As the difficulty of the task and the age of the subject increase, verbal exhortation seems to have less effect, and the performer's interest in the task becomes more affective of the quality of his efforts.[16]

Innumerable studies attest to the positive influence of praise upon the execution of a variety of motor tasks. Recent studies by Kelly and Stephens,[516] and by Strickland and Jenkins[861] support this basic assumption.

In addition to praising an individual or group for performing during or prior to beginning the task, onlookers may encourage optimum effort by various kinds of exhortation. Fleishman published findings in 1958 in which it was demonstrated that encouraging trainee airmen to "do your best," "the results of this test are important to you" and similar kinds of support significantly improved performance on a rudder-stick coordination task. Additional insight into the effects of exhortation upon motor performance is provided by Locke,[592] who found that the setting of specific performance goals more positively influenced scores on a complex coordination task than was elicited when subjects were simply encouraged to "do your best." It thus seems that encouragement toward the attainment of reasonable goals is more helpful than simply exciting the performer with non-specific attempts to activate him via verbal exhortations.

In general, younger boys and girls remain longer and work harder under conditions involving verbal approval.[16] Similarly performance increments will usually be elicited in complex tasks when approval is extended by a friend rather than by a non-preferred peer. In younger children the avoidance of criticism seems to be a more powerful motive to performance than eliciting approval for their efforts. The more mature children, adolescents, and adults will tend to work relatively independent of criticism or praise extended, deriving more of their satisfactions from an interest in the task itself.[16]

The influence of verbal exhortation upon performance is a function of the age of the performer, his past experience at the task, as well as the nature of the task. Similarly the previous relationships between the individuals offering encouragement or disapproval and the performers also influences the effects of this kind of social motivation.

The Motivating Effects of Another's Performance

In addition to individuals changing the performance output of another by passively observing him, or more actively engaging in some kind of verbal reinforcement, people stimulate each other as they perform at the same time on work teams, and as they compete against one another as teams or as individuals. These effects involve some kind of group or individual interaction involving the motor performance of two or more individuals, in contrast to social facilitation elicited by the mere presence of onlookers.

Competition. The American society of the late 1960's is a competitive one, in which apparent success is purportedly dependent upon the extent to which an individual can compete with his fellows in activities upon which the culture bestows status. One of these activities involves the performance of physical skills.

Individual and team sports have been justified in school curriculas partly because they have been hypothesized to be inculcating competitive behavior in the youthful participants. Competitive urges seem a rather basic component of the human personality, and indeed are observed in the behavior of animals at the lower levels of the evolutionary scale.

All other things equal, competition improves performance in simple strength tasks, as well as in tasks whose successful execution depends upon simple speed and/or reaction time.[156] On the other hand if the performers are relatively anxious and/or the task requires precision, competition may impede performance.

Generally the conditions which can be counted upon to elicit competition include individuals who perceive themselves as competitive and able in the performance of some task, as well as the presence of two or more individuals who perceive themselves nearly alike in ability. The competitors in motor skills must be reasonably mature; usually little structured competitive behavior is elicited before the age of three years. The similarities and/or differences of socio-economic levels of the antagonists can also influence their tendency to compete. Lower class individuals compete for different reasons and for different goals than do those more favored economically and socially. It has been found that differences in economic levels between two competitors may influence their interactions. Lower class individuals may be reluctant to challenge those of a superior economic classification.

Competition may be considered a form of "social activation" and may be expected to elicit performance changes accordingly. Simple tasks are improved, complex tasks are hindered; the performance of individuals working at below optimum levels of activation is improved, while the scores of those working at desirable levels may be depressed. Thus the effects of competition upon performance is a function of the current level of activation of the performers, the difficulty of the task, the individual's past experience in competitive circumstances, as well as his perceptions of himself as a competitor in the situation he faces.

People usually perceive competitive situations as satisfying, despite whether they have won or lost. Similarly mutual attractiveness of pairs or between members of larger groups has been demonstrated to be enhanced if they have competed with one another.

While competition seems a rather ubiquitous part of our society and an important component of social motivation, many facets of competition have not been explored experimentally, particularly in relationship to motor performance and learning. Additional research might concern itself with exploring in more depth the relationships between various personality traits and competitive behavior, perhaps in efforts to determine whether a "competitive nature" is a product of early training in childhood or elicited by needs immediate to the situation. Further investigations might also explore whether individuals generally tend to compete in a variety of situations, or only in selected tasks.

Cooperation. Individuals motivate each other when they perform in unison. Parallel play is first noted in children at about the age of two, as two children may engage in similar activity but do not interact directly. By the age of six, however, children stimulate each other directly by forming groups to accomplish various tasks. Affiliation is motivating, and grouping together to perform motor tasks usually affects the performance of the task. Frequently the problem of studying the effect of group interaction upon motor performance is complicated by the fact that individuals sometimes are performing both cooperatively and competitively at the same time. People form groups and engage in cooperative behavior in order to compete favorably with a similar group acting as their competitor.

Generally groups perform tasks better than do individuals, because of what has been termed a greater amount of "resource input" available to groups. However, as the group gets larger individuals will not be motivated to exert maximum effort because they may feel that their part in the total effort is diminishing; there is thus a measurable amount of performance decrement on the part of each individual. For example in one study conducted using a tug-of-war task, there was a decrease of 10 per cent in individual effort expended with the addition of each member over four.

Groups can be motivated to varying degrees by needs for affiliation versus needs for superior group performance. Studies by Cratty and Sage and others have described the tendency for affiliative needs to sometimes interfere with optimum group effort. An excess of "social noise," it was pointed out, may at times distract the group from focusing upon the task at hand.[220]

In general there seems to be an optimum amount of "we feeling" necessary to keep the group working together and to permit the leadership to focus upon the task at hand. However, if the individuals have formed the group primarily with affiliative motives in mind, their performance as a group may suffer.

Innumerable questions remain unanswered upon inspection of the available literature. The work-methods of the group may be more important than whether they are competing or cooperating in some task. Jones has found that how a group divides its labor, or whether they do at all, may be more influential of performance than whether they are competing or cooperating.[504]

Similarly the performance quality researched by Weist[964] et al. and Comrey and his colleagues is an important variable to consider. Some individuals perform particularly well when interacting with another in a motor task; they coordinate their movements with those of their teammates, anticipating the actions of the other group members with facility. Thus the performance of individuals in groups probably depends upon not only the mutual stimulation they afford one another, but the extent to which they can integrate their movements in a common task.[170-172]

Gaining Status Through Physical Performance

The gaining of status in childhood, adolescence, and adulthood depends upon innumerable qualities and upon a variety of situations in which human beings may interact. Generally status is bestowed upon group members who perform well the activities valued by the group, and/or those who enable the group to perform well by overcoming blocks to their efforts and by proposing helpful performance techniques. As the growing child reaches the age of five and six, physical ability contributes to some degree to his social acceptability and status within the play group. Fighting ability and superior motor performance have been found to enhance status on the part of older children.

The status conferred by athletic prowess is reflected in various personality measures on the part of growing boys. Research has documented the tendency for proficient boys to evidence traits which reflect the status this ability has bestowed upon them within their social groups. In general, these good-performing young males are more ascendent, and are socially more outgoing than are boys who are less proficient motorically. Early maturation which enhances basic physical capacities on the part of males also, as might be expected, correlates with personality traits denoting social adroitness.[687]

By the time adolescence is reached, athletic prowess has become an overriding means of achieving status on the part of males. Coleman, in the discussion of his findings in *The Adolescent Society,* points out that almost half of the boys interviewed wished to be remembered after high school as athletes rather than as leaders in activities, scholars, or the most popular. Male membership in leading social groups was mainly attributed to participation in athletics rather than to such qualities as appearance, common sense, and sense of humor.[168]

Although Coleman's findings might not be applicable to all communities or to adolescent societies of the late 1960's (the study was carried out in 1958 in ten high schools in the Chicago Area), they hold important implications for understanding the influence of social motives upon the performance and value systems of male adolescents in our society.

The effects of early maturation and physical proficiency upon the development of positive social skills is seen to carry over into adolescence and even into adulthood. In 1938 Jones carried out an investigation which revealed a relationship between physical development and social adjustment of boys. A follow-up to this investigation carried out in 1965 used the same subjects, now adults. It was found that these males tended to retain the same constellation of personality characteristics they had evidenced as boys. The late-maturing retiring youths grew up to be somewhat withdrawn men. Conversely the outgoing early-maturing male retained his ascendent behaviors in adulthood. Thus it was proposed that the advantages of early maturation on the part of males contributes to a positive self-concept which continues into adulthood.[542]

Girls in our culture, of course, do not derive the same status benefits from exhibiting proficiency in sports skills. Although there are some indications that girls are beginning to participate more in vigorous games, in general a girl must be selective as to the sports she attempts, while being careful not to exhibit too intense an effort to excel.

Status cannot be derived from proficiency in a variety of motor tasks— only in those involving large muscle activity deemed important by the culture. A chicken and egg relationship exists between status and physical prowess. Boys who excel in motor skills achieve status, and having achieved it continue to pursue its source. At the same time individuals with high needs for status will tend to work harder and to practice longer in various physical skills so that they may achieve social prominence. The "need for social approval" scored on various personality questionnaires is frequently correlated with proficiency in various gross motor activities.[218]

SUMMARY

Individuals are motivated by numerous components of the social clime when performing and learning motor skills. The presence of an onlooker will result in performance fluctuations, particularly if the spectator is a member of the opposite sex. More explicit modifications in performance will result if the audience voices approval, disapproval, or simply attempts to elicit maximum effort. The effects of such facilitation is a function of the nature of the task, as well as the maturity of the performer. Measurable indices of motor performance in children below the age of six or seven do not seem to be affected to the same extent as are children a few years older. As the child matures into late childhood and early adolescence, however, verbal exhortation by an onlooker begins to have less effect, and performance begins to be influenced more by the nature of the task, its novelty, and its complexity.

Competition and cooperative behavior in individual and group performance situations are at times difficult to separate. Competition is motivating in itself, independent of whether it results in individual or group success. However, if individuals are successful in groups, the attractiveness of the group is heightened, as is the cohesion of the members involved. If affiliative needs on the part of individuals in a group are paramount to their needs for success in the task at hand, performance may suffer. While there seems to be an optimum amount of group cohesion necessary in order to elicit maximum group efforts, facilitate communication, and make the most efficient use of the leadership available, groups whose members form primarily to satisfy social needs will not usually perform as well as do groups whose primary reason for collecting together is to execute a task successfully.

Status seeking is an important social motive, particularly influential of the peer group relation of growing boys in our culture. Early maturation together with the concomitant physical prowess—biological maturity—forms a base of success which results in the appearance of personality traits involving ascendency and social competence which extend into adolescence and adulthood.

Student References

Books

1. COLEMAN, JAMES S.: *The Adolescent Society,* New York, Free Press of Glencoe, 1961.
2. CRATTY, BRYANT J.: *Social Dimensions of Physical Activity,* Englewood Cliffs, N. J., Prentice-Hall, Inc., 1967.

Article

1. ROSEN, BERNARD C. and ROY D'ANDRADE: "The Psycho-Social Origins of Achievement Motivation," *Sociometry,* 22, 185-218, 1959.

Chapter 10

Anxiety, Stress, and Tension

MANY meanings have been assigned to the terms stress, anxiety, and tension. The definitions sometimes have been dependent upon the viewpoint of the researcher, the situation in which observations were made, or the measures employed. For example, with regard to *tension,* it is often reported that experimental subjects were "too tense" to perform well in movement tasks. In another context, it is sometimes observed that an individual evidences extreme "nervous tension" when attempting to meet the demands of life. In the first case, tension refers to a momentary task-related state, while in the second, a personality trait is described.

The meaning of the word *stress* has undergone change during the years. Earlier behavioral scientists considered the affecting situation as stress, while at other times definitions were based upon changes in performance characteristics. More recent medical researchers have inferred that stress is an intervening variable located between the situational input and the movement output. It has been further suggested that stress is best determined through biochemical analyses of various types.

Pinpointing the meaning of *anxiety* poses similar problems. Early Freudian psychoanalysts and many contemporary clinicians consider anxiety as a general fear of impending events based upon *unconscious* motives and upon circumstances in the organism's forgotten past. On the other hand, experimental psychologists have recently coined the terms *manifest anxiety* and *free anxiety,* suggesting that this syndrome of fear is a reportable and *conscious* experience.

An historical look at the manner in which stress, tension, and anxiety have been interrelated also indicates that shifts of opinion have taken place. For example, early researchers often used stress and tension as interchangeable concepts, with stress assumed always to produce tension, while the latter was considered indisputable evidence of the former. More recent investigations, however, suggest that stress is an internalized kind of preparation to meet an immediate or future threat, while tension is now considered to be a related, but separate and more peripheral, behavioral manifestation involving muscular contraction. It is further suggested that, although tension *may* be in response to emotional arousal, it can also be induced simply by increasing the task load.

Interrelating the terms anxiety and stress also has produced problems. In general, however, stress seems to be determined by the situation and is a rather short-range phenomenon. Anxiety, on the other hand, is usually considered to be a general and continuing state of the organism, a personality characteristic.

Stress and anxiety, however, are intimately related in several ways. The literature suggests that repeated exposure to stressful situations results in heightening general anxiety. In addition, a highly anxious individual evidences internal stress reactions to a wider range of events than does a non-anxious person and reacts more strongly to situations which to most would result in relatively mild reactions.

In summary, *anxiety appears to be a general fear or foreboding, a personality trait marked by a lower threshold to stressful events. Stress is an internal reaction, an intervening variable between situation and performance, evidenced by a marshalling of resources to meet a threat. Tension, on the other hand, is overt muscular contraction caused by an emotional state or by increased effort.*

Whatever definitions are attached to these terms, it is usually found that stress and anxiety are manifested in increased muscular tension. And, since the focus of the book is upon overt movement behavior, also a product of the skeleto-muscular system, failing to consider these major factors in performance would be a serious omission. Establishing more clear-cut boundaries between these terms, as well as demonstrating their inter-relationships will be attempted in the pages which follow. First, various theoretical viewpoints, which have been proposed, together with a "how-are-they-measured?" approach, will be discussed. It is hoped that, as stress, tension, and anxiety are related to movement behavior in the final portion of each section, the definitions presented above will assume more exact dimensions.

THE NATURE OF ANXIETY

To maintain internal balance, the organism must function with a certain level of anxiety always present. For anxiety, in its broadest sense, refers to the general state of alertness. It is related to the body's alarm system and provides for vigilance against disruptive forces in the environment. One must be anxious when crossing a street and transmit this anxiety to his children in order to insure their survival in the modern city. However, performance problems arise if anxiety-produced arousal is too great. If the organism is continually threatened, Malmo and Davis[584] suggest, heightened general anxiety, measured by increased muscular tension, is the result. Some psychiatrists utilize the term *anxiety* only in a pathological context, while suggesting that fear is a healthy respect for situations and objects which are actually threatening.

Anxiety is a central idea in Freudian psychodynamics. It is related to the ego concept, which is defined as the portion of the personality which interacts with actual situations in the real world, rather than with imagined events. It is suggested that, while the environment can reward and bring pleasure to the individual, it can also threaten and punish him. Freud[327] hypothesizes that anxiety floods the ego when it is overwhelmed with continual threats of pain and/or destruction with which the organism is unable to cope. It is further held that the dangers and insecurities of constant and pronounced threats will cause the individual to become generally anxious.

Initially, Freud emphasized that anxiety was primarily produced through frustration of sexual urges. Later experimental evidence, however, proved this assertion to be rather untenable. Freud divided anxiety into three categories, ranging from normal apprehension of real situations (*reality anxiety*) to the fear of punishment for future transgressions (*neurotic anxiety*). The third classification suggested was *moral anxiety*, or the fear of punishment for socially disapproved behavior.

Others differentiate between *general anxiety* and *situational anxiety*, the latter denoting a specific fear. It has been suggested that with increased exposure to a task, situational anxiety will tend to dissipate.[52]

The Freudian concept of anxiety, however, depended directly upon the existence of unconscious forces and was difficult to objectify experimentally. Contemporary psychological researchers, in a search for measures which would permit more exact investigation of anxiety and its relationship to objective performance measures and to other personality variables, have evolved simpler and more direct definitions. Terms recently have been coined which assume that anxiety best may be verified by the collection of reportable *conscious* behavior on the part of the individual.

In 1953, for example, Janet Taylor[876] developed a test to measure what she called *manifest anxiety*. It was based upon direct self-reports on the part of subjects. The device was validated by including responses which indicated marked differences between groups of "normal" individuals and those who had been clinically classified as needing psychiatric aid because of the general feeling of fear constantly attending them. This tool has been used, with some modifications, in numerous experimental studies during the past ten years.

Basowitz *et al.*[58] have suggested the term *free anxiety* to distinguish general fear. They also suggested that previous psychoanalytic descriptions did not lend themselves to precise measurement. Basowitz defines free anxiety as "the conscious and reportable experience of intense dread and foreboding." The concepts of *free anxiety* and *manifest anxiety* bear a marked similarity insofar as both are identified through similar measuring devices and are not dependent upon the identification of unconscious motivations.

Anxiety and Performance

The effect of anxiety upon performance is directly dependent upon the type of task considered. In most cases a heightened arousal state has been found to facilitate simple performances such as finger tapping, eyelid conditioning, and verbal memory tasks. On the other hand, as anxiety reaches a certain level, a breakdown of psychological and physiological integrative mechanisms is often seen to occur, resulting in less efficient performance in more complex tasks.

In a second frame of reference, anxiety has a temporal relationship to performance. The level of anxiety evidenced prior to performance may be different from arousal during performance. Following a stressful situation, abrupt changes in reportable anxiety are often recorded. In general, anxiety levels increase prior to a dangerous situation until they become relatively high just before it is encountered. During performance, anxiety is often lessened, since the individual must concentrate upon his own actions rather than upon his internalized fears. Post-task anxiety may then abruptly rise as the individual seems to lower his defenses and admit his fear more freely. This rise in post-task anxiety has been reported by Basowitz et al.,[58] investigating paratrooper training (and termed "the end phenomenon"), as well as by Menninger[650] and others, investigating anxiety under wartime conditions. It has been noted, for example, that more breakdowns took place after a soldier was removed from the front lines and placed in the rear rest areas than occurred during actual combat.

Two other kinds of anxiety have been identified in several kinds of experimental and real-life situations. Subjects often differentiate between what has been termed *harm anxiety* and *failure anxiety*. In addition to fear of the actual conditions which may cause injury (harm anxiety), individuals may evidence equal or stronger anxiety concerning the fear that they might not "measure up" or should fail under the stressful conditions to which they are subjected. Caudill[151] has pointed out the importance of social pressures and the manner in which they contribute to stress and anxiety in considering the fear of failure which is in addition to the real dangers in the situation.

Anxiety is intimately related to movement behavior. Malmo[614] and Meyer and Noble[656] indicate that there is an increase of muscular tension when an individual is characteristically in a state of heightened anxiety. Wassenaar also found that a factor named "general anxiety" was present in the performance of a variety of motor tasks. In a recent factorial study, it was found that this general anxiety was detrimental to a number of psychomotor performances, and that the resultant shortening of reaction time with heightened anxiety can interfere with the adaptation of the individual to new situations.[928]

Anxiety sometimes results in more activity on the part of the individual but often this activity is pointless, inflexible, and rigid. Since anxiety operates to increase tension levels within the organism, as might be expected inefficient performance is the result. It has even been found in studies by Brieson[111] and others that continued high anxiety will lead to physiological breakdown, measurable by nerve cell deterioration.

Still under investigation is the manner in which tension and anxiety interact to affect performance. While earlier researchers suggested that anxiety and tension summate to affect performance, an investigation by Lovass[600] indicates that anxiety and muscular tension interact separately to affect performance. Fenz[295] has also obtained findings which suggest that anxiety and muscular tension are separate factors. Anxiety, Fenz concludes, involves a "deeper level of inhibition," while muscular tension is associated with overt activity.

The relationship of anxiety to performances of both a simple and complex nature has been demonstrated in studies of verbal and motor tasks. Matarazzo and Matarazzo,[620] for example, found that subjects scoring within the middle portions of an anxiety scale performed best on a small maze task, while those scoring at both extremes evidenced inferior performance. At times, heightened anxiety will result in increased speed in simple conditioning tasks. However, as Matarazzo and Matarazzo[620] found in a maze problem and Taylor and Spence[877] discovered when studying a verbal choice-point problem, more complex performance is adversely affected by anxiety. Additional evidence that complex tasks requiring fine coordinations or fine discriminations are impeded by higher levels of anxiety is provided by findings of Wechsler and Hartogs.[937] These investigators found that high anxiety individuals took significantly more time to learn a mirror drawing task. Of particular interest to these experimenters was the continual evidence of "graphomotor blocks," tense small strokes made in a small area, which was taken to indicate that the neuromuscular integration had broken down.

Farber and Spence,[292] studying complex motor learning involving a stylus maze task, also found that high anxiety subjects were significantly retarded, particularly within areas of the maze containing difficult choice points. On the other hand, these experimenters found that these same subjects evidenced greater proficiency when their eyelid reflex was conditioned. It was concluded that the anxious and non-anxious groups differed primarily with respect to drive level, rather than to general learning ability. It was further suggested that the effect of variations in drive level upon performance is a function of specific task characteristics.

Thus, highly anxious individuals seem unable to adapt to novel situations. Their behavior is rigid and their integrative mechanisms, which permit efficient perceptual motor control, seem to break down. This assumption is confirmed by the findings of Ausubel, Schiff, and Goldman,[37] who found that, although anxious and non-anxious subjects performed the same during the initial trial of a blindfolded maze task, upon subsequent performances the high anxiety subjects were out-distanced. These researchers suggested that this was a lowering of the anxious subjects' "improvising ability" as the task progressed.

Anxiety, Induced Stress, and Performance

Numerous studies have been carried out to determine the effect of stressful events upon the motor and verbal performance of high and low anxiety subjects. Lucas,[602] for example, using a fear of failure to produce stress, found that high anxiety subjects performed more poorly than did non-anxious individuals when learning a verbal task. High anxiety, coupled with an increase in motivation due to instruction, was found by Sarason and Palola[781] also to impede performance in arithmetic and code-substitution tasks.

Baker[48] presented findings, in a doctoral study, which illustrate the effect of stress upon high and low anxiety performers of a task involving gross motor activity. The subjects were required to place their feet in a pattern drawn on a rapidly moving treadmill, much as a small girl would play hopscotch but involving more complex movements. The stress applied was an electric shock to the leg. It was found that significantly more errors were recorded by high anxiety subjects (as measured on Taylor's scale) than were recorded by low anxiety subjects subjected to the same conditions. The base performances of the two groups without shock, however, were not significantly different.

Experimental work by Kempe[519] has suggested that individuals can be differentiated according to the habitual manner in which they react to stress. On the one hand are people who tend to respond to stress with a general increase in muscular tension, who seem to remain aloof of social convention and can intellectualize quite easily. On the other hand are individuals who act by way of the autonomic nervous system. People within this second classification are emotionally sensitive, worry a great deal, and have fears of not being accepted by others.

Stress is more disturbing to the performance levels of individuals who are highly anxious; at times, however, performance of these people cannot be distinguished from the more tranquil subject until a stressor has been introduced into the situation. The effect of anxiety level upon performance, therefore, is a function of the amount of stress as perceived by the performer, his habitual manner of reacting to stress, as well as the complexity of the task.

THE NATURE OF STRESS

Stress may be defined as a temporarily induced physiological or psychological imbalance, caused by an event considered threatening by the organism. Several different approaches have been employed which place the concept of stress within a framework of total human functioning.

Selye,[802] physician and biochemist, has proposed a general stress theory, based upon research carried out over a period of thirty years. It is based primarily upon his observation that several kinds of bodily conditions were consistently noted to be present when various types of diseases or infections were diagnosed. He thus "bound these loose logs together" (observed facts), related them to solid supports (classical medicine), and evolved a general theory of stress, reported in 1956 in *The Stress of Life*. The basis of this theory involves the identification of a General Adaptation Syndrome, related to the nonspecific adaptation of the body to general impingement or to disruptive events. GAS is evidenced spatially, it is suggested, in adrenal, pituitary, and thymus gland activity by the mobilization of white blood corpuscles, as well as in internal visceral activity. Temporally, adaptation is believed to be divisible into the alarm stage, the resistance stage, and the stage of exhaustion.

Stressors, according to Seyle, are any disease, infection or injury, but also might include fatigue, aging, thirst, pain, as well as frustration and threat. Thus the theory is a broad one from which philosophical implications are derived concerning the manner in which one may optimally conduct his life.

Although earlier research often describes stress as a particular kind of event or situation which is likely to produce fear or task inefficiency, later investigation considers stress as an intervening stage between the situation and the performance. This is occasioned by the observation that individuals differ markedly in their reactions to a given stressful situation. An occurrence which might produce stress in one individual will often have no measurable effect on a second. It has also been observed that reactions to stressors take different forms. For example, one person may evidence marked physiological changes of various kinds, while no marked performance fluctuations are noted. Others may undergo perceptual distortion, while seeming to perform well and perhaps showing no measurable physiological changes.

Thus the measurement of stress and the definition of the term are intimately related to other intervening variables such as motivation, drive, and fear. For example, under sufficient motivation, an individual will often perform well under stress, while if the motivation level is reduced, marked performance breakdown will occur.

Stress will be considered in the present discussion, therefore, as a performance affector lying between the event and performance (as suggested by Lazarus, Deese, and Osler[570] in their 1952 synthesis of the research on stress and performance). To facilitate the study of the stress variable, consideration will be given to the type of stressor and the manner in which performance is affected under stressful conditions. The term *stressor* will be used to indicate the event, activity, or impingement upon the organism which produces stress.

The Measurement of Stress

Stress has been measured through the evaluation of various physiological functions, including cardiovascular measures and respiration, as well as finite biochemical changes resulting from hormonal activity. In addition, it has been evaluated by noting disturbances in perceptual organization and motor performance. Another measure of stress has been obtained by polling the subject directly about his level of concern during the application of a stressor, his ability to continue to perform under stressful conditions, and/or his feelings about an imminent stressor.

Generally, the measures which are selected are determined by the definition applied to the term stress. For example, if stress is considered to be a general reaction to events which disrupt normal homeostasis, then a wide range of measures are employed. If stress is considered to be dependent upon specific kinds of situations, then fewer measures have been used.

Physiological Measures of Stress. Physiologically, the measures may be divided into those which indicate that the body is preparing for some kind of action and those which imply that normal functioning is temporarily suspended so that the organism can concentrate upon meeting the interpreted threat. Most investigations utilize several kinds of measures, combining performance and psychological and physiological measures in order to obtain a comprehensive picture of the stress reaction. Examples are the studies by Funkenstein et al.,[334] Basowitz et al.,[58] and Wolf et al.[976]

Investigations concerned primarily with biological determinants of stress are too numerous to survey thoroughly in this text. Thus, in the pages which follow, only a sampling of the types of measures which have been used in recent years are presented.

Several researchers have suggested that secretions of the adrenal gland and changes in the presence of the various kinds of blood cells indicate that stress is present. Particular interest has been paid to the production of eosinophiles. Ulrich,[901] used this latter measure to evaluate stress levels before and after physical performance stressors have been introduced.

Blood pressure and respiration changes are other measures frequently used. Wolf et al.,[976] in an extensive study of the effect of stressful life events introduced into an interview situation, utilized blood pressure change as a stress measure. Hellweg,[437] studying stress before both examinations and physical contests, utilized respiration as one of her measures.

Mirskey and Stein[668] suggest that the presence of antidiuretic hormones secreted in the thalamus are reliable and valid indices of stress. This measure is an example of one which indicates that the usual bodily processes are being momentarily halted so that energies may be focused **upon the implied threat.**

Basowitz *et al.*[58] based a rather extensive study of paratroop training stresses upon the hypothesis that hippuric acid secreted by the liver constituted valid measure of stress. Although his hypothesis was not verified, several measures and the strict controls under which the investigation was carried out contributed much valuable information. For example, Basowitz found that the most predictive factors in differentiating potential paratroopers from those who might fail the training were the self-ratings of harm anxiety, while ratings of *failure anxiety* were not found to be highly predictive of success in training.

Selye suggested that pituitary secretion, which activates the adrenocortical hormone, ACTH, to produce a compound labeled F which, in turn, feeds back to the pituitary and decreases its activity, is a valid index of stress. Selye also pointed out that stress is accompanied by a decrease in rhythmic stomach movement, causing indigestion.

Increased palmar perspiration is often taken as a valid and reliable sign of stress. This is measured usually by collecting perspiration in a hand sponge and noting the volume. The study by Hellweg[437] is an example of one using this device. The most common measure of increased palm perspiration is the galvanic skin response. The GSR was used as early as 1915 and measures differences in electrical resistance of the skin as the result of increased perspiration during stressful conditions. Through the use of two small electrodes applied to the hands, it provides a sensitive, although at times unreliable, measure of stress. It has been suggested, however, that this increased sweating of the palms is caused by the need to increase the efficiency of the grip, much as could be accomplished by spitting on the hands before grasping an axe handle. This assumption, however, lacks experimental verification.

Many other physiological measures have been utilized to measure stress, including skin temperature, pupil dilation, and salivary secretion. A dermographic measure often used is obtained by stroking the skin with a rounded instrument and recording the time between the whitening of the skin and the return of the normal pink color to the area affected. Analysis of urine and the blood and measurement of metabolic rate, muscular tremor, eyelid blink rate, and muscular action potential have also been used as stress indicators.

Perceptual Disturbance. Several kinds of perceptual tests have been used in the study of stress. In general it is assumed, as Postman and Bruner[478] stated, that perceptual behavior is disrupted and becomes less accurate under stress than under normal conditions. The two perceptual measures most often found helpful are tests of closure and tests involving the ability to reproduce quickly presented geometric designs. It is assumed that individuals under stress will not be as sensitive to quickly presented incomplete circles and will produce more inaccurate figures (or may prove unable to draw anything) when presented with complex designs contained in the Bender-Gestalt test.

Direct Poll. In some investigations, less complex psychological measures have been utilized to evaluate stress. Basowitz *et al.*[58] and Erickson *et al.*[200] simply polled subjects concerning the level of stress they were experiencing, or the level of performance they expected of themselves under prolonged stress. Erickson concluded that "asking them" was the best way to predict individual performance under stress following the administration of psychological measures of personality, general adjustment inventories, and a group Rorschach.

Performance Measures. Various verbal and motor performance measures have been used as sole indicators of stress. The assumption usually advanced is that stress is indicated by a disruption of complex verbal, mental, or motor activity. Basowitz *et al.*,[58] for example, used an arithmetic task which involved subtracting rapidly by three's from a large base number. The problem with these measures, of course, is that it is difficult to separate learning effects from changes caused by stressors. Castanada and Palmero[149] and Benton and Whythe[73] base their measures of stress entirely upon motor performance scores. Benton used a manipulation task, while Castanada found that switch manipulation to light cues was stressful when changes in the task were introduced. Parson *et al.*[715] employed a hand steadiness test as a stress measure.

Muscular Tension Changes. Various changes in muscular tension also have been utilized as stress measures. Studies by Wenger,[950] Davis,[238] and Nidever[697] are examples. In general, these measures are more exact than the biochemical and/or psychological tests cited above. A more detailed review of these and their relationship to various kinds of performance are found in the section concerned with tension and performance.

Intercorrelations Among Measures of Stress. Although low correlations are usually found among various stress measures, a general fear pattern caused by autonomic nervous system functioning often is identified. In studies by Basowitz,[58] when several applications of a stressor were made, vast individual differences were seen not only in the indices of stress measured when a large variety of tests were made but also in the manner in which individuals adapted to stress. Holzman and Bitterman,[464] for example, found few meaningful relationships between perceptual, performance, and biochemical measures (urinary analysis) upon repeated administration of the stressor to the situation. Thus, there seems to be a difference in the manner in which individuals react and adjust to stressors, and the search for the most reliable and valid indicator seems likely to continue.

Stressors of Life and of the Laboratory. A number of kinds of stressors have been studied with respect to their influence upon performance. The two broadest categories include stressors present in real life situations and those experimentally induced. In addition, obviously disturbed individuals have been selected for study in the attempt to determine the kinds of stressors which caused the anxieties.

Various kinds of life situations have been studied relative to the production of stress, and several texts have been concerned with stressors operative in the "average" civilian community. Among these are *The Split Level Trap*[388] and Menninger's *Psychiatry in a Troubled World*.[650] These are clinical descriptions of the manner in which many aspects of daily living, such as raising children, attempting to succeed in business, and growing up, prove to be individual and group stressors.

Other experimental studies have been concerned with life stressors, but within more narrow confines. Funkenstein *et al.*,[334] for example, studied 125 Harvard students for a number of years, introducing several kinds of laboratory stress situations.

Many of these studies are concerned with participation in various kinds of training and with conditions which involve the continued application of stressors in wartime. Among these studies are *Men Under Stress*[396] by two World War II psychiatrists, *Breakdown and Recovery* by Ginzberg *et al.*,[396] and *War Stress and Neurotic Illness* by Kardiner and Spiegle.[511] The authors of these books arrive at some of the same conclusions regarding the performance and behavior of men placed under continual stressors, *i.e.*, imminent annihilation.

The effect of war stressors seems to culminate in nervousness, fatigue becomes a problem, and neuromuscular control lessens in the simplest of tasks. Additional problems result when closely knit combat units suffer casualties and buddies are seen to die. These authors also mention that not only were the men fearful of direct physical harm but also were "afraid of being afraid," of not measuring up as men and thus "losing face" with their peers.

Findings such as these emphasize the importance of studying stress in a total life situation, rather than only in the laboratory. Basowitz *et al.*[58] speak of the importance of examining stressful events within a total field of experience, since it is explained that "Stress is an experience which cannot be defined independently of the life situation and the response to it." Caudill[151] also advocates the study of stress as a total action picture, involving individual physiological measures and small group interactions within close proximity to the individual, as well as consideration of cultural pressures.

Laboratory Stressors. Stressors range from general and continual stressful situations of varying magnitudes, involving the close grouping of a number of stressful events, to situations in which stressful events occur rather infrequently. These latter circumstances are more compatible for study in the research laboratory. Numerous investigations have been carried out in recent years to determine the effect of various discrete kinds of stressors in controlled environments.

Four kinds of stressors are imposed upon the human subjects in the research laboratory. The one most utilized involves introducing various kinds of distractions, such as loud noises and electric shocks, and then studying their effect upon the performance of various perceptual-motor tasks. One of the most interesting of these was the sonic-confuser used by Funkenstein et al.[334] This test involves the delayed feedback of one's own voice while speaking, which results in thoroughly confusing the subject's reactions. Various perceptual-motor and/or biological measures are taken before, during, and after such sensory distractions are introduced.

A second main type of laboratory stressor involves the implication of task failure. This is accomplished in several ways: informing the subject that he is not performing up to required norms, presenting him with a task impossible of solution under highly motivated circumstances, or interrupting him before he can possibly finish. An example of a research program in which the failure stress was used extensively was carried out during World War II during the training of agents for the Office of Strategic Services. Since it was hypothesized that these trainees would be subjected to real life stress when operating later behind enemy lines, every effort was made to determine and to predict how their performance might hold up under stressful situations.

As reported in *The Assessment of Men,* the program included bridge building tasks and other individual and group endeavors which were at times insolvable. Numerous times the trainees were informed that they had failed the training program and were asked to reveal their real names (they were given "cover" identities during their training). Although the data collected from such situations were highly subjective, this program contributed materially to the understanding of men's performance under stressful conditions.[710]

A third method of creating stressful situations in a laboratory is to introduce a real life stress during an interview and then to determine various physiological reactions. This method was utilized by Wolf et al.[976] when studying hypertension. Individuals suffering from marked hypertension were interviewed in detail to determine the nature and cause of their disturbance, *i.e.*, what in their lives had probably caused them to become tense and susceptible to stressors. After this was determined, a second interview situation was set up and the subject was prepared so that various cardiovascular measures could be obtained. After a period of relatively innocuous give-and-take between the subject and investigator, a question relating to the stressful life event was suddenly introduced (*e.g.*, "How is your alcoholic husband?").

The marked cardiovascular changes produced when such a stressor was introduced suggested that hypertension can be caused by situational disturbances within the total life pattern. It was also noted by these experimenters that the blood pressure changes were most marked when the individual seemed to need to express hostile aggressive behavior, but the expression was suppressed by an equally strong need to remain calm. As will be noted in the following pages, activity has been suggested not only as producing stress but as alleviating stress within the individual. It is suggested here that a blocking of activity proves stressful, while other experiments suggest that mild activity relieves internal stress.

Environmental Stress. Another kind of stress frequently studied involves the production of rather long-term environmental changes and may involve a sustained exposure to heat, cold, weightlessness, disorienting movements, and the like. Most of these studies, of course, involve the ability of the body to perform well while under conditions which might be met in a military situation or in space flight. In other testing programs, however, an environment simulating industrial work conditions has been reproduced, and the effects of such sustained stressors as heat and noise have been related to performance measures.

Illustrative of hundreds of investigations of environmental stress is the study by Brozek and Taylor.[121] Various motor tests, including two of strength, three of speed, and one of "coordination," were administered under five kinds of environmental stressors, acute starvation, semi-starvation, deprivation of sleep, heat stress, and hard physical work. Brozek and Taylor found that motor performance was more susceptible to deterioration under stress than sensory and intellectual functioning. Of the motor tests administered, however, only the reaction time measure showed significant change under all five stressors. Strength showed the greatest decrement under semi-starvation, while speed of tapping and speed hand and arm movements exhibited greatest deterioration in acute starvation combined with hard work. In conclusion, the authors suggested that, rather than using one type of task, a battery of motor tests plus physiological indices best measure deterioration under stress.[121]

Although these and similar studies have contributed to general knowledge in this area, an extensive review of environmental stress research will not be undertaken, since the focus of the book is upon individuals moving in reasonably normal environments. The reader is directed toward summaries by Macworth[609] and others for further information.

Several problems loom large when attempting to assess the effectiveness of induced stressors in the laboratory situation. Initially, the assumption must be made that the induced stressor is as upsetting to the subject as it would be to the experimenter, and such is not always the case. For example, the subject's motivations, his past experience with similar distractions and/or tasks influence his reactions. In addition, great individual differences in psychological and physiological reactions to stress have been recorded.

One of the primary problems when studying stress-performance relationships involves taking into account cultural variables. As Funkenstein *et al.* point out:

The judgment as to what are mature or immature stress reactions depends to a large extent upon the values and expectations imposed by the cultural or sub-cultural system . . . for it must be remembered that man is a member of society and a bearer of culture and that stress reactions of man outside this context could not be completely understood.[336,484]

THE EFFECT OF STRESS UPON PERFORMANCE

Many stressor-performance relationships have been investigated. Essentially they have included the pairing of the kinds of stressors mentioned previously to various kinds of perceptual, motor, and verbal functioning.

Mental Performance

Although the focus is upon movement behavior, some of the initial principles of the stress-performance relationship may be illustrated by considering various kinds of verbal tasks. The introduction of failure stress into a verbal learning situation usually causes a deterioration of performance.

In a failure-stress experiment involving the learning of nonsense syllables, Sullivan[867] found that, while success produced the most rapid learning, failure was more harmful for a superior group than for an intellectually inferior group. The reverse of this is suggested in findings of research relating muscular tension to motor performance. Increased tension was found to facilitate the poor performers, while inhibiting the better performers who already are assumed to be operating at or near their optimal levels of tension.

In an unusual study by Beam[66] in 1955, involving simple conditioning and verbal learning tasks participated in just prior to three stressful situations, it was found again that stressors facilitate a simple conditioning task, while impairing more complex verbal ones. The stressful situations included doctoral examinations, taking part in a dramatic production before a large audience, and giving an oral report in partial fulfillment of a course requirement.

Perceptual-Motor Performance

The results of investigations of the effect of stressors upon perceptual-motor performance are similar to those involving verbal-motor performance tasks. In general, impairment is caused by either failure stress or situationally induced stressors when performing complex tasks. With simple motor acts, reaction time, movement time, and the like, the reverse seems true. Howell,[472] for example, found that time to move (including a summation of reaction time and movement time) was markedly improved when an electric shock was introduced.

Parsons, Phillips, and Lane,[715] on the other hand found that muscular steadiness was retarded when a stress was introduced. McClelland and Apicella, using a card sorting task, also found that failure stress produced less efficient performance in a complex task.[628]

A further problem, only superficially investigated, is whether stress reactions prior to physical exertion are similar to those prior to mental application. Confirmation of a generally stressful state regardless of the activity prepared for is shown in the findings of Hellweg.[437] It was found, however, that stress measured before physical activity (a game) resulted in higher blood pressure measures than stress measured before an examination. This might be taken as an indication that the organism seems to prepare itself for the specific type of task in which it believes it will ultimately take part.

Stress and Motor Learning

The effect of stressors upon motor learning is a more complex problem, and various influences have been demonstrated during different portions of the learning process. Castanada,[184] for example, points out that when stress was introduced a decreasing tendency to increase errors in a visual-motor task was shown. This was taken to indicate that a stress-adaptation factor was operative during learning. An investigation by Michael,[657] using a physiological measure of stress, also suggested that exercise can facilitate stress adaptation.

In general, however, various stress measures, when studied longitudinally, indicate that adaptability to stress depends upon the situation and the personality of the individual. Holtzman and Bitterman[464] concluded, following a factorial study, that few positive relationships existed between various stress measures, including perceptual tests, urinary analyses, and galvanic skin response. Parson, Phillips, and Lane,[715] hypothesizing the existence of a general stress-adaptation factor, were disappointed to find no significant correlations between circulating blood constituents which were felt to be indicative of stress and performance. They suggested that other psychological factors were important.

Basowitz et al.[58] also found that no significant correlations existed between performance tests, perceptual tests, physiological indices, clinical ratings, and other personal information. Funkenstein et al.[334] suggested that the various physiological patterns obtained in the data indicated that stress patterns were related to specific shifts in subject emotions (i.e., anger at the task or at the experimenter), rather than to the task itself.

Group Learning, Performance, and Stress

One of the most promising new directions in the study of the effect of stress upon learning behavior has been outlined by Caudill.[151] This anthropologist suggests that stress may only be considered within a total individual-group context through examining group feelings about bereavement, injury, and the like. Substantiating his argument, Caudill reviews research which indicates that individuals in close physical and psychological proximity often evidence similar kinds of internal physio logical reactions to stress. For example, quoting from a study by Watson and Kanter, Caudill[151] presents findings which indicate that the heart rate changes of the analyst and patient are similar when various kinds of stress occur during their interviews. Such emotions as anxiety, hostility, and depression, with the expected blood pressure changes on the part of the patient, were reflected in similar, but less marked, blood pressure changes on the part of the therapist.

More directly related to the focus of the text is the study by Hill et al.[458] concerning the stress relationship evidenced by members of athletic teams working in close physical proximity and performing a similar movement pattern. It was found that, when comparing the reactions to stress by two Harvard crews via an eosinophile count, the team which was noted to "swing together" evidenced less variability in this stress measure than did the crew which was not as successful. In another study with Harvard crews, Renold[748] found that while individual differences existed, there were characteristic patterns in the level of blood eosinophils in the crew, coxswain, as well as the coach during and when preparing for the traditional race with Yale. Caudill suggested that such research might be extended to determine whether physiological responses among team members in sports such as football and basketball, where individual roles are more differentiated, are also related.

Thus, the evaluation of the effect of stress upon motor activity requires an exact definition of the type of activity, simple or complex, the nature of the stress measure utilized, the stage of learning, and the motivational level indicated on the part of the subject.

Fuchs[232] has recently presented an explanation for the effects of stress upon motor performance which seems worthy of consideration. Initially, it is contended, human learning under normal conditions becomes progressively dependent upon more complex servo systems within the nervous system, as increasingly subtle cues are attended to. However, upon the introduction of some stress, a retrogression occurs; tension, which accompanied initial attempts to learn, returns, and the more finite aspects of the situation become again lost to the learner.

TENSION AND PERFORMANCE

The close relationship between levels of muscular tension and motor performance involving simple and complex movements is obvious. However, the exact manner in which tension affects motor performance and learning is not always as is expected. It is obvious that for movement to occur, a minimal level of muscular tension must be present.

Indeed, research findings suggest that, if subjects are trained to relax completely, no work is possible, and in addition they seem unable even to engage in imaginative pursuits.

Various theories concerning the relationship of muscular tension to general psychological processes have been advanced. Initially, a "peripheral" theory was suggested by Davis which held that any changes in tension patterns were intimately related to psychological processes.[239]

Meyer and Noble[420] advance one of the most comprehensive explanations involving the role of muscular tension and the manner in which it affects mental and motor performance. It is held that impulses from tension converge on motor patterns and interact with the responses. It is further suggested that the effect of tension on performance depends upon the amount of tension, the proximity of the tension to the performing limb, and the stage of practice during which the tension is induced.

There is an increasing amount of evidence which points to the existence of what has been termed general muscular tension. Goldstein[376] suggests that individuals may be ranged on a continuum from those who are relaxed to those who habitually exhibit a large amount of muscular tension in excess of that needed to perform life's activities. The extensive review of the research in this area by Duffy[259] also brought this authoress to the conclusion that while tension is many times manifested in specific ways, and has specific influences upon various facets of behavior, "there appears to be both some degree of 'generality' and some degree of 'specificity' in activation . . . activation is an organismic phenomenon, and it is recognized as such when we speak of an individual being relaxed or being excited, rather than of a particular system's showing this condition."[259,322]

The Measurement of Tension

Muscular tension may be requested by the experimenter of his subject, i.e., "keep your limb and/or body tense as you perform." But more precisely, it may be induced into the situation by subjecting the subject to a stressor. McTeer[644] and numerous other experimenters found that an increase in muscular tension was the immediate result of the administration of an electric shock. In addition, muscular tension may be introduced by placing an increased work load upon the subject as he attempts to perform a motor task. Studies carried out during the 1920's and 1930's induced tension via this method. In addition, muscular tension may be increased by having the subject squeeze hand dynamometers or handles a given number of pounds of pressure or by having the subject maintain pressure on a hand pulley or a foot pedal.

Davis[239] suggests several ways in which tension levels have been measured in a review of the literature. These included the measurement of pressure changes in the grip of various performing instruments (i.e., the handles of stylus mazes as per Stroud's experiment[863]) or upon the work or force with which subjects strike the keys of a typewriter or other type of experimental response key. More recently, the magnitude of electric impulses produced by muscular action itself, as measured by the electromyograph, has been used to determine tension levels. Computed in microvolts, it is generally assumed that the level of electrical output of the muscle is a direct measure of the tension present. In addition, Davis[239] points out that tension has been measured by determining the resistance to movements offered by a limb or muscle, by recording slight movements of body parts, by recording electrical properties of the skin, as well as by determining the magnitude of the stretch reflex of the knee.

Wenger,[940] in an attempt to determine what constituted muscular tension, compared individual subjective ratings of children in respect to the levels of tension they evidenced. It was found that these judgments were reliable. Then this experimenter attempted to determine what kinds of physiological variables correlated with these observational ratings. Galvanic skin response, respiration, diastolic pressure, and dermographic latency combined to produce a score which seemed to be most predictive of muscular tension.

Nidever,[697] a student of Wenger's, combined some of these same measures to determine whether a general factor of muscular tension existed. He found that in 19 of the 23 muscle groups tested such a general factor did emerge. Age, body build, and the time of day the measurements were taken were also found to be important variables. This researcher also found that mental work implied concomitant physical work, insofar as increased tension was found to occur in the frontalis muscles when a serial verbal learning task was engaged in. Eason[267] found that the neck muscles seemed the best indices of general muscular tension.

Freeman,[321] in research carried out in 1933, found that individual differences affected muscular tension. It was found, for example, that increased tension more adversely affected the performance of younger than of older subjects.

It appears that the measurement of muscular tension may be accomplished by several means. Although a general muscular tension factor does seem to exist, most of the investigations reviewed involve direct measures of the load of a secondary task (induced tension), the reaction to shock stressor, and the like. The measurement of electrical output of a muscle or group of muscles has been undertaken experimentally only since World War II.

The Effect of Tension Upon Performance

In general, the findings presented for stress and anxiety hold true with induced tension. Bills[82] carried out the pioneer work in this area task performance, depending upon the nature of the task, its complexity or simplicity.

Mental Performance. Mental tasks, if not difficult, usually are facilitated with induced tension. Bills[60] carried out the pioneer work in this area and found that tension produced by having his subjects squeeze hand dynamometers in both hands benefited the learning of tasks involving paired association learning and nonsense syllables, memorizing and adding columns of digits, and reciting scrambled letters. Zartmen and Cason,[991] on the other hand, found that solving complete arithmetic problems was not facilitated by having subjects keep a foot on a resisting pedal.

Freeman[322] studied both mental and motor tasks and found that tension-load, which is optimal for one type of activity, may be detrimental to another. He also suggested that the more complex the performance, the more likely that a tension increment will inhibit efficient performance. Freeman also suggested that theoretically it should be possible to determine the optimal tension loads for various kinds of tasks.

Bourne,[100] studying the effect of tension produced by squeezing a hand dynamometer, also found that, while tension affected performance in a paired word task, retention of these same words was not affected. Meyers and other researchers[656] have confirmed the fact that while tension seems to affect momentary performance, the integrative processes leading to retention (*i.e.*, learning) seem less, if at all, affected.

Visual Perception and Muscular Tension

Numerous studies have attested to the influence of muscular tension changes upon visual activity. Dowling found that motor activity (pushing and pulling a desk drawer) facilitated visual recognition.[254] Similarly Smock[838] found that moderate grip tension maintained at from ⅜ to ⅝ maximum, produced the best scores on a task involving the quick recognition of briefly viewed shapes. Proprioceptive return from the muscles perhaps heightens general activation level which translates into changes in a number of kinds of behavior. Weybrew found that moderate grip tension caused a reduction in perceived length of time.[959] Thus muscular tension seems related in a number of ways to the total sensorium.

The Effects of Induced Tension upon Tension

Hellenbrandt[436] and her student, Joan Waterland,[929] have enagaged in an interesting series of studies in which its was proposed to examine the effect of prolonged maximum strength efforts upon involuntary patterns of muscular tension manifested concomitantly. In order to examine this phenomenon, thousands of photographs were taken of subjects exerting all-out effort on a wrist ergograph.

As tension was maintained, the following observations were made: (1) there seemed to be an orderly expansion of involuntary motor responses which varied from subject to subject, but evidenced intra-individual consistency; (2) various reflexive patternings were seen—for example, the tonic neck reflex was elicited as the subjects usually inclined their heads toward the side on which the arm-flexion movement was being made; (3) the involuntary stress pattern of muscular contractions spread in an orderly fashion as voluntary tension was maintained, and was "immune to remodeling."

These researchers concluded that these involuntary muscular contractions indicate the body's reaction to exercise stress when voluntary control dissipates ("cortical noise" is minimal or absent). These involuntary flexions, extensions and grimaces are the result of the recruitment of reserve motor units under stress, and this recruitment proceeds in an orderly and expansive pattern within each individual. The findings of these investigations portray in a vivid way the manner in which excess tension can facilitate and at times interfere with voluntary movement patterns. The photographs depict the manner in which tensions specifically introduced may "overflow" and affect a number of voluntary and involuntary movement patterns in portions of the body far removed from the source of the original effort.

Tension and Motor Performance. Numerous investigations have been devoted to the study of the influence of induced tension upon motor performance. In general, the findings parallel those of verbal-tension comparisons. Some tasks, usually the less complex, have been facilitated by tension, while others, the more complex, are usually inhibited.

Consideration of the effect of tension upon performance involves two auxiliary considerations. Freeman found that the relationship of the limb in which tension is produced to the performing member is important. The nearer the produced tension to the performing hand, for example, the more such tension affects performance.[209] Courts[182] suggested that there are two kinds of tension: one which reflects effort and a second which reflects emotional upset. Although it is suggested that the effort-tension facilitates performance while emotional-tension inhibits it, little experimental work separating the two phenomena suggested by Courts has been undertaken.

The earlier studies used rather inexact means for determining and/or inducing muscular tension. But, in general, they were predictive of the findings of more recent investigations in which more sophisticated measuring devices were utilized. Duffy,[261] for example, used subjective ratings of the tension observed in children and concluded that tense children evidenced awkwardness in their movements, were weaker in a hand dynamometer test, and indicated less ability in a perceptual test involving the tracing of figures. In addition, Duffy observed that the tense youngsters showed less tendency to engage in direct physical contact with the other children, although their social contacts did not seem inhibited.

13

Russell[771] in 1932 used as a variable the experimenter's request to subjects "to tense," "to remain as normal," or "to consciously relax the body" when throwing a tennis ball for accuracy. It was found that the normals threw best, while the individuals who had been requested to relax were next, while, as might be expected, the most inaccurate throwers were those who had been requested to keep their bodies tense. The validity of Russell's findings might be questioned, however, even if his manner of inducing tension is ignored, for Freeman[321] suggests that individuals trained to tense or to relax their bodies will show benefits from such training in subsequent trials. It has also been noted that induced tension has aided simple maze learning, the amplitude of the knee-jerk is greater, and finger tapping rate is also improved. On the other hand, more complex performances, including mirror-tracing and the like, are often inhibited by an increase in tension levels.

Tension and Motor Learning.   Stroud,[863] one of the initial investigators to measure tension changes during the learning of a motor task, used the downward pressure his subjects exerted upon a stylus in a maze problem as the tension score. It was found that more tension occurred as the subject learned the more difficult portions of the maze, containing numerous cul-de-sacs, than was recorded when they traversed the easier portions of the pathway. It was also noted that tension decreased as learning progressed, with the exception of an "end spurt" during the last trials. The subjects were informed that they had to complete three perfect trials to finish the experiment successfully. Therefore, as might be expected, tension levels rose during the final three trials, particularly on the last one. Stroud also found that when additional tension was added by requiring that the subject hold a pulley weight with the non-performing hand, more tension also was evidenced in stylus pressure. Stroud explained his findings by using the concept of facilitation and hypothesized that the nerve impulses having different sensory origins summated to aid in the production of a response.

Daniel,[231] using action potential as a tension measure, produced findings which parallel those of Stroud. It was found that as learning progressed, a decrease in tension occurred. He also reported that a slight increase in action potential was noted just prior to the completion of the maze problem. Daniel also found that decreased tension was associated with error elimination, while increased tension produced greater speed. In general, tension levels were greater, measured by action potential, the closer to the performing hand they were recorded.

Ghisseli[359] also found that as the individual learned a visual-motor task, tension tended to decrease. The tension measure utilized in this investigation was the pressure exerted on keys which were struck in response to light cues. Ghisselli did not find that an end-spurt occurred, indicating a rise in tension level, since his directions omitted mention of a requirement involving the learning of the task to a given criterion. It has also been found that at times skill may improve with tension remaining constant. Eason[200] found that performance improvement was recorded on a tracking task while muscular tension, measured in the neck muscles, remained the same.

Pre-Task Tension. Several investigators have studied levels of tension occurring within the period prior to task performance. It has been shown by Davis[240] that tension during this "set" period is usually gradually increased if the period is relatively short. If the fore-period is extended, however, the tension level often falls. It is, therefore, suggested that there is an optimal length of time prior to motor task performance during which an individual can prepare himself to best advantage. To cite an example, in Japan the referee of a Sumo westling match must decide when both contestants are in psychological resonance (called *ki ga au*) before starting the match. It is suggested that he is attempting to determine when both performers are at their optimal levels of tension, or at least at equal levels prior to starting the bout. At times, four or five starts are attempted before the bout is permitted to progress.

Seen frequently in gymnastics, weightlifting contests, and track and field meets are athletes who attempt to raise their tension levels to the optimum prior to performance by pacing back and forth or through similar activities. A high tension level at the end of the fore-period, results in shorter reaction time, according to Davis. When the fore-period was varied so that the performer was not certain when the task was to begin, it was found to affect reaction time adversely. Davis suggested that the effect of tension plus glandular activity combined to influence pre-set conditions.

Theories Relating Performance to Tension

Several hypotheses have been advanced to explain tension-performance-learning relationships. Some investigators suggest that the constancy of kinesthetic stimuli as the result of tension raises the level of excitement in all muscle groups via cortex action. This heightened excitation level, which brings about a general readiness to act, results in increased speed and accuracy of performance.

Freeman[203] on the other hand, first proposed that muscular tension levels, when increased, lower the threshold of excitability in the higher nervous centers. And, as a result, accurate complex performance may be inhibited. More recent investigations by Pineo and Kempe point more clearly to the relationships between muscular tension and more basic neurological and physiological measures.[519,733] Pinneo found that induced tension of the muscles via a hand dynometer resulted in widespread changes in various indices of activation including heart rate, respiration rate, palmar conductance, frontal and occipital EEG, as well as EMG readings elicited from passive limbs. Pinneo concluded that "proprioceptive return from induced muscular tension produces generalized behavioral and physiological effects in the reticular activating system." It thus seems that the relation of tension to total behavior is a function of the amount of tension induced, the unique characteristics of the nervous system of the individual, as well as the locale in which such tension occurs.

RELAXATION AND PERFORMANCE

If there is an optimal tension level for a specific task, as the literature indicates, the present discussion would be incomplete without brief reference to the role of *relaxation* and its relationship to performance. Several writers have presented programs for producing relaxation and for alleviating tension through various mystical or pseudo-scientific approaches to mind-body problems. For example, one writer presents suggestions relative to the alleviation of tension which involve "transplanting the mind" to thoughts which are tension-free.

A widely accepted method for promoting relaxation was advanced in 1938 by Jacobson[488] and described in his book *Progressive Relaxation.* It embodies a principle of nervous re-education (*i.e.,* learning to relax the total body) based upon first acquiring a heightened kinesthetic awareness of tension within specific muscle groups. Jacobson's method is concerned with dispelling *residual tension,* which is defined as the excess tension exhibited as an individual reclines on a couch and is based upon external signs and manipulative tests. Residual tension, it is hypothesized, consists of "fine tonic contraction along with slight movements or reflexes." The underlying principle of the Jacobson method, therefore, is to heighten the self-awareness of tension so that the individual can more fully and efficiently relax. Thus, subjects are instructed first to fully tense various body parts, then to "let go" and relax. They are then asked to tense the same muscle group about half as much as they had previously and then to relax again. Thus, it is hypothesized that, as the individual learns to induce tension progressively and to relax, he becomes able to recognize and to control minute amounts of tension within his body and to reduce residual tension to a minimum.

An unpublished study by Benson[71] in 1958 indicated that the application of the Jacobson method contributed positively to efficient total body movement. It was assumed that the ability to relax plays an important role in learning to swim and that training in relaxation would speed the learning process of beginning and intermediate swimmers. It was found that the swimmers who were given relaxation training progressed more rapidly than those who were not. And, although little improvement in swimming speed was noted between the control and experimental groups, the group trained to relax evidenced a generally lower tension level and showed significant improvement in an arm stroke test. In addition, all the non-swimmers in the experimental group learned to swim at least 20 yards, while half of those in the control group did not at the end of the testing period.

Benson's study points out the continuous nature of the tension relaxation continuum. It was demonstrated that tension may be increased until movement cannot occur. Complete relaxation also prevents movement. But while numerous experimenters have been interested in the problem of inducing tension, relatively few have investigated the role of relaxation upon gross human movement. It would seem that to move efficiently, or to promote efficient movement in others, one must clearly grasp the "optimal tension" principle, to be as proficient in producing increased tension in himself (or in others) as he is in achieving relaxation.

SUMMARY

Anxiety appears to be a general fear or foreboding, a personality trait marked by a low threshold to stress. Stress is an internal reaction to a specific threatening situation. Tension, on the other hand, is overt muscular contraction caused by an emotional state or merely by increased effort.

The effect of anxiety and stressful situations upon performance is a function of the task, of the general anxiety of the individual, and of prior practice in the task. In general, induced tension results in performance improvement in simple conditioning tasks and when an individual is performing at an inferior level in some more complex task. Stressful situations interfere with task performance of superior performers and within complex tasks.

It has been found that individuals interacting within close proximity often evidence similar kinds of internal reactions to stress. Exploratory research indicates that well-functioning athletic teams often are in accord physiologically, just as are the psychotherapist and his patient in the medical interview.

In general, it has been found that stress affects high anxiety subjects and disrupts both mental and motor performance. Stress is alleviated by moderate physical activity. General adaptability to stress is often evidenced, but, with repeated stress imposed, a general anxiety state can be produced which may eventually lead to physiological breakdown. In addition, as the task is learned, tension levels decrease as the performer adjusts to the demands of the situation.

Student References

Books

1. BASOWITZ, H., PERSKY, H., KORCHIN, S. J., and GRANKER, R. R.: *Anxiety and Stress, An Interdisciplinary Study of a Life Situation,* New York, McGraw-Hill Book Co., 1955.
2. EYSENCK, H. L.: *The Dynamics of Anxiety and Hysteria,* London, Routledge and Kegan Paul, 1957.

3. JACOBSON, EDMUND: *Progressive Relaxation,* Chicago, The University of Chicago Press, 1938.
4. SEYLE, HANS: *The Stress of Life,* New York, McGraw-Hill Book Co., 1956.

Articles

1. CATTELL, RAYMOND B.: "The nature and measurement of anxiety," *Scientific American,* March, 1963.
2. CAUDILL, W.: "Effects of social and cultural systems in reactions to stress," Social Sciences Research Council, New York, June 1958.
3. COURTS, F. A.: "Relations between muscular tension and performance," *Psych. Bulletin,* 347-367, 1942.
4. FREEMAN, G. L.: "The optimal muscular tensions for various performance," *Am. J. Psychol., 51,* 146-150, 1938.
5. HILL, S. R.: "Studies on adrenocortical and psychological response to stress in man," *Arch. Int. Med., 97,* 269-298, 1956.

SECTION IV

MOVEMENT BEHAVIOR AND ABILITY TRAITS

Chapter 11

Neurological Foundations of Voluntary Movement

DESPITE emphasis upon movement as *behavior*, an understanding of the nervous control of muscular action is necessary. Man is not a hollow tube, despite the view taken by some learning theorists, but a highly complex organism capable of receiving a vast number of messages through his sensory end-organs and having the ability to execute movements of remarkable complexity and variety.

It is the purpose of this chapter to examine briefly some of the neurological mechanisms which are involved in the integration of movement output. The initial portion of the chapter will deal with the simple and basic units of nervous control, the neuron and the motor unit. Following a brief examination of the functional anatomy of the central nervous system, an effort will be made to summarize recent findings concerning the neurological control of voluntary movement patterns.

EVOLUTION OF THE NERVOUS SYSTEM

Throughout the evolution of organic life upon the earth, from the simple one-celled animals to mammalian species, including the Homo sapiens, examination of organismic control mechanisms reveals an accompanying developmental pattern. Living matter is modifiable, and all organisms evidence mechanisms which facilitate irritability, contractility, and conductivity, characteristics which permit adaptation to changing conditions.

Even the one-celled amoeba, capable of only avoidance or approach responses, evidences these basic qualities. Simple locomotion is facilitated by sequential contractions of cellular parts. To facilitate movement, a wave of excitability passes from one portion of the cell to another, just as a nerve impulse travels along branching nerve pathways within the human organism at a developmental level eons of years removed from the amoeba. In seeking or avoiding a stimulus, the amoeba thus evidences the three basic functions which are inherent to human neuromuscular control: (1) irritability (affectability by stimuli), (2) contractility (controlled movement), and (3) conductivity (sequential undulations).

Among the higher mammals, more complex functioning is, of course, apparent due to the proliferating structures and mechanisms which have evolved within the nervous system. An increasing number of cells and structures permit more kinds of stimuli to be dealt with, while at the same time more complex action patterns become possible.

In general, it appears that the mechanism for nervous control has evolved through three functional stages, from the ability to handle instinctual reflexes to simple learned movements to the highest level of behavior, evidenced primarily in the human being. At the lower level, innate stereotyped performance is integrated; at the intermediate stage, acquired adaptive behavior is monitored; while at the higher levels, abstract thinking, discrimination, symbolization, and communication are mediated.

During the course of evolution, parts of the nervous system making their evolutionary appearance most recently did not displace more primitive structures. Less complex parts within the peripheral and spinal systems, upon which the lower animals are primarily dependent for control, remain in the human nervous system. *Encephalization* is the term coined to denote the addition to and dominance of the more primitive structures by the higher components of nervous control. As will be seen later, however, all portions of the human nervous system interact to provide a mutual series of checks and balances to facilitate the control of voluntary movement.

BASIC STRUCTURES WITHIN THE NERVOUS SYSTEM

The Neuron

The type of cell specialized for functioning within the nervous system is termed the neuron. It is different from other types of cells because of the characteristic fibrous processes (dendrites and axons) which permit a single cell to exert functional influence over a considerable distance. Although microscopic in diameter, a single neuron may extend from the feet to the base of the skull.

Neurons are found within the central nervous system (brain and spinal cord) as well as in nerve trunks and in peripheral nervous tissue in various nerve centers of the body. The neuron is usually covered by a myelin sheath, a white fatty tissue which reduces the effect of adjacent nerve fibers upon each other and thus insures the more exact transmission of an impulse. Complete development of the myelin sheath is believed related to performance of coordinated movement patterns and is completely developed sometime between the ages of four to seven.

The neuron originates from the neural tube, the outermost layer of cells in the embryo, and at birth the human's full quota of neurons is present. When one is destroyed, no replacement of the cell takes place.

The Nerve Impulse

The specialized function of the neuron is to conduct a nerve impulse, evidenced by a change of electrical potential along the cell membrane. The nature of the nerve impulse is studied by recording electrical potential changes between active and inactive neurons through the use of delicate metering equipment. Through such techniques the following seems apparent: (1) There seems to be a *threshold of excitability*, a level of electrical stimulation which, unless exceeded, will fail to elicit conduction through the nerve cell. (2) Positive and negative after-potentials are recorded, after-effects dependent for their duration upon the extent of the previous activity and surrounding chemical conditions. (3) There seems to be a maximum number of times that a given fiber can be stimulated within a given period, ranging from 100 to 1000 times per second. This is termed the *absolute refractory period* and relates to the amount of times a neuron retains an impulse. (4) A single nerve impulse seems governed by an all-or-none law, which suggests that a fiber responds to its limits or not at all, depending upon whether its threshold of excitability has been exceeded. However, *summation* can occur, the effects of two or more rapid and brief sub-threshold stimulations can evoke a reaction by combining to exceed the threshold. (5) Nerve impulses vary greatly in speed from 120 meters/second to 17 meters/second, depending upon the diameter of the neuron and its location and function within the nervous system. (6) Nerve cells evidence a kind of impairment through use (sometimes termed fatigue). It has been found after repeated stimulation that fiber recovery is impaired. Such a condition, however, does not correspond directly to general mental or muscular fatigue as the term is commonly used.

The Synapse

The term synapse has been given to the point of physiological space connecting a neuron to a neuron. It is the point between the axon of a neuron and either the cell body or dendrites of another. The synapse permits a complex of functional arrangements, because the axon leading from one neuron may branch and synapse with several other neurons.

It requires slightly more time for an impulse to pass through a synapse than to run along a single fiber. In addition, because of the absence of a myelin covering at the synaptic junction, an easier access of drugs to the axon is possible here. It has also been determined that a single synapse is capable of only one-way transmission of the impulse, thus establishing a regularity of functioning to the nervous system.

Two theories have been proposed to explain the manner in which an impulse traverses a synapse: (1) Transmission is simply a summation of sufficient electrical potential to affect the crossing; and (2) A chemical substance, *acetylcholine*, secreted at some synapses, enables one neuron to cause a second to discharge. These two concepts have been utilized as the basis for several learning theories. The summation for more than one impulse seems necessary in order to traverse a synapse, since the available evidence renders it unlikely that a single impulse is capable of crossing this neural junction. In addition to synaptic transmission, the effects of one neuron upon another may also be exercised as parallel fibers electrically activate each other. When neurons are placed in tight bundles, the excitability of adjacent fibers, caused by the effects of common electrical fields, may occur along their length.

The Motor Unit

The term *motor unit* was first used in 1925 by Liddell and Sherrington[584] who defined it as a "motor neuron-axon and its adjunct muscle fibers." In general, a motor unit is a functional unit composed of a neuron lying within the peripheral portion of the nervous system, the ventral horn of the spinal cord, the axon branches of which extend outward and terminate in groups of striated muscle fibers where they end in flattened oval-shaped end plates.

Since there are many more striated muscle fibers in the body than there are myelinated nerve fibers that might innervate them, it is apparent that one nerve innervates many muscle fibers. Great differences are found in the innervation ratio for various muscles. In muscles which seem to demand immediate, quick, and precise actions, such as those of the eyes, the ratio is only 5:8, while in some of the larger muscles utilized primarily for locomotion and posturing, the ratio is greater. It may be as great as 1:1775 in the large calf muscle (gastrocnemius) and 1:609 for the tibialis anterior muscle.[10]

Thus, the number of motor units in a given muscle and their innervation ratios will affect the precision and range of contraction of which the muscle is capable. Muscles with many motor units are capable of finite coordinations. Muscles with few motor units, while at times able to exert more force, are less capable of precise, graduated action.

Previously outlined qualities of the neuron, of course, are applicable to the motor unit, of which the motor neuron is an integral part. For example, it has been found that motor units have gradient thresholds; some begin firing to induce minimal contractions, while others do not fire until stronger contractions are required. Thus the intensity of muscular contraction is explainable upon determining the frequency and the number of motor units firing. Motor unit territories overlap upon connecting with a particular muscle. As many as six motor units have been found to overlap, so that, for example, a bundle of from 3 to 50 fibers may contain the axon endings from two or more motor units.

Further complicating the picture is the fact that the rate of nerve impulse conduction varies from fiber to fiber. Thus impulses begun at the same time at a receptor organ arrive at the muscle fiber at different times.

Modifying the final muscular response is the nature of the muscle fiber which has been innervated and the action of muscles opposing the action of the one stimulated. For a muscle to move a body member, there must usually be a controlled movement of an opposing muscle.

The unique arrangement of the muscle fibers in bundles is also an effector of the final action produced. Some are placed across the line of pull (termed penniform), resulting in more force with a sacrifice of speed. Other fiber bundles are arranged parallel to the line of pull, which thus makes available all contractile power and results in a maximum range of motion. The fiber size is another factor and varies from 1 to 45 mm. in length, while maximum diameters range from .01 to .10 mm.

Thus, at the periphery, controlled, forceful, and/or sustained movement is dependent upon the innervation ratio, the number of motor units affecting the muscle, the duration and rate at which the stimulation occurs, the differential in nerve conduction rate, the arrangement of the muscle fibers, the nature of opposing muscular activity, and the size and formation of the fibers composing the muscle affected.

THE CENTRAL NERVOUS SYSTEM AND
THE CONTROL OF VOLUNTARY MOVEMENT

Structures

The Spinal Cord. Basically, the spinal cord is a channel located along the back which permits integration of reflexive and voluntary actions into a blend of total behavior. A cross-sectional view of the cord reveals columns of white matter on the outside and the characteristic "butterfly" of gray matter on the inside. The white matter consists of conducting tracts of myelinated nerve fibers, while the gray consists of cell bodies and unmyelinated fiber terminations.

Thirty-one pairs of spinal nerves connect the spinal cord with the peripheral parts of the body and are connected to the cord through a dorsal and a ventral root. The two general functions of the spinal cord involve conduction of impulses upward to higher centers and the conduction of impulses in the opposite directions. Its third function is a reflex one, the integration of simple unlearned responses to discrete stimuli requiring no mediation by discriminative process in the brain stem.

The Brain Stem. Immediately at the upward portion of the spinal cord lies the brain stem the primary structures of which are, first, the medulla and, then proceeding further upward and on the dorsal side, the cerebellum. Although the medulla is primarily involved in reflexive coordination, the cerebellum is involved in the coordination of voluntary movements and acts primarily as a smoother or check-point through which movements initiated in the higher centers are mediated and controlled. The important *reticular formation,* a column of scattered portions of gray matter, is also located on the brain stem and contributes to the energy of cortically initiated movement, the production of muscle tone, and also may suppress or inhibit muscular activity.

The Cerebrum. The cerebrum or cerebral hemispheres consist of the corpora striata covered by the cerebral cortex. Two important landmarks of the cerebral hemispheres are folds, which cause ridges called *gyri* and grooves or *sulci*. The two most important grooves are the central sulcus dividing the front and parietal lobes and the lateral fissure setting off the temporal lobe.

The cerebral cortex, or outer covering of the cerebrum, may be divided into two major subdivisions: (1) the neocortex, the newer in terms of evolutionary development, and (2) the allocortex, or "other" cortex. In general, the allocortex is concerned with visceral activity, with smell, rage, or other emotional patterning. The neocortex, on the other hand, may be divided into lobes, as delineated by sulci and fissures, or according to the type of cell structure found within various areas.

To the cortex the following generalized functions are attributed: (1) In connection with the thalamus, it serves to arouse or alert the organism; (2) It organizes and interprets sensory impressions, including formation of a general body image; (3) It initiates and aids in the control of general motor functioning; and (4) The frontal association areas, not specifically concerned with sensory or motor functioning, are believed to involve perceptual memory, as stimulation of portions of this region may evoke images of familiar objects or scenes.

Two basic classifications of theories purport to explain cerebral functioning: (1) nerve impulse theories, and (2) the field theories. In general, the former theories suggest that the billions of cells within the cortex act as individual cells, much as the single tubes of an electronic computer may be activated or not. While not denying that patterns of neurons may fire together to create patterns of thoughts, of perceptions, and the like, it is felt that a simple all-or-none principle of nerve excitation exists in the central nervous system much as is found within peripheral nervous functioning. The field theory, on the other hand, suggests that nerves within the central nervous system may influence each other not only through the synapse and that generalized fields of electrical activity can be induced within the nervous system. Since nerve fibers may activate one another along their length, as well as at the synapse, credence is given to this argument. In pages which follow, a generalized field theory is further explored as a basis for explaining the coordination of voluntary movement.

Methods of Examining the Neurological Control of Motor Behavior

Ablation. Ablation involves removing or destroying some portion of the central nervous system and then determining the resultant alterations of functions that are produced. The method must be carefully examined in order to circumvent several difficulties: (1) Careful appraisal of the extent of the tissue damage must be carried out; (2) It is sometimes difficult to determine whether a change in function is due directly to removal of the structure or whether the structure acted as a check on the function of other portions of the nervous system.

Electrical and Chemical Stimulation. A more frequent technique has been to stimulate electrically portions of the nervous system and then study the resultant responses. In general, it involves setting up a false nerve impulse. Humans as well as animals have been studied in this manner in a variety of ways. A disadvantage lies in the inability, in most cases, to initiate experimentally a discrete impulse; the usual result is that several neurons discharge simultaneously, including those which might interfere with the response in which the experimenter is interested. It was through electrical stimulation of various portions of the cortex that the motor areas were initially mapped.

The electroencephalogram is an example of an electrical recording method utilized from outside the skull and is a routine procedure in clinical and experimental situations. Strychnine is the usual chemical applied to nervous structure to study its function. Occasionally, electrical and chemical stimulation are used concurrently, as when one is used to desensitize a given area, while the other is used to study more exactly the functions of another area.

Clinical: Functional Changes Induced by Structural Abnormalities. Another frequent method of studying the relationship between neural structures and human behavior is through studying individuals, animals or humans, which have received some injury or are subject to some condition which renders portions of their nervous system apparently inoperative.

In general, however, attempting to predict alterations in behavior upon knowing various cerebral lesions in man becomes a perilous undertaking. Teuber[878] and others have found that changes in behavior after various kinds of brain damage are not obvious; in fact, they often prove to be subtle and elusive and even might go undetected. The adaptability of the human nervous system after damage to one of its parts, the taking-over of function from one structure by another, makes difficult the prediction of movement alterations by knowing the injury involved.

When studying human beings after injury or similar clinical problem, it is also difficult to determine what the patient was really like before his atypical condition occurred. Of paramount importance is not the performance after injury, but the change in performance or function produced by the injury to portions of the central nervous system.

THE FUNCTION OF THE CEREBRUM AND ASSOCIATED STRUCTURES AND VOLUNTARY MOVEMENT

Through the use of electrical stimulation, it has been possible to determine what areas of the cortex give rise to what general kinds of voluntary movement. In general, it is found that an area just in front of the central fissure, the precentral gyrus, might be termed the motor area and that the effects of stimulation on one side of the cortex result in movements on the opposite side of the body. It has also been found that the upper part of the cortex gives rise to movements in the lower part of the body, while the lower portions of the cortex elicit movements in the upper part (facial region) of the body. In general, it is also noted that more finite movements (face, hands, *etc.*) are controlled by relatively larger portions of the cortex than are gross, less accurate movements of the legs or trunk.

However, the exactitude of this "mapping" of the brain is open to question from several standpoints: (1) Repeated stimulation does not elicit the same precise effects. Such factors as the intensity and timing of the stimulations seem also to influence the observed functioning. (2) Other areas of the cerebrum, the somesthetic areas and various cortical supressor areas (*i.e.,* the corpus striatum and reticular formation) serve to reduce or increase activity. In addition, the cerebellum serves to reduce and to smooth movement.

In general, stimulation of a portion of the cortex fails to elicit an exact controlled or complex movement but rather produces a simple jerk or spasmodic action. It would seem that all of the structures in the central nervous system must be continually activated and balanced in order to produce a complex movement response.

Pathways and Loops for the Transmission and Control of Voluntary Movement

The human action system can be said to be dependent upon both external as well as internal loops. Visual-motor integrations and other movement modifications based upon information from auditory sensations, the verbal directions of others, and the like (external loops), form the basis for much of the material in the remainder of the book. We are concerned here with internal neural loops which control movement.

It has been stated that all neural structures seem to cooperate to integrate and "smooth" voluntary movement, some facilitating, some initiating, while others inhibit and modify the form of the movement output. These modifications and controls may be represented by neural loops which represent mutually affecting pathways. These internal loops may be complex and dependent upon internal control from remote reflexive and postural mechanisms located in the anti-gravity muscles of the trunk; proprioceptors located in muscles, tendons, and joints; or perhaps skin receptors receiving pressure cues. Some of these loops, however, are smaller and operate within the upper portions of the central nervous system, from cerebrum to cerebellum and corpus striatum and back again. These loops can be said to have two main functions: (1) to restrain or inhibit movements, thus serving to smooth jerky and uncoordinated movement patterns, and (2) to strengthen the effect of patterns initiated at the cortex level.

In general, two major types of pathways have been shown to influence voluntary movement. At the lower level (termed the "Lower Motorneuron Keyboard" by Paillard[711]) is the functional organization represented by the medulla oblongata and spinal cord neurons which acts directly upon muscular systems. At the second (or cortical) level are the assembled neurons emanating directly from the cortex in what are termed the *pyramidal pathways.* Studies reviewed by Tower[895] have indicated that these upper corticomotorneural tracks are essential in conveying impulses necessary for the manifestation of skilled movements.

The activation of motor units within the lower level is initially dependent upon the creation of a central excitatory state contributed to by central elements. Thus the activation of peripheral muscle structures is carried out within "programs" established in the higher centers. The lower track, however, has the ability to delicately control movements through temporal patterning (pacing) of the impulses to the affected muscle.

Experimental findings[711] have confirmed that a direct corticomotorneural path exists from the central nervous system to the lower levels. These direct pathways from the cortex serve two main functions:[584] (1) They contribute to the general excitatory state of the organism and, to facilitate general tension level, contribute to the state of readiness for action; (2) The other function of the cortical tracks are "specific contributions to individual acts of performance."[584] Thus the role of these centralized tracks are twofold, general and specific, contributing to the general state of arousal as well as to specific action patterns. Paillard,[711] in summarizing the research, concludes that ". . . The corticomotorneuronal system . . . can be considered as the chief executor of skilled movements."

Electrical stimulation of the cortex in itself never gives rise to complex coordinated movement, although superior influences seem to initiate a skilled response. Therefore, final manifestation is dependent upon activation from sensory structures in the cortex, "smoothing" by the lower portions of the brain stem, as well as upon the aforementioned peripheral and central feedback systems. The cortex, in the final analysis, seems to act as a funnel, or an integrator of movements, organizing a stream of patterned impulses from sensory structures in the periphery as well as in the central nervous system.

SUMMARY

Through the course of evolution *encephalization,* the addition and dominance of primitive structures within the nervous system by higher components of nervous control, has occurred. Within the human being, it appears that the higher centers, cortex, and associated structures function to integrate and funnel available sensory information and to initiate an appropriate movement output. The lower structures, cerebellum, reticular formation, and the spinal cord serve to monitor and smooth the action through a system of interdependent loops.

At the peripheral level, the motor units serve further to modify the final response and exert the final control over muscular output. Primary variables at this level influencing controlled muscle action include the innervation ratio, the number of motor units affecting the muscle, the duration and rate at which stimulation occurs, differentials in nerve conduction rate, the nature of opposing muscle activity, as well as the size and formation of the fibers composing the muscle affected.

Student References

Books

1. HERB, D. O.: *The Organization of Behavior,* New York, John Wiley & Sons, Inc., 1949.
2. WENGER, M. A., JONES, F. N., and JONES, M. H.: *Physiological Psychology,* New York, Holt, Rinehart and Winston, 1956.

Articles

1. HARRISON, VIRGINIA F.: "Review of the neuromuscular bases for motor learning," *Research Quarterly,* 33, No. 1, March 1962.
2. PAILLARD, JACQUES: "The patterning of skilled movements," *Handbook of Physiology,* Am. J. Soc., Washington, D.C., 1960.

Chapter 12

"Personal Equations" in Movement

THE majority of studies involving motor performance and learning are concerned with optimum all-out effort. The subject in such experiments is usually informed that he should "do his best," exert "maximum effort," or should move "as rapidly as possible." These experiments, while providing important information concerning performance attributes, tend to obliterate innumerable components of movement behavior which relate to how an individual *chooses* to move in the absence of some kind of exhortation for maximum effort. To an increasing degree these subtle components of motoric functioning are being accorded experimental attention. It is the purpose of this chapter to discuss these studies and to draw conclusions from them of importance to the physical educator.

In many tasks on the playground and in the gymnasium the manner in which the individual *prefers* to move will influence the total effort he exerts and the nature of the observable pattern elicited. The dance teacher is frequently confronted by evidence of these personal equations in movement as she attempts to encourage individuals in her charge to "break out" of well-established habit patterns involving rhythm; or perhaps to elicit movements within a larger amount of space than members of her class would prefer to use. Most performances in athletic skills represent a compromise between the maximum effort an individual can manifest versus what he *prefers* to do.

The available research indicates that there is a remarkable consistency in this kind of personal performance quality, both in action patterns[14,222,498] in which the total body is moving through space, in limb movements,[222,498] and in tasks involving smaller amounts of space.[754] This category of variables denoting a personal equation in movement might be termed *individual preferences in movement, personal equations of performance,* or perhaps *individual biases in movement behavior.* Essentially these components of movement seem to be the result of instructions the performer extends to himself prior to and during the performance of a motor task. These "personal equations" are also manifested in movement behaviors independent of structured performance situations—in walking, handwriting and in similar daily activities.

In the pages which follow, material relative to *task persistence, personal rhythm, preferred speed,* and *spatial preference* will be discussed. *Task persistence* relates to individual differences in the inclination to continue performance while undergoing varying amounts of discomfort caused by continuing a task. "Personal rhythm" is obtained by experimental directions which ask the subject simply to "tap rhythmically," or instructions of a similar nature. "Preferred speed" is measured in tasks whose apparent emphasis is not upon speed, but upon accuracy, or by simply clocking movement patterns (*i.e.* walking) elicited from unsuspecting subjects.

Spatial preference relates to the amount of space an individual habitually utilizes when moving. Studies involving naive subjects who are asked simply to "move their bodies to the music" have elicited data of this nature, as have studies evaluating the amount of space characteristically used by people as they have been asked to engage in a relatively unstructured manual skill.[754]

These personal preferences, taken together, may be indicative of *personality* expressed in movement. Several behavioral scientists during the 1930's became interested in these general movement attributes.

Early Investigations

Allport and Vernon carried out experiments in the 1930's which attempted to determine relationships between expressive movement and personality. The first battery of tests used consisted of speed of walking, length of stride, handwriting measures, hand and finger tapping, estimation of distances, the drawing of geometric figures and similar tasks. Their first investigation resulted in the identification of three stable movement characteristics.[19]

Two of these characteristics seem related to the previously mentioned spatial preference. One was termed an *areal factor* by Allport, based upon the amount of space characteristically used in tasks. Allport also identified a *centrifugal factor*, indicative of whether an individual typically made movements away from, or toward his body during performances of various tasks. A third factor was named *emphasis* by Allport, and was identified by quantifying the amount of force and tension characteristically present in the performance of various finger tapping and handwriting tasks.

Further studies by these investigators purported to establish relationships between personality traits and various movement characteristics. Conversely it was claimed that through observation of movement characteristics various personality traits could, with moderate accuracy, be accurately predicted. However, Allport and his students caution the reader to proceed cautiously in the interpretation of the findings, stating that:

> "The unity of expression turns out entirely a question as to
> degree, just as the unity of personality is largely of degree.
> Expression is patterned in complex ways exactly as personality
> itself is patterned."

In 1932 June Downey devoted a text to the elaboration and explanation of experimental findings which related "temperament" to movement. She used paper and pencil tests, together with handwriting analyses to evaluate various movement traits which included speed of movement, freedom from tension, the tendency to vary a movement (flexibility), speed of decision, forcefulness, perseverance and the like.[255]

From these groups of tests the following classifications were formulated:

1. The mobile type
2. The mobile-aggressive type, exploding with great force
3. The nonspecific type (difficult to classify)
4. The deliberate type, having great care for detail
5. The low-level type, easy-going, not forceful
6. The psychotic type, high degree of tension and little tendency to vary movements

Downey concluded that individuals might be characterized by their individual "profiles" based upon movement traits evidenced within these categories.

Although the reliability and validity of the test used by Downey were not established, this program represents one of the initial attempts to evaluate personal equations in movement. She is one of the first to show an awareness of the influence of tension upon motor performance. Later researchers took a less global approach to the problem than did Downey, and usually investigated specific portions of this personal preference of movements.

Task Persistence

Various researchers within the past thirty years have attempted to determine whether a general quality termed *persistence* is evidenced when a variety of motor tasks are engaged in. Although much of this work is not of a high caliber, the study by MacArthur in 1952 seems to point to the existence of a general factor involving the inclination of certain individuals to prolong their performances in a variety of tasks.[607]

MacArthur found, after intercorrelating twenty-two measures, that after intellectual differences were partialled out, a general persistence factor involving motor performance did exist. This investigator revealed that persistence was at least a dual factor, one part reflected in the relationships between various physical tasks, and the second in tasks of a more intellectual nature (*i.e.* how long an individual is willing to read from a book). This factor of motor persistence was revealed in correlations obtained from tasks which included the time an individual was willing to hold one foot straight out from the hip while seated, time of holding breath, of maintaining hand-grip pressure, and the time during which an individual was willing to extend his arm at the shoulder. MacArthur's data also revealed that persistence under conditions which involve some kind of social motivation, *i.e.* the exhortation from others, seems to be a factor apart from persistence, evidenced by an individual in the absence of some kind of obvious social motivators.

Ryans,[776] Crutcher,[226] and others have also identified a general factor of persistence in a number of motor tasks. Thornton has isolated a general factor which he describes as "ability and/or willingness to withstand discomfort in order to achieve a goal," with high loading in "time holding breath, time standing still, maintained hand-grip, and similar measures."[884] Rethlingschafer also named a factor "the willingness and/or ability to endure 'discomfort.'" Such studies involve the evaluation of a quality similar to pain.[151]

Although I am unaware of investigations which relate such measures of persistence to vital capacity and to other basic indices of optimum physical capacities, it is apparent that persistence could be an important variable influencing the results of experiments involving endurance, or in other studies in which repetitive movements lead to some degree of stress.

Typical of the methods used when evaluating persistence is to first obtain maximum capacity (*i.e.* grip strength), ask the subject to maintain 50 to 75 per cent of his maximum and then clock the amount of time he is willing to do so. In common with the other *personal equations* discussed in this chapter, the experimenter must be certain that the subjects remain naive to the purposes of the investigation.

Although the physical educator and athletic coach frequently are heard to explain that encouraging a boy to persist in athletics will elicit similar fortitude when he is confronted with classroom lessons, the available data do not usually support this assumption. At the same time the possibilities of research in this area are limitless. Determining whether persistence is a predictor of courage under stressful circumstances, studying the generality versus specificity of persistence, as well as relating persistence to various measures of absolute capacity which undergird cardiovascular endurance would seem only some of the studies which could be profitably undertaken.

Personal Rhythm

Studies by Lewis,[582] Harding,[412] and others have presented findings which are somewhat inconclusive concerning the existence of a general factor of personal rhythm. Such a factor is studied by analyzing the speed an individual selects when confronted with directions to "tap rhythmically." In general there is a reasonable consistency between measures obtained when the same limb is engaged in this kind of task on several trials.[718] At the same time, contrasting total body rhythm, foot tapping, and finger tapping with various physiological measures including heart rate, respiration rate, and the like usually reveal low relationships.

Personal rhythm seems to be related to other kinds of sensory experiences. Dinner, Wapner, and McFarland[250] found that when an individual was asked to tap faster than he preferred, it led to an apparent shortening of an objective time period by the subject. On the other hand when he was asked to tap at a rate slower than he would usually choose, it led to an apparent lengthening of his perception of a time interval.[250]

Other characteristics of tapping behavior have also been explored as possible indices of personality. Eysenck[287] found that extroverts took more involuntary rests, after being instructed to tap rhythmically, than did introverts. Similarly subjects informed that their rate of tapping would be a criterion for admittance to a training course, of course evidenced increased speed versus subjects who had already been admitted to a training program. Thus the personality of the subject as well as various motivating circumstances can alter personal tempo to a marked degree.

In general the identification of a personal tempo by asking an individual to engage in a few tapping tasks is a somewhat tenuous undertaking;[754] at the same time, given a specific tempo involving a single portion of the body, marked consistency is usually indicated. Rimoldi found relatively consistent measures obtained on tests of personal rhythm between tasks administered several weeks apart.[754]

Preferred Speed

Relatively few investigations were carried out prior to the 1950's exploring preferred speed. In 1947 Kennedy and Travis found a unitary speed factor when the scores obtained from a number of tasks were contrasted.[520] These investigators coined the term "irritability" to indicate the general work rate evidenced by an individual. Frischeisen-Kohler also suggested that a unitary speed factor exists, based upon evaluation of preferred rates on tapping and on metronome tests.[329]

Another study which attempted to verify the existence of a general speed quality in movement was carried out by Harrison and Dorcus somewhat earlier. Comparisons were made of the speed at which individuals characteristically moved, by measurement of their speed of arm and head movements in tasks in which speed was apparently not being evaluated. The speed with which the subjects walked to the experimental area was also measured without the subjects' knowledge. These latter investigators concluded that no unitary speed trait was present, although speed in specific tasks evidence inter-trial consistency.[423]

In the most comprehensive study available, carried out in 1951, Rimoldi found that both specific and general speed factors were evidenced when the work rate at which individuals preferred to perform various tasks were contrasted. Rimoldi used fifty-nine measures in which seventeen subjects participated; measures included those evaluating preferred speed in perceptual, cognitive, clerical, as well as motor tasks. The motor tasks included preferred arm swinging speed of various kinds and in various planes, tapping tasks carried out by the feet, fingers and arms as well as speed of walking. The perceptual tasks included various reaction and discrimination time problems. Writing activities were also included, as were reading speed, preferred metronome rate, cancellation speed, writing speed, and tests evaluating mental ability.[754]

Rimoldi found that habitual motor speed in various tasks evidenced moderate to high relationships, but that preferred speed in motor tasks was not indicative of the speed elicited when his subjects performed non-motor tasks. Two separate motor factors emerged, relative to preferred speed. One factor was composed of scores from tasks involving rhythmic and tapping movements; a second factor was composed of scores from tasks which required rather exact movements of the limbs (*i. e.* parallel movements of the legs while seated).

Rimoldi suggested that his data support the existence of different tempos, rather than acceptance of a universal one. For example, one could not predict preferred metronome speed by knowing the speed at which the same subject chose to bend his body. At the same time speed in bending the body is reasonably well predicted by knowing how fast the same person is willing to swing his arm. It is possible to predict speed of small movements by knowing the speed of large ones; prediction of movement speed by measuring preferred rate of drawing, for example, is not possible, based upon the present data. Acceptance of the extreme "piece meal viewpoint" relative to preferred speed is, Rimoldi concluded, not a sound approach. It seems, states this investigator, possible to accept the existence of a motor speed factor of quite a general kind.

Rimoldi concluded that his study as well as others have supported the existence of at least four areas in which preferred speed of performance are relatively independent of one another. These include speed of cognition, speed of perception, speed of reaction time, and speed of movement.

In common with the findings of Harrison and Dorcus[423] and those by Frischeisen-Kohler,[329] Rimoldi found that the time between test periods has relatively little influence upon the scores. Individuals are relatively consistent about the rate of movement they evidence when performing various kinds of motor tasks. Rimoldi concluded that "Each individual performs a particular act following a specific temporal pattern which he keeps constant." This pattern chosen seems to be, for him, the most economical way of performing. The speed of another person imposed upon an individual's personal way of performing may prove detrimental.[754] The more recent study by Jones and Hanson also found marked consistency in measurements obtained fifteen months apart, evaluating both time and space patterns evidenced when subjects arose from chairs.[498]

The available evidence thus supports the existence of a general factor indicative of preferred speed which is common to a number of motor tasks and relatively consistent over a time period. Although the correlations between preferred speed of movement, and maximum movement speed, and other physiological measures are low,[754] it would seem that each individual has a characteristic and efficient movement speed which he prefers when performing a number of tasks. Further research would seem indicated relative to how these temporal patterns are developed in children, the extent to which they are resistant to different kinds of external conditions, and their relationship to various other psychological and physiological measures. Preference of personal tempos in movement is also probably related to an individual's perceptions of time; thus further research might also explore the relationship between various aspects of personal tempo in movement, and factors influencing the perception of time itself.

Of particular importance to coaches and to teachers of dance are the possible effects of the imposition of "unnatural" movement speeds upon the performance in various tasks in which all-out speed is not requisite. The best procedure in such situations might first be to evaluate the effects of the individual's preference for speed when performing the task, and then proceed cautiously when attempting to inculcate any marked changes in the individual's chosen "movement speed."

Spatial Preference

Early observers of human behavior suggested the presence of a general spatial factor present in relatively unstructured movement tasks;[19] the experimental designs with which this quality was explored left much to be desired. More recent evidence from several sources indicates there is a given amount of space through which individuals prefer to move their limbs and total bodies in relatively unstructured situations.

This general problem area has two primary questions which have been subjected to varying amounts of experimental exploration. (1) In a given type of task, *i.e.* line drawing, facing movements, dancing to music, etc., just how much space do individuals prefer to utilize (*i.e.* how long a line do people prefer to draw?), and (2) Are there individual consistencies in the space individuals utilize in several tasks, and/or in the same task from trial to trial?

The first question has not been explored extensively. The available evidence, however, indicates that in various kinds of tasks there is a given distance people prefer to move despite directions extended from an outside source. When individuals are asked to draw a line 4 inches in length, they tend to draw a longer one; conversely people seem to resist drawing a line 15 inches long when requested to do so. In other terms there seems to be a preferred length of line people like to draw despite instructions extended by another person.

In another study it was found that when sighted and blind adults and children are asked to make facing movements of 90, 180, and 360 degrees while deprived of auditory cues (and sight in the case of the sighted), they were found to turn past 90 degrees by about 7 degrees, to underturn 180 degrees by about 10 degrees, and to underturn full turns by about 40 degrees. There thus seemed to be an amount of turning these subjects preferred despite experimental directions, probably somewhere between 90 and 180 degrees![222]

These findings are rather intriguing. It would seem that a simple factorial analysis might be helpful in the initial exploration of this phenomenon. The extent to which this kind of preference for space utilization in movements has long been speculated upon in the clinical literature, however, relatively little objective work has been carried out.

Consistencies in individual differences in the amount of space utilized in various movement tasks has been also subjected to rather scant experimental treatment. These studies were initially concerned primarily with writing movements in both structured handwriting tasks and in relatively unstructured activities.

Various modifications of the draw-a-person test have been explored as indicative of some kind of personality trait structure, usually without marked success. Similarly, graphologists have been diligently at work for years attempting to prove that character is reflected in handwriting with little to show for their efforts. The most recent review of the findings of the graphologists is by Vernon in 1953.[911] By far the greatest number of studies has been concerned with attempts to match personality sketches or case studies with assessments from handwriting. The results of such studies are usually negative. Most of the European studies have failed to incorporate acceptable statistical procedures; and most of these seem to be based upon the claims of intuition, rather than upon scientific veracity.

Lewinson and Zubin[579] have presented a number of objectively scorable scales and certain combined ratio scores which are claimed to be valid measures of handwriting characteristics. However, few investigations have been forthcoming utilizing these techniques. Perhaps Pophal, a research graphologist presently holding a chair in graphology at the University of Hamburg (Germany), will contribute research illuminating the relationships between personality and handwriting characteristics.

Generally the hypothesis that introversion and/or anxiety produces restriction in the amount of space utilized in various movements has little experimental verification. Exceptions are the studies by Craddock and Stern who found that introduction of stress produced a constriction in a design copying task,[186] and the parallel findings of Brengelmann[109] relating confidence to the space utilized in a task involving the arrangement of figures around a radial pattern of lines.

A recent investigation by one of my students presents findings which seem an inroad to the understanding of spatial preferences in movement.[14] In this investigation, movement of the entire body was measured. Using 60 teenage girls with no previous dance experience as subjects, Ahrens requested that each one "move as she would like" to recorded music. The subjects were then one at a time left alone in a gym, and "watched" by a television camera of which they were unaware. The space they utilized was traced in an adjacent room through the use of a monitor upon which a grid was superimposed.

Three trials were given the subjects on three separate occasions. The scores obtained were measures of the distance they moved, the number of squares in the grid they "visited" as well as the greatest distance they moved from the starting point.

Analysis of the data revealed that there were remarkable consistencies in the amount of space the subjects used under the conditions described. Correlations exceeding .8 were obtained when the scores from the various trials were compared. In addition there were marked individual differences evidenced in these spatial measures.

The investigation did prove the possibility of obtaining reliable measures from participation in a relatively unstructured movement task. It is believed that this investigation made an important contribution to our knowledge of human movement, and should be followed by others similar in intent, in which the influence of innumerable variables upon spatial utilization might be explored. These additional factors might include various personality traits, stressors in the form of social harassment, verbal encouragement, and the presence of members of the opposite sex and of friends and disliked peers.

It is not difficult to locate various assumptions about the purported relationships between spatial qualities in movement and various other factors. Experimental verification of these associations are more difficult to locate, however.

Other "Personal Equations"

In addition to the four personal equations discussed on the previous pages, experimental evidence points to several other possible individual differences in movement characteristics which are consistent from task to task. For example, the work of Duffy summarized in her text indicates that there is a typical level of activation manifested in muscular tension and in other measures characteristic of an individual.[259] It is not unreasonable to suggest, therefore, that there is a personal equation which might be termed *habitual force*, which may be evidenced in such tasks as handwriting, which in turn may correlate positively with various personality traits indicative of assertiveness.

Similarly there seem to be individual differences in susceptibility or suggestibility to instructions which probably exert an influence upon the extent to which an individual asserts his personal movement character- istics versus accepting control and incorporating instructions from an outside source when moving. This *suggestibility factor* has been investi- gated by Sarazon and Rosenzweig[782] as revealed in relationships between body sway and susceptibility to hypnotism.

Further Investigations Needed

The available evidence is suggestive rather than conclusive. The amount of information presently available is not so extensive when compared to the bulk of data concerned with other problem areas con- tained in the text.

Further studies might explore the relationships between various motor tasks in which maximum performance is desired versus those in which various personal equations are exposed. The relationship between vari- ous structural and biological characteristics and individual preferences movement might also be subjected to the scrutiny of the scientific method of problem solving.

The relationship between selected measures of personality traits, *i.e.* introversion, extroversion, ascendency, aggression, hostility, succorance, and various manifestations of the personal equations described would seem a fruitful field of investigation. Similarly the extent to which a movement as performed is influenced by some kind of personal pref- erence versus maximum capacities is also an important avenue of scientific exploration. Contrasting various measures indicative of these personal equations with measures reflecting characteristic ways of per- ceiving should also prove interesting.

Overall these kinds of investigations should provide a deeper under- standing of some of the subtle influences upon perceptual-motor be- haviors manifested by human beings. Correlation of some of these personal equations to various motor ability and motor learning scores might explain some of the findings presently attributable to "experimental artifacts." Consideration of some of these types of variables might also aid teachers to work more effectively with children in the classroom and on the athletic field and to better accommodate to individual differ- ences in movement and perception evidenced by the students in their charge.

SUMMARY

Performance data elicited from subjects under no specific instructions to perform maximally have revealed several classifications of attributes which may be defined as personal equations, or personal preferences in movement. Persistence at a task is one of these, which describes the inclination to continue performing under conditions involving varying degrees of discomfort. Persistence at motor tasks seems independent of persistence at intellectual tasks. Other personal equations include personal rhythm, preferred speed, as well as the amount of space preferred in movements. In addition, the extent to which force is habitually expressed may be a sixth dimension within this category of movement attributes.

Student References

Book

1. EYSENCK, H. J.: *The Structure of Human Personality,* London, Methuen, 1953.

Articles

1. MACARTHUR, R. S.: "The Experimental Investigation of Persistence in Secondary School Boys," *Canad. J. Psych.,* 9:42-54, 1955.
2. RIMOLDI, H. J. A.: "Personal Tempo," *J. Abnorm. & Psych.,* 46:283-303, 1951.
3. THORNTON, G. R.: "A Factor Analysis of Tests Designed to Measure Persistence," *Psych. Mono.,* 51:1–42, 1939.

Chapter 13

Communication Through Movement

CLOSELY related to investigation of personality-movement relationships is the study of the manner in which human actions may contribute to the communication process. Although early investigations were relatively subjective, having their genesis in phrenology, palmistry, and the like, in more recent years studies of movement communication are found in such respected fields as psychology, anthropology and sociology. As a result of the development of more objective evaluative instruments and sounder theoretical frameworks, studies in this area have become increasingly scientific.

Most investigations of movement communication are based upon the assumption that interpersonal relations are facilitated as one becomes better able to assess and to utilize such factors as facial expression, posture, and gestures when judging meanings transmitted by a second individual. Conversely, it is hypothesized that by failing to interpret correctly the thoughts expressed by another, by omitting consideration of accompanying movements, one may leave out an important dimension of interpersonal communication. Thus, much of the research seeks to gain general information which will enhance the productivity of various group endeavors.

Members of the performing arts have evidenced an interest in the manner in which movements communicate ideas, although little material which could be termed scientific has been forthcoming from this source. Acting "methods" recently coming into prominence have emphasized the subtle and overt use of bodily movements to communicate the intended emotions and ideas to the audience.

Expert dancers also have used an understanding of the manner in which gross limb and body movements suggest internal emotional states. Recent efforts on the part of researchers in movement communication to evolve a shorthand system with which to describe various facial expressions bear a marked resemblance to systems of dance notation, which translate bodily movements to the printed page.

Literature in movement communication may be classified in several ways. Two main areas, for example, seem clearly delineated: (1) studies in *movement expression,* including the part overt bodily expression plays in communicating internal emotional states and various movement-verbal relationships; and (2) the study of *movement interpretation,* concerned with examining the variables which influence the manner in which individuals *judge* the movement behavior of others. In addition, recent investigations have considered actions manifested at three different levels, based upon the area of the body involved in the movement; the study of *facial expressions, gestures* formed by the limbs and/or hands, and, at the gross end of the continuum, the manner in which posturing of the *total body* communicates meaning.

Two other important problem areas will be treated within the following pages. The first is concerned with whether gesture communication is innate or learned; the second, a close parallel, with what kinds of communicative movements occur of which the individual is unaware and what kinds are consciously sent and received.

COMMUNICATIVE MOVEMENTS: LEARNED OR INNATE?

As is the case with other facets of human behavior, motivation, personality, and the like, one of the major questions considered by various scholars is whether characteristics and individual differences in action cues are molded by socio cultural factors or whether they are determined by basic structural constituents of the organism.

Several lines of evidence support the viewpoint that movements and posturing are innate. Darwin, studying the relationship between animal emotions and their "facial" and bodily movements, concluded that many of these actions are functional in nature. For example, he contended that baring the teeth in anger enables the wolf to maintain a better grasp of his prey as it allows the teeth to become more effective as weapons. Since Darwinian theory naturally assumes that man has direct evolutionary linkages to the animals, it is therefore suggested that various human expressions have their basis in primitive action patterns.[151]

Cannon[139] offers another line of reasoning to support the innate nature of movement communication. Through numerous physiological studies investigating the characteristics of emotional states produced in dogs and cats, it was found that the methods by which they reacted to stress seemed identifiable. Furthermore, it was found that these various rage and/or fear responses were mediated by subcortical portions of the nervous system. Since these were not dependent upon integration by the higher centers of the cortex, Cannon hypothesized that such innate movement responses to stress are "built-in" and not formed by learning.

Investigations in another area also support the contention that expressive movement communication may be inherited. Goodenough, studying the facial expressions of a ten-year-old child, blind and deaf from birth, concluded that distinct movement patterns were evidenced, indicating rage, fear, disgust, and shame, which roughly corresponded to these same actions in sighted individuals. This was taken as evidence that such emotional states produce inherent kinds of gesture patterns unrelated to learning, as in this case the opportunity to observe others and to imitate them was, of course, not possible.[380]

Studies in growth and development provide further evidence. Watson,[931] an earlier researcher in this area, concluded that three motion patterns are observable in the emotional patterns of infants. These he labeled x, y, and z and hypothesized that they represented evidence of fear, rage, and love, respectively. Since these three patterns were noted by Watson to be present in newborn infants, it was suggested that such movement traits were innate.

Studies by Bridges,[110] however, suggested that Watson's findings might be questioned. This later researcher was unable to identify Watson's three patterns and proposed that the only significant movement pattern discernible in newborn babies was one of *general activity*. It is not until infants are about three weeks of age, Bridges argued, that other kinds of movement communication take place, including a *distress pattern*. At about two to three weeks of age, a *delight* pattern was noted to emerge, but not until the fourth month of age did movements which indicated *joy* become expressed in facial movements. Thus Bridges seems to infer that most patterns which involve movement communication are learned rather than instinctive. It is interesting to speculate the dissimilar backgrounds of Watson and of Bridges, or the divergent frames of reference they employed, resulted in their different interpretations of infantile action patterns.

Crying and Smiling in Infants

The crying response seems present at birth and initially is caused by internal kinds of discomfort. After the first month of age, the percentage of time given to crying decreases, reaching its lowest point at about four months. After four months, the time given to crying increases up to about one year, and then decreases again to about eighteen months, according to Bayley.[163]

As the child grows, causes of crying become more related to external environmental conditions. The manner in which the child is handled and the like become increasingly important. After the child organizes his proximal world, strange objects or conditions seem increasingly to elicit a crying response.

Smiling is absent at birth and thus seems learned. Smiling does not appear until about the twentieth day with the total response developing during the third, fourth, fifth, and sixth months. By the age of six months, Buhler[124] found the smile becomes a normal response to social stimulation and is utilized in communication.

In an ingenious study designed to determine various causes of smiling in infants, Spitz[849] found that the human face, when presented to the infant between the ages of three to six months, elicited a smiling response. This researcher then covered various portions of the face viewed by the infant with a mask to determine exactly what stimulated a smile. Was it movement, the eyes, the mouth, or what? On the basis of many observations, Spitz concluded that it is not another human face in itself that elicits a smiling response from infants, but a configuration of elements within a total stimulus pattern. This configuration was found to consist of two eyes combined with motion of various facial muscles, which could consist of nodding, sticking out the tongue, or some similar movement.

Movement and Emotion in Adults

Wenger,[950] devoting considerable study to the electro-physiological activity of the autonomic nervous system, has produced findings which relate to movement communication. He found that there are about eight distinguishable patterns of electrical activity which seem related to internal emotional states. Furthermore, he stated that: "There seem to be certain patterns, such as the flexion pattern in fear and pain, and the extension pattern in anger, as well as the unique relaxed 'bowed-back' flexion pattern in grief or depression."

Another question of prime importance, assuming that emotions and movements are moderately related, is whether one can objectively measure, and thus predict, one from the other. A pioneer study in this area by Meyers[655] suggested that in the case of anxiety this can be accomplished. He found that there was a significant positive correlation between eye-blink rate and anxiety. It would seem that more such exact measures are needed.

THE CULTURE AND LEARNED MOVEMENTS

The view that emotional patterns expressed in movement are learned rather than innate is supported by anthropological studies. Anthropologists found long ago that peoples in various cultures use dissimilar gesture systems when expressing themselves. Cushing[230] suggested, upon studying Zuni Indian sign language, that the more primitive the culture, the more the recourse to gesture communication. However, such a simple hypothesis is open to question when it is realized that, even in a given culture, a gesture may have different meanings for various situations and for different socio-economic groups.

Misinterpretation or lack of knowledge about the characteristic gesture signs used by an ethnic group has caused the death of more than one anthropologist who mistakenly used gestures which threaten rather than signifying friendship when first encountering an isolated tribe. The actions of actors in motion pictures produced in one country often misunderstood, because of the habitual use of a different set of gestures in countries to which the films are exported.

Although a large number of gestures are culturally oriented and seemingly not dependent upon innate characteristics, in most cases a

15

one-to-one relationship between internal emotional state and movement cues is difficult to demonstrate. Indeed, in many primitive tribes, emphasis is placed upon the concealment of internalized fear through the presentation of a relatively immobile countenance to the world.

Hewes[448] and other observers of various cultures find that there are a vast number of movement patterns characteristic of ethnic groups which apparently are learned, since they seem to be unique to specific groups. Such patterns have been used in studies of personality, status, and emotional state. For example, it was found that there are specific and nonspecific movement customs which govern the actions of individuals while eating and playing that are unique to citizens of the United States. In some cases, the social status group in which an individual belongs may be accurately identified through observing his mannerisms in various situations.

Although the instinctive vs. learned question is difficult to resolve in relation to movement communication, it seems that rather intense emotional states result in innate movements of the face and body which indicate fright or fear. On the other hand, less intense kinds of communicative behavior, which transmit information or add a dimension to verbal behavior, seem largely a learned product of the cultural setting.

The learned patterns of movement expression seem to fall upon a continuum, from actions of which the sender is totally unaware to those clearly practiced. Many of the more conscious patterns, such as shrugging the shoulders and turning the palms upward to indicate bewilderment, are used to augment, emphasize, and speed communication. Toward the subtle, reflexive end of the continuum lie minute facial expressions and overt flexings of the body of which an individual may be unaware.

The importance of such subtle clues is emphasized in an investigation by Eisenberg and Reichlane.[276] It was found that observers successfully differentiated between women who had been labeled dominant and submissive, through the administration of a personality inventory, by observing films of their walks.

The contention that gesture patterns are both unique to the individual and also culturally determined is supported by research by Hebb.[430] It was found that gestures were highly individualized in both animals and man. Observers of primates had to become familiar with each animal before they could correctly interpret the meanings of their gesture patterns. Similar findings were forthcoming when the gesture patterns of humans were analyzed.

THE INTERPRETATION OF MOVEMENT CUES

A number of articles have reported upon the ability to interpret facial expression and larger bodily movements. The results often have been contradictory; however, the findings of one investigation seem worthy of review. Kline and Johannsen[532] found that correct interpretation of another's movements is dependent upon the number of kinds of movements observed. And conversely, when viewing isolated portions of the body, less accurate estimates were possible. More accurate judgments were made when facial expressions, gestures, and posturing were observed in combination than when only one or two of these subdivisions were inspected. Kline *et al.* also presented evidence indicating that observations of moving pictures, rather than still pictures of individuals, resulted in more accurate judgments of emotions.[532]

Also important to correct interpretation of movement "language" is consideration of the context in which the action occurs. Research by Frijda[328] suggests that if the total situation is known, the judge may better project himself into it and thus become able to form more accurate judgment about the movements observed. For example, if expressions of joy are seen in a context which seems pleasant and truly happy, interpretation is not difficult. However, if these same gestures and movement patterns are viewed within a situation calling for grief, judgmental confusion is likely to result.

Although Ruesch and Kees,[770] among others, have supported the accuracy of Frijda's statements, relatively little research has been devoted to exploring the effect of the context upon the interpretation of movement cues or the possible "overriding" of contextual cues by intense action patterns.

Innumerable cultural variations in gestures which communicate can be cited.[541] For example, the gesture meaning "come here" in America is used to denote "good-bye" in many parts of South America. Similarly stroking the chin in Italy means that the individual is "starting to grow a beard" because he is so bored with the speaker. The typical gestures of Jewish immigrants from Lithuania and Poland were studied by Efron, and it was found that they could be easily distinguished by reference to gesture patterns alone. The children of these immigrants, however, failed to utilize the amount or the kind of gestures which characterized their parents' efforts to communicate. Efron is one of the few individuals who has bothered to devise a reasonably objective system for coding gestures, although it is somewhat complex to use.[272]

These cultural variations, of course, indicated that the judgment of gesture patterns will be made more accurately by people of a similar background. Dusenbery and Knower found that ability to judge the meaning of gestures within one's own cultural context was good; but when people of one culture attempt to judge the communicative movements of another, little accuracy was possible.[264]

While awareness of the cultural situation seems important to the interpretation of gestures, other variables do not. For example, Morrison[675] found that sex, intelligence, occupational rank, and religion did not seem to be related to the accuracy with which individuals were able to judge gesture-language.

THE MEASUREMENT OF MOVEMENT INTERPRETATION

It is generally agreed that individuals continually interpret the gestures of others. In answer to the need for objective measuring tools with which to evaluate consistency of judgments, Morrison developed a Gesture Interpretation Test (GIT). The task evaluates whether individuals were consistent in the manner in which they interpreted the emotions and meanings suggested by 37 outlines of individuals pictured in various postural and gestural attitudes.[675]

Morrison found that his subjects were able to attach meanings to commonplace postures, gestures, and apparent movements with some consistency. This was rather remarkable, because the pictures contained *no indication of facial expression*. The fact that even mentally abnormal individuals were found to judge the pictured postures accurately was interpreted by Morrison as indicating that ability in gesture interpretation is a skill formed early in childhood and is not easily forgotten.

TACTILE COMMUNICATION

Movement may communicate, of course, not only as the receiver observes the movements of another, but also as he is touched by another. In recent years, several researchers have indicated an interest in tactile communication, although little objective evidence has been forthcoming in this area.

Frank suggests that the growing infant reacts first to *signals*, then to larger and more complex kinds of tactile cues, or *signs*, and later to *symbols* which indicate still more complex meanings. Frank also discusses various cultural influences upon tactile communication and suggests that personality development and increased tactile sensitivity are closely parallel.[318]

SUMMARY

Movement communication is an important aspect of man's movement behavior. Mobile cues often accompany verbal expression, but at times stand by themselves to suggest meanings. Movements which communicate may be either learned or innate, dependent upon the intensity of the emotion directing them. The more intense emotional types of movement expressions are probably more instinctive, while actions which only communicate information are largely learned and related to the culture.

An understanding of movement communication is important from several standpoints. Initially, it seems important for an individual to become sensitive to the exact meanings emanating from another; therefore, accurately interpreting movement cues heightens an individual's perceptions of the feelings, needs, meanings, and wishes of another. An understanding of the nature of movement communication is important also for the sender of communication, insofar as more exact meanings may be transmitted, thus establishing clearer channels of interpersonal communication.

It also seems clear that when a total complex of movements is regarded, including facial, postural, and bodily actions, accurate meanings may be interpreted or transmitted. And as Icheiser[483] has pointed out, failing to interpret properly movement cues may pose serious interpersonal misunderstandings.

A primary problem is the need for the development of objective measures of the ability to communicate through movement, as well as instruments to assess the ability to interpret movements. Morrison's GIT test provides a vehicle through which investigators might better assess the manner in which individuals judge the posturing and gesturing of others.

The primary area for further research, it would appear, concerns the nature of socially determined movements. Cooperative research among sociologists, anthropologists and psychologists might prove productive. More research also seems called for to explore the manner in which the sender becomes accustomed to utilizing various gestures that they are engaged in without thinking. In line with this problem, an investigation concerning the classification of various gestures into conscious and unconscious categories would be worthwhile.

The role of gestures in manipulating the behavior of others, of groups, or of individuals, the subject of a study by Stratton,[858] also seems important for future consideration. No one who has ever attended a group meeting in education or business can deny the importance of the facial and bodily movements of ranking members to the channeling of discussion.

Student References

Books

1. RUESCH, J., and KEES, W.: *Non-Verbal Communication*, San Francisco, University of California Press, 1956.
2. BIRDWHISTLE, RAY L.: "Kinesics and Communication," in *Explorations in Communication*, edited by Edmund Carpenter and Marsha McLuhan, pp. 54–65, Beacon Hill, Boston, Beacon Press, 1960.

Chapter 14

Ability Traits

Motor performance has been described as observable human behavior characterized by voluntary, task-centered movement. It has also been explained that learning may be studied only by observing progressive performance changes. This second concept permits *motor performance* to be defined also as *the segmented evidence of motor learning.* Before accepting either explanation, it is important to examine in some detail the nature of motor performance (the part) prior to considering the broader concept of motor learning.

Numerous physiological and anatomical factors limit the individual's ability to utilize force (dependent upon the contractile strength of various muscles), to move with speed (governed by the mass of the limb, or portion of the body moving), and to react quickly (dependent upon the type of stimuli reacted to) the speed of the nerve impulse, the complexity of the movement to be carried out, the state of the organism (fatigue, and the like). Within these capacity limitations, however, individual motor performance is extremely variable. Two men of similar physical make-up, having the same scores on strength tests and in other measures of physiological capacity, might vary markedly when asked to perform a complex motor skill. Our concern, therefore, is not in defining absolute limitations of movement, time, reaction time, or strength but of determining how performance potentials might be reached within these limitations. Basic to the achievement of performance is whether one may cultivate basic factors, which seem superior, to underlie a number of tasks or whether skill is highly specific.

General or Specific?

The answer to the question as to whether motor skill is task-specific or general in nature is complicated by several kinds of problems. (1) How are the two skills being compared—through correlation techniques; by looking at "clusters" within factorial studies; or by examining transfer (the effect of performing one task upon the performance of a second)? (2) Is heredity vs. environment or nature vs. nurture being equated with generality and specificity? (3) What efforts have been made to control such variables as learning and the relative dependence upon sensory information (*i.e.*, visual control) within the two compared tasks? (4) What is considered a motor skill; a simple arm-swing, involving reaction time and movement speed; or a complex act involving spatial accuracy?

Correlation as a Technique for Determining Generality or Specificity

One of the most direct methods of determining whether factors are common to two or more motor skills is to compare performances through correlation techniques. A correlation coefficient relates the order in which a group of individuals is ranked (from least to most proficient) in one task to their ranking in a second.

If an individual's score in shooting basketball free-throws may be predicted by knowing the accuracy with which he is able to throw a baseball, it might be said that a general "throwing for accuracy" factor underlies performance of the two skills. If no such prediction is possible, since the subjects seem to reshuffle the order in which they rank on the two tests, these may be considered specific measures of performance.

To interpret a correlation coefficient correctly, one must square it to determine the extent to which proficiency in one skill may contribute to the other. The final number achieved is in the form of a percentage of "common variance." Thus a correlation coefficient of $+.45$ between push-ups and sit-ups indicates that the ability to perform sit-ups probably contributes about 20 per cent ($.45^2$) to the ability to do push-ups. The word *probably* was used in the previous sentence insofar as a relationship, evidence in a correlation coefficient, may not indicate *causality*. Thus a logical examination of the two tasks, or groups of tasks, which are related statistically must be made in order that a valid conclusion can be reached concerning the actual relationship.

FACTOR ANALYSIS

When three or more scores have to be compared, experimenters frequently utilize factor analysis in order to determine what "basic" qualities underlie performance. While a detailed analysis of this technique is beyond the scope of this text, it will be attempted here to explain some of the basic assumptions which underlie this helpful mathematical tool.

Essentially a factor represents a "cluster" of test scores which intercorrelate highly with one another. If we have, for example, twelve tests and five correlate highly with one another, we have identified a single factor; if four or more of the test scores correlate with one another but not with any of the initial five, it may be said that a second factor has been identified.

In addition we may determine how predictive a single test score is of the total factor by obtaining a "factor loading." This loading is a number, in the form of a correlation coefficient, which represents the relationship between the total factor to one of its parts.

Some of the test scores of the twelve mentioned above may not correlate with any other score, and thus represents specific abilities, unrelated to other attributes which are common to the other tests in the battery. The practical outcomes of factor analysis may include the identification of common factors which may then be incorporated into a testing or training program. Similarly if a number of tests are being given to a population which purportedly evaluate different attributes, application of a factor analysis may reveal that fewer tests may be utilized as indeed there may be a marked overlapping between the qualities evaluated on the tests. Initial exploratory studies in relatively unresearched areas are best accomplished by simply obtaining numerous measures and then ascertaining which seem to "cluster." This saving of time and effort in many testing and research programs is a helpful outcome of this statistical method.

It must be kept in mind, however, that the value of factor analysis is not intrinsic to the method but depends upon the insight and interpretative abilities of the individual utilizing the technique. The experimenter, for example, using his subjective judgment, selects items originally for inclusion in his battery; after the computer helpfully arranges his scores in clusters he must, using his best insight, name the factors which appear, utilizing his knowledge about what *seems* to be common basic attributes underlying the performance of the related tasks. In addition the type of factorial analytic technique selected by the investigator influences the nature of the clusters obtained.

The reader is directed to texts by Fruchter,[331] and Harmon[417] to obtain a detailed account of various factorial techniques.

Trends in the Research

Research delving into the specificity vs. general question has evidenced the following trends during the past sixty years. Initially the earlier, more subjective investigations carried out during the early part of the 1900's indicated that various general performance characteristics *do exist.* The research by Downey and Allport[19,255] previously discussed, as well as a study by Garfiel,[344] are examples. During the 1930's, as intelligence testing was separated from motor skills evaluation and as more objective performance measures were developed, research indicating the specific nature of motor skill was published. Investigations by Perrin,[724] Seashore[796] and others during this period substantiated the independent nature of skilled performance.

In the late 1950's and 1960's Franklin Henry and his colleagues[443,446] demonstrated that tasks involving movement, speed, reaction time, and strength seem largely based upon factors unique to the movement. Although at times their concept of a coordinated movement seemed somewhat narrow and appeared to exclude tasks emphasizing spatial accuracy, these findings have generally served to shake the traditional concept of "general coordination" formerly espoused by physical educators as underlying a number of sports activities. That some individuals seemed to be "well coordinated" was explained in several ways: (1) They were able to perform well since they possessed a number of specific performance qualities. (2) They frequently placed themselves in a position, or the culture encouraged them, to practice a number of activities. Their success was but the result of extensive practice. (3) Their general personality resulted in a need for success or approval in motor skills, so they were motivated to work hard to improve performance in a number of tasks (the relationship between "need for social approval" and performance measures has been previously discussed).

The specificity concept has been crystallized recently by Karl Smith in *Neurogeometric Theory of Motion.*[831] It is hypothesized that there are several specific types of neurons in the brain (termed "neurological recorders") which are sensitive to different patterns of stimulation and motion. Smith theorizes that these neuron systems are differentiated at three levels to integrate independently the component movements of posture (movement of the body through space), of body transport (limb movements), and of manipulation (hand-finger movements). The specificity of skilled movements, it is explained, is caused by the refinement of neurological functioning at these three levels.

The Search for General Factors

Researchers concerned with human factors problems, using visual tracking tasks, have recently demonstrated that psychomotor performance is predictable upon controlling practice variables. It has been particularly emphasized that final skill levels, having a fewer number of factors which contribute to performance, are more highly correlated with other tasks. Thus, as practice occurs, it is suggested motor skill[85] becomes more general in nature, echoing the findings of Hollingworth in 1913.[463]

Factorial Studies. Researchers, however, have continued over the years to search for *general factors* which seem to underlie the performance of more than one task. They seem interested in constructing a framework in which skilled performance may be considered rather than merely dismissing motor skill as specific. Independent "clusters" of correlations in studies by McCloy[629] and Jones[500] studying gross motor skills and by Fleishman and his colleagues[311,314] using both fine and gross tasks indicate that it is possible to isolate basic, although independent, factors contributing to the performance of various types of motor tasks. McCloy, following a survey of studies concerned with this question, concluded that 10 factors contributed to the performance of gross motor skills. These were listed as:

1. Strength
2. Dynamic strength or energy
3. Ability to change direction

4. Flexibility
5. Agility
6. Peripheral vision
7. Good vision
8. Concentration
9. Understanding the mechanics of movements
10. Absence of disturbing emotional complications

Guilford[400] evolved a matrix of factors in 1958, upon reviewing the work of McCloy, Fleishman, and others, by which psychomotor ability may be classified. The independent "clusters" of abilities, previously noted, are apparent upon inspection of Table 1. Broad areas seem to consist of the accurate utilization of space, the maximum and immediate use of force and balance, and the ability to move rapidly. The independence of these "clusters" is revealed when it is noted that many are present only in the functioning of specific parts of the body.

Table 1. Matrix of the Psychomotor Factors, with Columns for Kinds of Abilities, and Rows for Parts of the Body *

	Strength	Impulsion	Speed	Static Precision	Dynamic Precision	Coordination	Flexibility
Gross Body	General Strength	General Reaction Time		Static Balance	Dynamic Precision	Gross Body Coordination	Flexibility
Trunk	Trunk Strength						Trunk Flexibility
Limbs	Limb Strength	Limb Thrust	Arm Speed	Steadiness	Aiming		Leg Flexibility
Hand-Finger		Finger Tapping Speed		Hand Aiming	Finger and Hand Dexterity		

* From Guilford, J. P., A System of Psychomotor Abilities, *American Journal of Psychology*, *71*, 164–174, 1958.

Recent Factorial Studies. In recent years investigations of the factors of motor performance have become more substantial. These studies constitute an important contribution to the literature for three major reasons: (1) A large number of subjects have been used, in some cases from 500 to 700 individuals have participated in the testing programs. (2) A larger variety of skill and capacity tests have been included in these batteries of tests. (3) A more careful selection of these skills has been made to include tasks evaluating a wide variety of performance traits. These recent investigations fall within two major areas: those investigating the components of manual dexterity and studies concerned with the analysis of gross motor skill and capacity.

Components of Manual Skill. In one of a series of studies concerned with manual skill Fleishman and Ellison[307] produced findings which further point to the specificity of motor performance. Using 760 subjects and 22 tests of manual dexterity including paper-and-pencil tests and apparatus tasks, five primary factors were isolated.

(1) The initial factor identified was termed *Wrist-Finger speed,* and was evaluated through the use of paper-and-pencil tests which involved tapping speed independent of accuracy.

(2) A second factor was termed *Finger-Dexterity,* and has been repeatedly identified in factorial studies of manual skill. Tests which evaluate the rate and accuracy of the manipulation of small objects by the fingers delineate this performance quality.

(3) *Speed-of-Arm Movement* was a third factor identified, and as we shall see later (p. 222) is perhaps only a component of a larger factor termed *Speed-of-Limb Movement.* This factor was identified through the application of various arm-aiming tasks, involving an accuracy component.

(4) *Manual-Dexterity* was identified by tasks which involved rapid and precise hand-and-finger movements, as opposed only to finger movements.

(5) The fifth component of manual skill identified by Fleishman and Ellison was termed *Aiming,* and involved hand-eye coordination, and appeared most clearly when the aiming required great precision; *i.e.* attempting to place a pointer in a small circle.

It is thus apparent that manual skill of adults involves several kinds of qualities. The influence of findings of this type has been to expand the kinds of tasks included in batteries to screen the selection of industrial employees.

Components of Gross Action Patterns, Recent Factorial Studies. Although the initial studies reviewed identified a general gross coordination factor involving the integration of arm and leg movements, more recent investigations using a broader range of tasks and larger number of subjects have further dissected such apparently "pure" qualities as strength, flexibility, balance and the like. In one of the most recent and comprehensive of these, Fleishman, Thomas and Monroe[314] used 30 tests of gross motor ability. Six Primary factors were identified.

(1) *Speed-of-Change-of-Direction,* was the initial factor isolated. It was evaluated by tests which included the quick propulsion of the total body in running tasks, and is related to the ability to quickly mobilize energy.

(2) *Gross body equilibrium* was a second factor identified. It was seen in the performance of various static and dynamic balance tests, and is evaluated by the length of time an individual can balance on an edge of a balance beam, as well as the proficiency with which an individual can walk a narrow beam (dynamic balance).

(3) A separate balance factor termed *Balance With Visual Cues* was isolated, and was apparent in tests of static balance, performed with the eyes open.

(4) A fourth quality was termed *Dynamic Flexibility,* and involved the ability to quickly execute repeated trunk and/or limb movements. The tasks involved speed in the movements through a wide range of motion.

(5) In contrast to the fourth quality the fifth factor identified was termed *Extent Flexibility,* and was evaluated by tasks requiring the demonstration of range of motion of the back and trunk in slower stretching movements.

(6) A performance quality identified was called *Speed-of-Limb Movement,* although it was originally hypothesized that arm and leg speed were separate components of performance. Tasks involving both leg speed (*i.e.* foot tapping) and arm speed (via number of arm circles within a time period) clustered to form this fifth performance quality.

Components of Muscular Force: Strength. Another factorial study[311] has further fractionalized strength. Thirty carefully selected strength-endurance, flexibility tasks were employed, and 201 subjects performed them. It has been suggested earlier (p. 220) that strength lies within three broad areas (dynamic, explosive and static). This investigation hypothesized that in these general areas might lie some more specific kinds of "strengths." Specifically the role of endurance in strength tests was also investigated; as was the possibility that strength was specific to various muscle groups (*i.e.* flexor versus extensor strength). It was finally purposed to discover tests which provided the best assessments of various strength qualities. Seven factors were identified.

(a) *Dynamic Strength;* evaluated by chin-ups and push-ups to limits, and in time periods (fifteen seconds), dips on the parallel bars and similar tests of arm strength. As the best measures involved arm support tasks, as might be expected, height and weight were negatively correlated to performance in these kinds of measures.

(b) Factor two was named *Static Strength,* and has repeatedly been identified in strength studies: It is evaluated by tasks in which force is exerted against immobile object. This factor seems rather general and involved muscle groups in the hand, arm, back shoulder and legs; and was common to both flexors and extensor muscle groups.

(c) *Explosive Strength* was the third component of muscular force. This factor emphasized the ability to expend a maximum of energy in one explosive act and was measured by tasks which extended to both the arm and shoulder regions (softball throw, as well as the vertical jump).

(d) The fourth factor was termed *Trunk Strength,* and involved primarily tasks evaluating abdominal strength.

(e) The fifth factor involved the ability to handle and manipulate weights with both the arms and feet. Tests measuring the number of pulls or pushes within a short time period (usually twenty seconds) evaluated this quality. It was termed *Weight Balance.*

(f) A questionnaire was administered to the subjects polling their athletic experience, and a scoring system was applied to the amount and type of experience they reported. Relating this score to their performance scores resulted in the identification of two sub-factors which taken together were termed "Athletic Experience;—General." This previous experience in athletics, however, seemed divisible into two components, involving two patterns of participation: (one involving football-basketball-track, and the second a basketball-baseball combination).

Practice as Effecting Generality. Two early studies searched for general factors which might emerge as the result of *practice.* Hollingworth[463] in 1913 found that as motor skills were practiced positive correlations increased: from 0 to +.28 at the 5th trial, to +.32 by the 25th, to +.39 by the 80th, and to +.49 by the 205th. The tasks included those evaluating complex coordination, tapping, and various discrimination problems. Hollingworth concluded that a "true sampling of ability" emerged as learning progressed. It was hypothesized that other variables, such as momentary attitude, motivation, and initial methods used, became less important as task practice is continued

In 1943, Buxton and Humphries[136] also attempted to ascertain the effect of practice upon generality of motor skill and arrived at findings disagreeing with those of Hollingworth. Nine cycles of tests, in which pursuit rotor and other fine motor skills among other tasks were used covering a three-hour period produced a drop in positive correlations, from +.25 to +.16. It should be noted that in this latter study only nine trials were allowed in each task, while Hollingworth's subjects participated in over 200 trials.

Within recent years, research using various tracking tasks confirms the findings of Hollingworth. It was found that correlations between scores on the same task increase as practice prior to the first score is continued. It has thus been suggested that the factorial structure of visual-motor tasks becomes simpler as learning progresses. It has therefore been hypothesized that, due to the multiplicity of factors present during the early stages of learning, relationship between the early trials of two tasks could be expected to be low, while, when trials in two tasks are compared after considerable learning has transpired, more inter-task generality can usually be demonstrated. Jones,[500] among others, suggests that with increasing practice, pre-experimental experience exerts a decreasing influence performance. Adams,[8] in research for the Air Force, obtained higher inter-task correlations between final than between initial trials and also found that final performance level can be better predicted by extra-task measures than by intra-task measures.

Fleishman[310] published a study relating predictability of motor performance as related to the stage of learning. His findings imply that although at times relative predictability may change as the task is learned, the same task factors are probably present throughout the learning process;

they change only in percentage of involvement. Some abilities were shown to increase in importance, while others were demonstrated to decrease as learning progressed in various hand-eye-feet coordination tasks. Thus whether generality or specificity is demonstrated during the learning stages of various tasks probably depends upon the ingenuity of the researcher in devising tests which will best correlate to the factors which are of paramount importance during the stage in the learning process under consideration.

Generality of Skill as a Function of Intellect. It has sometimes been assumed that the younger the child or the lower the intelligence of the individual tested, the higher will be the intercorrelations obtained.[209] Recent research suggests that indeed this is true. In an investigation of six perceptual-motor qualities using trainable as well as educable retardates as subjects, it was found that the children less well endowed intellectually (the trainable retardates with I.Q.'s from "untestable" to about 40) achieved scores which when correlated averaged +.52, while the educable retardates (I.Q.'s of about 70) achieved scores whose average intercorrelation was only +.32.

Thus it would seem that with increased intelligence comes the increased ability to profit from a variety of specific experiences. The youngster or adult who is retarded, on the other hand, will give less evidence of specificity of functioning, as indeed they have been unable to profit from the variety of past experiences to which they have been exposed.

A General Factor of Spatial Accuracy? The results of two other studies seem to suggest the existence of a spatial factor contributing to the performance of certain types of skilled performances. In an investigation carried out in 1943 by Patricia Woodward[980] it was found that practice in one industrial task aided the performance of a second when the movement patterns in both were similar. Cratty[204] in a more recent study found a spatial factor present in the performances of tasks in various sizes of mazes. These findings seriously strain the neurogeometric theory of motion and question the findings of studies which point to the independence of fine and gross motor skill.

Heredity vs. Environment. The traditional question concerning the importance of heredity vs. environment is also important to the discussion of specific vs. general factors in motor performance. One could assume that general factors are dependent upon constitutional factors, while specific factors depend upon the opportunities an individual has had to explore his environment. A study by Goodenough and Smart,[383] indicating that more general factors are present when children's motor performance scores are compared, as well as investigations revealing the same phenomenon when performance scores of the feeble-minded are compared, add substance to such a position. Studies of Co-Twin Control summarized by Gesell,[351] reviewed in some detail in Chapter 7, on Maturation, further suggest that basic motor activities involve inherent capacities.

In a study completed by Cratty,[188] moderately high correlations were obtained between father and son performance in the 100 yard dash (+.49) and the broad jump (+.80), obtained from measures taken at the same time of life and on the same facilities. Although such relationships may result from opportunities the father afforded his son to run and to jump, no significant correlations were found between father and son scores in more complex gross body skills (bar vaulting and ball throwing). Recent studies by Smith and his colleagues[831] indicate that improvement of movement speed seems to resist practice, while manipulative ability (as part of the same complex task) showed marked improvement under the same conditions. Taken together, one might hypothesize that the locomotor speed and efficiency may be a basic inherent factor, while accurate and complex movements of the upper limbs are more dependent upon experience. However, further research is needed to explore this supposition.

The Specificity of Movement Time, Reaction Time, and Strength. Within recent years there has been proliferation of studies demonstrating that movement time, reaction time, and strength are largely independent and are combined in specific parameters to produce a simple, direct movement. Examination of the underlying peripheral structure controlling motor output, the *motor-unit*, which is discussed in Chapter 11, demonstrates the anatomical possibility of such specificity.

Neuromotor specificity has been demonstrated in the time honored measure of grip strength. Henry and Smith[445] presented findings which pointed out that individual differences in strength were 54 per cent specific to the hand tested, while a general hand strength accounted for only 46 per cent of grip pressure.

In a series of studies, Henry, Whitley, Smith, and Lotter[446,445,443] have demonstrated the independence of strength and maximum arm speed. In addition, limb speed and limb reaction (time taken to initiate the movement after the stimulus is given) were demonstrated as largely independent. Arm mass and speed of movement were also found to be independent phenomenon. Nelson and Fahrney[694] on the other hand obtained moderate to high relationships between measures of strength and movement speed. In this latter study angular velocity was measured in an elbow flexion movement, while in the studies by Henry and his colleagues the movement speed measure was usually elicited by a movement which combined angular and linear velocities of the limbs. Helen Eckert[271] also found moderate correlations between speed of limb movement and strength when linear velocity was employed as the measure of speed.

While working in this program, Henry, upon finding that response time increased when more complicated movements were to be initiated, suggested that a "Memory Drum" theory might explain the basics of neuromotor reaction.[442] It was proposed that an unconscious mechanism channels stored information to the appropriate neuromotor coordination center, thus causing the desired movement. The lengthened reaction time prior to a complex movement may, therefore, be explained by the increased time necessary for the more diverse pattern of impulses to manifest itself.

The contribution of these researchers has been important in the understanding of rather direct motor acts. Their terminology might be criticized, however, since they generalize findings obtained from simple movement speed experiments to explain "the high specificity of neuromotor *coordination skills*."[446] In one frame of reference, coordination seems to imply the monitoring of neural impulses involved in muscular contraction controlling a rather direct simple movement (*e.g.*, a horizontal arm swing). In another context, "coordination" might be construed as a series of movements of varying speeds and force combining into a motor act of a more complex nature. Basically, the question seems to be whether coordination implies internal integrations of the nervous system to produce finite variations in a simple act or whether it means complex outward manifestations of movement. The studies of Henry *et al.* seem to imply that the former definition is the more acceptable. However, acceptance of the latter meaning of coordination indicates a broader outlook rather than rejection of processes underlying the former.

A Four-Part Theory

Fitts,[298] a pioneer researcher in the area of human factors, has identified general capacities of movement which were found typical of individuals performing a variety of perceptual-motor tasks. Among the qualities considered were amount of information assimilated, facility in dispelling psychological interference ("noise"), channel capacity (ability to receive information and to organize it), and rate of movement. He concluded that:

> The performance capacity of the human motor system plus its associated visual and proprioceptive feedback mechanisms, when measured in information units is relatively constant over a considerable range of task conditions, reflecting a fixed capacity for monitoring the results of on-going motor activity, while at the same time maintaining the necessary degree of organization with respect to magnitude and timing of successive movements.[298]

Consideration of the information contained in the previous chapters leads to the conclusion that a four-part theory of perceptual-motor behavior is tenable. Underlying performance of movement tasks are several levels of general abilities, which although somewhat independent nevertheless explain the individual consistencies and differences in performance exhibited.

The argument concerning the specificity versus generality of skill permeates the contents of the text, appearing not only in this chapter but in the discussion of the transfer of training, of motor educability, and in the sections dealing with anxiety and motivation. In general, the major conflict arises when skills are measured and compared, as contrasted to the observation that some individuals seem generally "coordinated" and are apparently able to perform and to learn well a variety of perceptual-motor activities.

Arguments concerning the generality and specificity of behavior have their genesis in literature dealing with the human intellect. Spearman[845] around the turn of the century, and later Thurstone,[886] Guilford,[400] and others suggested that cognitive behavior is highly specific and could be fractionalized into several parts. The research previously described by Fleishman[312] and Seashore[796] also gives further impetus to the supposition that perceptual-motor functioning is highly specific.

The following theoretical model attempts to explain perceptual-motor performance in both general and specific terms. Spearman[845] for example, spoke both of a "g" (general) factor and an "s" (specific) factor in intelligence, while Kelley,[517] Burt,[135] Eysenck,[289] and Vernon[910] share the opinion that human behavior is molded by a general or universal factor in addition to a hierarchy of second-level factors.

The theory presented here assumes that variables of four kinds influence performance output. At the basic level are what have been termed Behavioral Supports[196] and include general aspiration level, state of arousal, ability to analyze a task, typical amount of muscular tension present, as well as the individual's need for and susceptibility to social stimulation. These basic *supports* are believed to influence a variety of human behaviors in addition to perceptual-motor performance, including verbal and cognitive abilities.

The second part consists of two types of attributes—personal equations of movement, described in detail in Chapter 12, and ability traits described in this chapter. Generally these two types of attributes interact in the formation of performance. Personal equations in movement are more influential of motor behavior when the situation is unstructured, and maximum performance is not called for. On the other hand, ability traits are more closely related to performance when optimum effort is expended. The ability traits within this part change as sustained performance is engaged in, influencing perceptual-motor behavior in a direct way, and do not exert the comprehensive effects upon other categories of human behavior as do the *general supports* mentioned previously.

In the uppermost part are components of the performance situation which result in marked skill specificity seen in the various experimental studies cited. Such variables as the social stimulation within the performance situation, instructions (or lack of them) accompanying task performance, the unique spatial and force requirements of the task at hand, as well as the performer's past experience in the same and in similar tasks, are placed here.

16

The importance of the various parts may change as a function of age and intelligence. Younger children, for example, are probably influenced more by the basic behavioral supports than are older children and adolescents. The retarded, perhaps unable to profit from specific past experiences to any degree, also may exhibit perceptual-motor functioning which is more highly dependent upon the basic behavioral supports than upon unique performance characteristics of the task and situation.

Several types of investigations suggest themselves upon inspection of this theoretical structure. For example, the generality and specificity of human skill may depend upon the extent to which vision is incorporated into the task's performance. The generality or specificity of aspiration level of situational anxiety, and of persistence in the performance of tasks, needs further clarification. Particular emphasis should be placed in future studies upon the importance of various perceptual factors important to the performance and the learning of motor skills.

FOUR-PART THEORY OF PERCEPTUAL-MOTOR PERFORMANCE

UNIQUE PERFORMANCE FACTORS

Specific Instructions
Force and Accuracy Components
of Task
Social Conditions Present
(etc.)

4

ABILITY TRAITS	*PERSONAL EQUATIONS*
Static Strength	Persistence
Dynamic Balance	Preferred speed, tempo
2 Agility	Space Used 3
Hand-Finger Speed	
(etc.)	(etc.)

BEHAVIORAL SUPPORTS

Aspiration	Social Needs
Tension	Analytical Ability
Arousal Level	(etc.)

1

SUMMARY

Ability is a basic facet of motor behavior which underlies a number of more complex skills. These traits emerge in a number of factorial studies which have been carried out over the past twenty years, and include those involving limb, hand, and total body movements. The extent to which these attributes are related seems to be a function of the amount of learning which has taken place, the sex and intellect of the performer, as well as the complexity of the task.

Variables of four types of influence the final performance output of an individual. Basic behavioral supports include general arousal level, residual muscular tension usually present, ability to analyze a task, and similar attributes. In addition to these, various personal equations or preferences involving movements interact to varying degrees with basic ability traits. Acts which are structured and in which all-out effort is expended are more closely related to basic ability traits which are measured under similar conditions; on the other hand, in unstructured tasks various personal equations emerge. The final classification of variables underlying an expression of motor ability are those unique to the task, the specific social conditions, the unique force, temporal and spatial characteristics of the task, the type of sensory feedback available, as well as the instructions given at the time the task is performed.

Student References

Books

1. FLEISHMAN, EDWIN A.:   *The Structure and Measurement of Physical Fitness.* Englewood Cliffs, N.J., Prentice-Hall, 1964.
2. WOODSON, WESLEY: *Human Engineering Guide for Equipment Design.* University of California Press, 1956.

Articles

1. FLEISHMAN, EDWIN A. and HEMPEL, WALTER E., JR.:   Factorial Analysis of Complex Psychomotor Performance and Related Skills. *J. Appl. Psych.,* 40, No. 2, 1956.
2. GUILFORD, J. P.:   A System of Psychomotor Abilities. *Am. J. Psych.,* 71, 164-174, 1958.
3. HENRY, FRANKLIN M.:   Increased Response Latency for Complicated Movements and a "Memory Drum" Theory of Neuromotor Reaction. *Res. Quart.,* 31, No. 3, October, 1960.

SECTION V

LEARNING

Chapter 15

Neurological and Biochemical Bases of Learning and Retention

SINCE early man began to have time to think, a considerable amount of his thoughts have been directed toward the attempt to understand thinking itself. Early Greek philosophers speculated that within the head lay wondrous mechanisms which aided man to imagine, to dream, and to ponder. With the gradually emerging dawn of the age of science these inexact speculations have been translated into both simple and complex experimental designs.

Luigi Galvani, discovering the nature of the electrical properties of neural transmission in the late 1700's, has been designated as the father of experimental neurology. Contemporary personages—Magoun,[612] Burès,[130] Paillard,[711] Olds,[978] Hebb,[732] Sperry,[847] Penfield,[722] and others—have further advanced knowledge about the central and peripheral nervous systems and their effects and controls upon human behavior.

These latter researchers have attempted to elucidate the apparent capacities of the human brain to carry out four major functions related to learning and retention. (1) *How* is experience recorded within the nervous system? (2) *Where* are memory traces stored? (3) *What* are the biochemical and anatomical mechanisms for this storage? (4) *How* are learned experiences "called up" and utilized when appropriate?

In recent years the search for the answers to these and related questions has more and more come to occupy the time of the biochemist, the neurologist, and the physiologist. At times the background of the experimenter has, of course, determined the avenue traveled. At other times a productive "wedding" has occurred between the various disciplines, and the result has been a deeper and more penetrating analysis of these problems.

The experimenters constructing these neurological and biochemical "models" to explain learning and/or memory have been beset with several momentous problems. The remarkable experiments of Wilder Penfield have suggested that humans seem a record within their nervous systems literally everything to which they have attended during their lifetime. Thus an individual by the age of twenty has somehow recorded (although not consciously remembered) literally billions of "bits" of information. When the surgical patients of Dr. Penfield had their speech areas stimulated electrically, they would report a kind of "double consciousness," and could vividly recall the details of experiences in their pasts. When the electrical stimulation was removed, the imagery would stop, and when it was re-applied, the "picture" of the past would continue without interruption to unfold.

However, Penfield's studies indicate that the individuals would only report components of the scene to which they paid attention at the time. The subjects did not recall particularly critical periods within their lifespan, but would relate everyday situations in which they had participated. Consideration of this evidence has led to speculations concerning the apparent need for memory storage by the human brain that range from about 30 billion memory storage units[913] to "only" about 50 billion units by other writers.[978]

Thus any theory of learning and retention has to present a sufficient number of structures and modifications of structures to contain the remarkable volume of information which is apparently absorbed by the human mind during a lifetime.

Individuals constructing neurological and biochemical models of learning and retention have attempted to deal with other problems of a similar magnitude. For example, there seem to be storage components within the mind involving memory of various durations. Man seems to be able to remember vividly events of the previous day, as opposed to occurrences of a week ago. At the same time one can recall some important events occurring many years in the past. These subjective experiences lead to several knotty questions, including the neurological and biochemical mechanisms which seem to implant certain "important" events and people within our nervous system, and the processes which result in a "blurring" of less vital events and situations.

Important questions related to the focus of this text revolve around whether there are differences in the memory storage characteristics of motor skills versus learning is dependent more upon thought than movement. If as some would have us believe, motor skills are more lastingly retained than are verbal materials, does movement somehow better impregnate the neural memory mechanisms than does simply thinking about or discussing a problem? Can one truly hypothesize a difference between motor learning and the learning requiring other kinds of behavior? Or, as some have suggested, at the neurological level are there no differences in learning? Or do the differences between motor learning and problem solving, the forming of associations, the selection and classification functions of the mind occur only at the periphery when the individual is engaged in some overt act to evidence the acquisition of a concept or a motor skill?

The answers to these and to other questions are not neatly spelled out in the experimental literature. The discussion which follows contains more questions than answers, but recent scientific evidence presents hopeful evidence of a more scholarly approach taken by theoreticians and experimenters to the problems outlined above. Essentially there have been no differences found at the neurological level between motor learning and any other kind of learning. At the same time these differences *may* exist. The learning of a motor skill is different from pure problem solving insofar as the nature of the input to induce retention has been different, and a movement or series of movements has accompanied the resultant learning. At the same time whatever is stored triggers series of movements which if practiced often enough seem to rely less and less upon conscious thought as they are performed. Further analyses of the biochemical and anatomical mechanisms which accompany the learning and re-practice of a motor skill thus probably will uncover several stages of mechanisms operative at different periods in the learning process; whereas events, problems, associations formed more independently of volitional movements probably may not evidence similar successive bio-neurological changes as they are remembered and reproduced.

Some of the models elaborated upon in the pages which follow are based upon examinations of the electrical processes within the nervous system, others are the result of biochemical analyses at the molecular or synaptic levels. Still others concentrate upon various anatomical structures and the manner in which the elusive "engram" is stored within brain tissue.* In any case, these models are primarily the result of theoretical speculations, rather than of direct evidence relating changes in measurable behavior of humans to biochemical and/or neurological changes within the nervous system. The best that can be said for them is that at the present time they seem to provide only tentative answers to the difficult questions raised by the learning theorists. Further progress will probably be forthcoming when students of behavior acquire extensive knowledge of biochemistry and neurology so that an amalgamation of the knowledge about external behavior and internal functioning will occur. Improved research methodology should also contribute to further knowledge, including more refined techniques to carry out chemical analysis of the intact and healthy human brain as the individual is confronted with various tasks, as well as the development of methods to examine the deeper lying electro-biochemical processes in the brain as they accompany various kinds of human behavior.

Four classifications of neuro-biochemical models for learning and retention may be identified. Both a molar and molecular model of neural functioning, and molar and molecular models of biochemical functioning have been presented by various authors. Molar models of neural functioning are concerned with more gross anatomical and electro-

---

*An engram is a term introduced into the literature in the 1920's to represent a memory storage unit. It has usually not been related directly to an anatomical structure.

physiological phenomena connected with learning, while the more molecular models delve into the location, retrieval, and disruption of discrete memory traces within the human and animal cortex.

A molar biochemical model of learning and retention is concerned with chemical changes occurring at the synaptic levels. The more molecular biochemical theories of learning and retention have focused upon finite changes in the components of nucleic acid and similar substances in the nervous system.

Furthermore, theories attempting to explain some of the internal processes accompanying learning and retention may be classified according to their dependence upon biochemical-anatomical concepts, or whether they focus upon electro-physiological processes within the central and peripheral nervous system. Theories of this nature are often based upon reasonably objective evidence due to the more sophisticated electro-monitoring equipment which has been recently made available to researchers. Several theoretical constructs revolving around the electrical properties of the brain are discussed in the pages which follow.

Molar Theories of Neural Functioning

Theories of learning and retention utilizing anatomical concepts suggest that accommodations within the brain to repeated stimuli and situations involve a functional integration of innumerable brain structures facilitated primarily by cortical activity. Paillard, for example, presents evidence that learning of motor skills is facilitated according to the extent to which the organism can break down previously established patterns.[711] Examples taken from experiments in which the innervation to reciprocally functioning muscle groups has been reversed are drawn upon to substantiate this hypothesis. These clinical studies indicate that the higher the organism resides on the phylogenic scale, the more able they will be in adjusting to differences from the normal innervation-muscle relationships. The rat, for example, will seldom be able to function adequately when this type of surgical incoordination has been induced; the monkey will make some slight adjustments; while the human being by inspecting and thinking about his attempts at motor re-education will be able to establish new patterns of movement between muscles and nerves previously unrelated.

Furthermore, such theories suggest that as learning occurs, decreased dependence upon a variety of neural structures is apparent. For example, as a motor act is acquired, there is less dependence upon and involvement of the visual centers of the brain as the individual does not continue to need to accompany movement with vision. Similarly, the speech centers become less involved in the total act as symbolic-verbal behavior becomes less important as learning occurs. Such evidence indicates that the capacity to learn motor skills relates closely to the extent to which connections between the higher and lower centers of the brain controlling motor functions are related. The direct influence of the cortico-spinal system as well as the indirect influence of the reticular activating system have been both looked upon as vertical integrators of the nervous system important in the acquisition of motor skills.

Modifications in more peripheral structures within the nervous system have also been considered as influential of learning. The contact surfaces at the synaptic junction were once considered facilitative of learning. It was hypothesized that the presentation of a more extensive surface permitted greater contact between neurons which in turn facilitated transmission of the impulse over the synapse during the acquisition of the learned act. Within recent years, however, more microscopic changes at the synapse are being accorded more careful scrutiny.

It has often been speculated upon that as an act is learned its mediation is progressively assumed by structures within the lower motor levels. Lashley's earlier data on this question, although far from conclusive, suggest that an acquired habit never becomes independent of the cortex. The refinement of feedback circuits, while making a well-learned skill seem almost reflex-like, in essence only seems to improve the delicate adjustment of the act in the latter stages of learning.[563]

A molar theory of neural functioning does not consider the nervous system as a simple tablet of wax which only needs to be impregnated. But rather the nervous system is described as a delicate balance of interactions of complex mechanisms and structures with learning, serving to bring the complexity into various functional relationships supportive of the final behavior desired. Thus improved functional interactions rather than finite molecular changes are emphasized within these theoretical frameworks.

Electrophysiology, Learning and Retention

Seemingly random and specific electric activity is synonymous with neural functioning. Even during the deepest sleep the human brain seems to function as a miniature electric motor and transformer. It is therefore not surprising that the nature of these electro-physiological processes have been explored as possible indices of learning and retention.

Lachman, for example, has recently evolved an "oscillation theory" of brain function to explain learning capacity.[550] This researcher suggests that the amplitude of the oscillations of various brain wave patterns are indicative of the flexibility with which an individual brain functions, and thus is related to the extent to which an individual can organize, interpret, and acquire new patterns of behavior. Learning will be facilitated, according to Lachman, to the extent to which the oscillations of a given individual's brain correspond to the complexity of the stimuli. It is hypothesized that the extent of these oscillations is evidence of the readiness of the brain to receive information.

It is hypothesized that complex patterns are recorded less readily than are simple ones. However, if a complex pattern is somehow congruent with what Lachman calls "optimal brain recording points" they will be more easily received. Furthermore, it is assumed that the greater the variability of brain activity level, the more effective the learning.

Lachman states that the best indices of "brain readiness" or receptivity is a figure obtained from subtracting the lowest percentage of the alpha rate from the highest percentage, *i.e.* the alpha wave variation. This figure, it was found, correlates well with rote memory scores.

Russell also alludes to the presence of electrical activity in the brain when attempting to explain reminiscence—the tendency to learn even though no practice is engaged in. According to Russell, patterns laid down faintly within the brain after brief practice result in pathways through which the random and ever-present electric activity will naturally flow with little resistance. With increased rest, these trace pathways will thus become strengthened and will result in better performance when the individual re-performs the act.[773]

Several experimenters have studied, with some success, the extent to which a "memory trace" becomes ingrained within the nervous system by attempting to disrupt this integration at various periods after practice has been discontinued. Most of these experiments have been carried out with animals, but others have ascertained the extent to which electro-shock therapy has obliterated learning in humans.

Electric stimuli introduced cortically in humans and in animals have been studied as influential of various stages of retention, as well as being used to ascertain the location of various memory traces within the cortex. Generally, it is found that this kind of electric impingement upon the nervous system obliterates most of a skilled act if administered directly after the act has been practiced. If a delay is permitted after learning and prior to the electric shock, less impediment to retention will be evidenced. Thus if the memory trace is given time to become ingrained into the nervous system, it seems to be less resistant to destruction by an externally applied electric stimuli.

Typical of the research on this subject is the recent investigation by Weissman, who found that a shock administered to rats resulted in amnesia only when given within forty minutes or less after learning.[940] This tendency to consolidation of the memory trace in animals was originally hypothesized by Heriot and Coleman.[447] Experiments on humans corroborate this "consolidation" theory.

Experiments in which both animals and humans have taken part attest to the presence of a three-stage memory mechanism: a short-term, medium-term, and long-term memory storage capacity. Electro-shock administered a few minutes after learning will tend to obliterate more of the learned response than shock after a wait of thirty minutes. Similarly, if the electro-shock is administered more than an hour after some learned response has been acquired, little disruption in retention will be elicited.

Some have criticized these kinds of experiments on the grounds that the electro-shock simply results in a general trauma and avoidance by the animals, rather than in the disruption of specific memory traces for a given act. However, carefully controlled experiments by King and others have indicated that consolidation of memory and experimental disruption can occur independent of fear and competing responses elicited by electric shock itself.[528]

Experiments of this kind have also confirmed the frequent observation that the middle years of life are those in which learning is more likely to take place, and in which new skills are acquired with least effort. Doty and Doty found that memory consolidation takes longer among animal subjects of extreme ages (*i.e.* rats under thirty days old, and over six hundred days old). Massed practice, as well as various electro-shock and chemical inhibitors, delayed memory consolidation in the young and old animals, while animals intermediate in age were significantly less affected by the various noxious stimuli applied directly to the brain.[253]

In human retention Eysenck and others have hypothesized that there are two stages in the consolidation of the memory trace termed *primary consolidation* and *secondary consolidation*. During the former stage, retention is susceptible to retrograde amnesia in humans, to loss due to electro-shock, and also to a traumatic brain injury. After the second stage is reached, *secondary consolidation*, the learned acts tend to be protected against these kinds of traumatic influences. It has been suggested that both stages probably go on simultaneously with primary consolidation lasting a matter of minutes immediately after learning, while secondary consolidation takes place over a longer period of time.[288]

The Location of the Memory Trace

Experiments with electro-shock as well as Sperry's classic "split-brain" studies have attempted to ascertain the location of the storage areas for various types of memory traces.[847] For example, in studies by Zamora and Kaelbling,[989] as well as in those by Gottlieb and Wilson,[389] it was found that only when electro-shock was administered to the dominant cerebral hemisphere was verbal recall affected (the left hemisphere in right-handed subjects). More difficulty was noted in the obliteration of memory traces via electro-shock to the left hemisphere, in the latter experiment, when individuals of mixed dominance were involved as subjects. In general, such investigations indicate that the more electro-shock administered, the more the resultant memory loss, thus indicating that quantitative aspects of the trauma influence memory and retention in rather direct ways.

Sperry produced findings which indicate that the memory of visual discrimination tasks seems to be duplicated in both hemispheres almost immediately after the learning has taken place. He sectioned the cortices of both cats and primates so that the corpus callosum was divided. This procedure done immediately after learning produced no effects upon learning, after the animals had been exposed to a discrimination problem. However, if the animals' brains had been split prior to learning, they functioned almost as separate animals (*i.e.* what had been learned with one eye, in the split-brain animals, was not learned by the other covered eye as it was later exposed to the tasks).[847]

In further elaboration of this approach and by utilization of drugs to depress one of the hemispheres in animals, Burés[131] and his co-workers produced competing reactions in either hemisphere. For example, with the activity in one hemisphere depressed, the animals might be taught to avoid a box, and when the depressant had worn off in the initial half of the brain, the second would be anesthetized and a competing response would be learned (*i.e.* to approach the box). The implications of these experiments are too global for a thorough review here, but in general they provide ingenious means for investigating primary integration of memory traces, the manner in which memory traces compete, add, subtract, or otherwise interfere with one another.

Although initially the whole neuron was looked upon as a possible candidate for memory storage at the molecular level, within recent years other structures have been hypothesized as possibly aiding in this critical function of the nervous system. Indeed the vast amount of input feeding into the nervous system during a lifetime makes it apparent that there are probably not enough single neurons available for this extensive classification and storage job.

Classical neurological doctrine attributed only a housekeeping function to the glial cells which compose about 75 per cent of the bulk of the brain. These cells tightly packed between the neurons, and having about a 10:1 ratio to them are believed to participate in memory storage.[482] Findings that the neuron to glial ratio is greater during the middle years of life further substantiate this contention.[481]

It has been hypothesized that the glial cells, which lie within a millionth of an inch from the bodies and dendrites of the neurons store information by modifying the specifics of electric conductivity to local spots on the neurons, thus further modifying dendritic currents. This arrangement permits storage capacity within the brain much greater than theories holding that a single neuron is responsible for the storage of a single "bit" of information.

The findings of these investigations raise more questions than answers. However, it is clear from the results that human retention is dependent upon traces of the activity residing somewhere in the cortex, which becomes deeply ingrained and resistant to forgetfulness after a period of time has passed. Furthermore, these studies indicate that verbal memory seems to reside primarily in one of the two hemispheres—the dominant hemisphere—whereas the memory for other kinds of problems may be duplicated in the two sides of the brain.

In addition these findings point to the detrimental influences of cerebral stresses upon human retention, and included in these stressors are not only drugs and electro-shock, but massed practice! The presence of memory storages of short, medium and long duration are also substantiated by these ingenious experiments.

Biochemical Mechanisms for Learning and Retention

Within the past ten years increasing attention has been devoted to the molecular mechanisms influencing learning and retention in humans and animals. These more refined intraorganismic theories and experiments have stemmed from the previously cited investigations of retrograde amnesia, controlled electro-conclusive shock experiments, and research concerned with more molar aspects of synaptic functioning.

Initially experimenters considered the fact that a calcium increase at the synapse seemed to influence learning. Later, when it was found that neuronal activity increased the amount of RNA (ribonucleic acid) at the synapse, attention was turned toward various components of nucleic acid as a possible explanation of learning and retention.

Both DNA (deoxyribonucleic acid) and RNA are found in great abundance within the nervous system and at the same time their structure is complex enough to explain the numerous vicissitudes of human learning. For example, a single DNA molecule consists of thousands of units (about 40,000), and there are about 800,000 DNA molecules in humans. It has been estimated that there is enough DNA in a single cell body to encode about 1,000 books.[339] DNA is found in the cell nucleus, and RNA is in both the nucleus and cytoplasm. In nerve cells about 90 per cent of the RNA is in the soma of the cell and about 10 per cent in the dendrites.

Theoretical statements have been advanced within recent years to explain both learning and retention by reference to these components of nucleic acid. For example, it has been suggested by the Belgian chemist Hyden that a nerve cell responds differently, depending on whether a different new RNA molecule is shaped, which in turn shapes a protein molecule which then reacts with a complementary molecule causing the triggering of an inhibitory or excitatory substance across a synapse. If the impulse is familiar, protein molecules will already be present which will dissociate rapidly, thus a more rapid response will be forthcoming. Each cell may perpetuate a large number of unique patterns of RNA and protein. A giant RNA molecule may accommodate along its length to many different sequences shaped by different impulse patterns that have coursed through its neuron.[554] Acceptance of such a theory does not require strict localization of brain function, since a single RNA molecule can be a link in many neuronal networks.

Learning, it has been further hypothesized, occurs when a transfer occurs in the RNA from the surrounding glial cells into conducting neurons and the subsequent transfer of protein synthesizing apparatus of the neuron. Similarly, retention has been explained as occurring when a neural membrane can become tuned by alteration of its protein structure. Indeed both functions can occur at the same time.[554]

Developmental changes in animals and humans support the importance of RNA and DNA to the learning process. As would be expected, there is an increase with age in the ratio of glial cells to neurons.[339] Similarly, the presence of RNA in the motor nerve cells increases from the third year of age to the fortieth year of age, remaining constant until about the age of sixty, after which it declines sharply.

Since the early 1960's intravenous and oral doses of RNA and DNA have been administered to humans in attempts to improve learning and retention. Cameron[137] reported an experiment in which the aged and the senile were injected with RNA, with the result that their memory was improved. These researchers, while suggesting that RNA is essential for operation of memory, also pointed out that the evidence they presented was far from conclusive.

There is little direct evidence that these findings are as clear-cut as they seem. For example, Gaito has pointed out that DNA may be too stable a molecule to function as suggested, while RNA may be too unstable a molecule. In addition, there is little experimental evidence directly linking the production and presence of RNA and DNA to specific changes in human behavior caused by practice. It is uncertain whether RNA and DNA participate in learning and retention in direct ways, or simply serve as stimulants or nutrients to the nervous system, thus facilitating the general receptivity of the neural structures in an indirect way.

Ignoring the possible inadequacies of these molecular theories of learning and retention, several experimenters within recent years have attempted to elicit transfer of training by the injection of refined and unrefined biochemical extracts from one trained animal to another untrained one. Initially, these experiments carried out by McConnel and his colleagues involved the feeding of flatworms which had been trained to respond to simple light cues to flatworms which had not been trained in this manner. The positive transfer which was seen to occur prompted other more refined experiments involving rats in which RNA was extracted from the cortex of trained animals and injected intra-peritoneally into untrained rats. Rats trained to respond, via food rewards to both clicks and lights, were found to transfer their training somehow to their untrained compatriots via the injections described.[487]

Jacobson and his colleagues at the University of California at Los Angeles have apparently succeeded in eliciting intra-species transfer of this nature via injections from hamsters to rats. Additionally more elaborate controls enabled the experimenters to determine in more detail the specificity of the transfer effects elicited from these kinds of experimental conditions.[486]

While Jacobson's findings are provocative, other experimenters have had problems replicating them.[387] In addition, it is difficult to determine how RNA injected into the peritoneum would reach the brain of the animal with biochemical obstacles in the form of the "blood-brain barrier" interposed. In general, the questions such experimental findings pose include elucidating the biochemical mechanisms involved, outlining the extent to which the transfer effects are specific or general, and describing what behavior arrangements and biochemical agents are important in obtaining the transfer effects.[338]

The veracity of these experiments can only be verified after further attempts are made at their replication, and with additional refinements in their experimental methodologies are carried out including more rigorous controls. In any case, they indicate that learning may someday be improved with the injection of certain biochemical substances. While it would be several years before such chemical agents are available in experiments involving human learning, the fascinating possibilities for the improvement of motor performance and learning are apparent.

Although it is apparent that physical educators cannot observe the biochemical concomitants of learning and retention, it is equally apparent that no component of human behavior is without its neurological and biochemical bases. Understanding the concepts presented above should result in a more thorough understanding of learning and retention expressed in behavioral terms.

SUMMARY

Biochemical and neurological theories of learning and retention may be concerned with either gross or finite changes within the nervous system. These theoretical models attempt to explain how information is obtained, stored, remembered, and brought to recall when appropriate.

The various neuroanatomical theories of learning and retention have recently focused upon the glial cells as possible repositories of information. The more molar neural theories, on the other hand, have been intent upon explaining learning and retention by reference to the interaction of larger neural structures. Other theories have attempted to explain learning and retention by reference to structural changes at the synaptic level, or by reference to various electro-physiological changes which seem to parallel the acquisition and recall of information and skills.

Student References

Books

1. Eiduson, Samuel, Eiduson, B. T., Geller, Edward, and Yuwiler, Arthur: *Biochemistry and Behavior,* Princeton, N. J., Van Nostrand Publishers, 1964.
2. Magoun, H. W.: *The Waking Brain,* Springfield, Charles C Thomas, 1958.
3. Woolridge, Dean E.: *The Machinery of the Brain,* New York, McGraw-Hill Book Co., 1963.

17

Articles

1. JACOBSON, A. L., FRIED, C., and HOROWITZ, S. D.: "Planarians and Memory: I. Transfer of Learning by Injection of Ribonucleic Acid," *Nature, 209*:599-601, 1966.
2. LUTTGES, M., JOHNSON, T., BUCK, C., HOLLAND, J., and McGAUGH, J.: "An Examination of 'Transfer of Learning' by Nucleic Acid," *Science, 151*:834-837, 1966.

Chapter 16

Perceptual-Motor Learning, Based Upon Performance Measures

Learning is defined as *the rather permanent change in behavior brought about through practice.* Based upon this explanation, *motor learning* may be termed as a *stable change in the level of skill as the result of repeated trials.*

It was also explained that *learning* might be considered the *potential to perform,* and reference was made to motivation as one variable which sometimes invalidates the assessment of learning solely as depicted by performance changes. The findings of recent studies concerned with the effect of "mental practice" upon skill acquisition also point to the validity of the "learning potential" concept. It has been found that, in addition to practice, learning a complex motor act may be facilitated by "thinking through" the movements and/or by viewing others perform. Skill improvement may thus be assumed to take place as the result of silent, inactive contemplation. These findings indicate that learning is occurring even though performance improvement measures are not recorded. The amount of "latent" learning achieved is later found by comparing the progress of the "thinkers" to groups who had no such opportunity.

These "mental practice" studies, as well as others which have dealt with the types of cues influencing motor learning, also point to a basic difference between animal and human learning. The performance of humans is superior to that of animals because of many factors, such as greater facility in integrating movements and anatomical specialization. The paramount difference between animal and human learning, however, is that human beings attach symbols to a motor task, which usually results in an increased ability to remember and to organize information. Humans may rehearse a skill by prior manipulation of symbols while animals are unable to do so. Although reference will be made to animal experimentation when discussing theoretical considerations, because of this basic difference, emphasis will be placed upon research investigating human capacities to learn motor skills.

Initially, it is also important to differentiate between the terms *performance* and *learning.* Delineation between the two concepts is most often accomplished by reference to a time dimension. *Learning* is a long-range change, demonstrable in retention measures collected over a period of time. *Performance,* on the other hand, is a one-attempt phenomenon influenced by such short-term variables as motivation, fatigue, and nutritive state.

The movement characteristics of human beings cannot be neatly designated as either learned or innate, however. There are increasing indications in the literature that perhaps a second kind of acquired behavior is influential of human actions. Zoologists for the past fifty years have studied with various degrees of objectivity the phenomena known as imprinting, which involves apparently automatic sets of behavioral sequences which seem to be "triggered" by specific events occurring early in the life of the organism. For example, the "following" response of chicks and ducklings is believed imprinted when the animals are exposed to a moving stimulus pattern during a critical period of their early life.

The studies by Goldfarb examining the influence of maternal deprivation upon later development,[374] the research by Brodbeck and Irwin concerning the emergence of speech behavior,[117] the findings of Spitz, who studied factors which elicit smiling,[849] the wolf-child histories summarized by Gesell,[353] as well as the investigations of Green and Money of effeminate behavior in boys[393] raise the possibility that at certain times in the lives of infants and children critical events trigger certain components of their motor behavior. Although the present evidence is suggestive rather than conclusive, it might be hypothesized that several facets of movement behavior may be the result of imprinting—including throwing, running, unique gait characteristics, and a variety of gesture patterns.

INTRODUCTION TO LEARNING THEORY

A learning theory is a set of theoretical assumptions which attempt to explain such phenomena as forgetting, retention, the role of practice, performance variations, learning limits, the influence of rewards, and the types of cues which cause learning to take place. Learning theories dwell mainly upon two basic concepts and may be classified by the relative emphasis placed upon each.

The initial dimension is the relative importance accorded *reinforcement* as a condition necessary for learning. Reinforcement, although a somewhat nebulous concept, may be defined as some *reward* within the learning situation, as obvious as satisfaction gained from hitting a target or approval from a coach or as subtle as the lessening of tension or a feeling of task-mastery. Opposing the theory that reinforcement is indispensable is the "contiguity theory," the concept that learning will occur when a stimulus (or event) and a response occur at the same time.

A second dimension with which learning theories are concerned is the nature of the sensory stimulation which causes the organism to respond. In essence the argument deals with whether an organism reacts to discrete stimuli (chained together, or in groups) or whether action is elicited by some meaning or significance attached to the situation or object. The former theories are termed "stimulus-response" (S-R theories), while the latter are "associative" or "field theories."

Learning theories may also be classified by more explicit criteria. Some are classified by the extent to which they emphasize central thought processes, as contrasted to simple muscular movement (central vs. peripheral theories). Some utilize objective mathematical formulas, while others use more subjective philosophical assumptions to explain learning. Other theories may be identified by whether more than one type of learning is presented to explain simple and complex performance, or intellectual vs. motor behavior, and whether importance is attached to intermediate factors (emotion, reward, motivation, and the like).

In the pages which follow an attempt has been made to outline briefly theories which represent a sampling of the various conceptual frameworks available which treat learning. An extensive review of learning theories is beyond the scope of the book and has been ably carried out by Hilgard[453] and others.

Thorndike—S-R Theory

Thorndike[881] developed one of the most accepted S-R learning theories and has had an important influence upon educational practice from the 1890's to the present. Experimentation with animal and human subjects resulted in the hypothesis that learning consisted primarily of the strengthening of the connections (bonds) between stimulus and response. Important implications for both animal and human learning are contained in Thorndike's theory. *Motivation* is emphasized as an important intervening factor influencing learning. Consequently, Thorndike's "connectivism" may be considered an S-R theory emphasizing the importance of reinforcing or rewarding conditions.

Three laws of learning were proposed in this conceptual framework: (1) *The Law of Readiness* stated that learning is dependent upon a readiness to act or prior "mental set," which facilitates the response. Generally, this preparation was believed to consist of physiological accommodations within the conduction units of the nervous system. (2) *The Law of Exercise* assumed that S-R connections were strengthened through *frequent* pairing. Later, it was expostulated that mere repetition did not strengthen the S-R bonds but that motivating conditions (including knowledge of results) were necessary for learning to take place. (3) *The Law of Effect* emphasized the importance of the annoying or satisfying results of the act in influencing the chance of its recurrence. In later experiments, Thorndike found that the effects of satisfaction and displeasure were not equal and that the satisfying results facilitated performance more than did punishment. Discussions of "Teaching Method," emphasizing the importance of reward as opposed to punishment upon learning, indicate an acceptance of these later findings.

Thorndike suggested that learning was specific to the task at hand. Extension of the concept to motor performances has been referred to previously. His "transfer of identical elements" theory, holding that the practice of one task would contribute to proficiency in a second only when elements within the two are identical, is currently being tested by motor skill researchers.

While Thorndike's assumptions did not deal specifically with learning athletic skills or gross motor performance, considerable attention was accorded to fine motor skills. Handwriting, typing, and other such class-room tasks were investigated and accorded as respectable a place in his research as more "intellectual tasks." His "specificity theory" provided the impetus which prompted educators to include typing and other vocational courses in school curriculums.

Thorndike is considered a behaviorist because he based theories upon evidence obtained from direct and observable performance rather than from subjective reports from subjects. His contribution to the study of motor learning lies in the formulation of (1) the specificity theory, (2) the importance accorded motivation, and (3) the objective approach he took to the study of learning problems.

Gutherie—Contiguity Theory

Gutherie was an S-R theorist who, while de-emphasizing reinforcement, placed importance upon the occurrence of stimulus and response together in time. His theory was derived to a large extent from research based upon study of kinesthesis. Gutherie hypothesized that all learning, complex and simple or verbal and non-verbal, consists of the contiguous pairing of movement stimuli and response. He postulated that all thinking and remembering is dependent upon the repetition of subliminal movements of the vocal apparatus. His experiments involved small animals, mice in mazes, and cats in "escape" boxes. From the results, generalizations were extended to human learning. It was assumed that the gradual improvement in performance shown by sloping learning curves was the result of the joining of various pairs of stimuli and responses within complex tasks until a whole "family" of connections were formed.[404]

The explanations reported by Gutherie have been rejected by many as too simple to explain complex human functioning. And later experimenters demonstrated that mice were able to learn maze pathways even when nerves carrying kinesthetic impulses were cut. However, the basic assumptions formulated by Gutherie deserve serious study as they have led to additional research concerned with movement learning.

Hull—Mathematical Model for Learning

Moving on from more traditional S-R theories, Hull developed a highly objective theory based upon animal experimentation. The central concept in this theory was habit formation. To explain learning phenomena occurring within the stimulus phase, variables intrinsic to the organism and various motor "output" variables, postulates involving exact mathematical formulas were devised. They were modified if subsequent experimentation proved them questionable. Hull's theory could be likened to Woodworth's S-O-R theory,[982] with emphasis placed upon the organism's integrating role, or "O," within the learning process.

Hull relied heavily upon mathematical symbols to explain behavioral changes, quantifying the effect of the number of trials, the amount of reward, the intensity of the stimulus, and other variables in order to predict behavior more exactly in various experimental environments. From his experiments, Hull developed the concept of *habit strength* ($_sH_r$), which, he concluded, was the direct outcome of reinforced, spaced trials at a given task. The concept of *reaction potential* ($_sE_r$) is also central to the theory and represents the organism's *tendency* to respond. With these two terms, Hull explained learning in absolute performance units (habit strength) and in units of learning potential (reaction potential).

He considered seven "input" variables, including the intensity of the stimulus, the amount of reward, prior practice, drive, and the work required in responding. Several factors intrinsic to the responding organism included habit strength, strength from related habits, the extent to which a given stimulus affects the learner, and the variability of performance from trial to trial. The final "output" variables considered important included strength of reaction (reaction amplitude) and the persistency and endurance of unrewarded responses.

Hull proposed that at the basic level several primitive types of learning occur, including those based upon inborn tendencies, adaptation to primitive situations, the ability to generalize and to discriminate, and trial and error learning. At the final level, to explain complex behavior and learning, Hull presented concepts based upon the integration of behavioral sequences through *anticipatory responses*, believed to be the steering mechanisms formed by conditions affecting the learner. It was from this latter concept that the formation of "families" of habits was explained.

Hull's theory is extremely complex, and further elaboration is beyond the scope of this discussion (see Adams[9]). His main contribution, however, was the objective manner in which learning was explained. Objectivity does not imply rigidity, however, as Hull's postulates were subject to change when experimental evidence seemed to warrant it.

Tolman—Sign Theory

Tolman[891] was one of the first to emphasize the integrative function of the nervous system in contrast to concepts dealing with the formation of peripheral stimuli-response connections. It is assumed that human learning depends upon the meaning (sign or significance) an individual attaches to situations or objects in his environment. The theory may thus be considered *molar,* or based mainly upon the observation of total behavior, rather than *molecular,* or based upon the anatomical-physiological phenomena underlying S-R theories.

Tolman was one of the first "field" theorists. He used the term "behavior space" (similar to Lewinian "life space") to represent the individual's immediate environment. Contradicting the findings of S-R behaviorists who felt that learning implied the acquisition of simple responses, Tolman postulated that organisms become familiar with places, that mice, for example, form "cognitive maps" of the maze pattern. The meanings attached to a situation were not assumed to be only spatial, since it was also proposed that time factors and "logical" considerations aid in performing the task at hand.

Behavior is considered to be goal-directed and concerned with avoiding or approaching something in the environment. The concept of *confirmation* replaces *reinforcement* in Tolmanian theory. An individual is assumed to repeat an act as its consequences become known and predictable. The term *carthexes* (negative or positive) was coined to explain the relative attraction or repulsion individuals attach to objects or situations.

Tolman considered himself a strict behaviorist, concerned mainly with observable evidence. However, it was hypothesized that numerous "intervening variables" existed between the situation and the resultant behavior. While the list of variables was often modified, it generally included demand, appetite, differentiation, motor skill, and bias.

Tolman was criticized for generalizing human learning from animal experiments. However, the findings of his "latent learning" studies carried out with animals, which indicated that maze learning, unverified by performance, might take place as maze exploration remained unrewarded, seem to be confirmed by "mental practice" research carried out with human subjects. It was explained that complex motor skills are learned because of the formation of "motor patterns" rather than because of the acquisition of movement stimuli-response chains. Motor learning was felt to be dependent upon the perceptual process which resulted in meanings attached to the situation which in turn produced a readiness to act or to remain inactive.

While some feel that Tolman's assumptions did not cover all problems of learning, many believe that the value of his theory lies in this incompleteness. It seems to have provided an impetus for further study which many more "complete" systems failed to do. The "cognitive-map," or "sign-significant" theory, forms a bridge between the strict behaviorists who deal only in S-R terms and the later Gestaltists who accorded an increasing importance to perceptual processes in formulating more "holistic" concepts of learning.

Gestalt Theory

In the 1930's, the simplicity of approach advocated by the S-R theorists was challenged by German psychologists who advocated the importance of insight in learning. These Gestaltists evolved a "field theory" based initially upon the problem-solving behavior of apes. Learning laws were formulated, the validity of which depended upon an accurate assessment of perceptual processes. Particularly emphasized was the sudden recognition of factors involved in a problem, with the subsequent correct action. This was in direct opposition to the trial-and-error concepts advanced by Thorndike in the United States at about the same time.

As was the case with Tolman's theory, Gestaltism may be termed "holistic." However, the latter conceptual framework depends more upon introspective evidence and *anthropomorphic* observations, or putting oneself in the place of the animal, than did Tolman's theory. Awareness of relationships and meanings among various parts of a problem, between problems, and between the part and the whole are emphasized. Transfer of learning, or "transposition," is assumed to take place as a pattern of dynamic relationships are found to be similar in two situations.

Woodworth, Skinner, Miller, and Hebb

Several traditional theories combine concepts of the Gestaltists and the S-R bond psychologists as well as several views of reinforcement. Woodworth, for example, explained complex learning in terms of S-R sequences, while at the same time emphasizing the importance of the perceptual process, dependent both upon biological and behavioral cues (*i.e.*, the need on the part of the organism to use its capacities). A framework of ideas is constructively based upon a variety of evidence (behavior, introspection, and experimental observations). Although termed by some as "eclectic," Woodworth's functionalism seems to be a most comprehensive theory of learning and has been outlined in his publications appearing over a period of sixty years.[982]

Skinner[824] also reconciled certain aspects of the S-R and field theories as he proposed two types of learning: (1) respondent behavior, smooth muscle activity elicited by an identifiable stimulus, and (2) operant behavior, movement of the skeletal muscle, not necessarily caused by an identifiable stimulus, but which may result from the demands of the whole situation.

Neil Miller's liberalized S-R theory is another example of the more comprehensive theory formulation within recent years. He presented a broad definition of a *stimulus* as "anything to which a response can be learned," and *response* as "anything that can be learned to a stimulus." Thus, it is proposed that, while specific biological needs often determine initial behavior, the behavior may later prove rewarding in itself. This idea is similar to the Allport "functional autonomy of drive" concept and to Woodworth's emphasis upon the existence of exploratory and play drives as basic human needs.

Hebb's physiological models for learning and perception are also worthy of consideration. It is suggested that learning occurs as cell linkages are formed in the nervous system. As these linkages are combined and interact within phase cycles, or systems of linkages, it is concluded that complex patterned thinking occurs. Learning, it is suggested, is physiologically manifested through the formation of protruding knobs at the synapse level. While admittedly speculative, Hebbs' theories, since their publication in *The Organization of Behavior* in 1949,[432] have had an important impact upon learning theorists.

Information Theory

Although earlier learning theorists, particularly Hull, have utilized mathematical constructs when explaining modifications of human behavior, the more contemporary learning theories draw further comparisons between components of an electronic computer and the functioning of the human nervous system. While it is doubtful that electronic engineers studied the brain and spinal cord before developing these complex devices, the reverse has been noted. Several contemporary learning theories use computer terms to explain human functioning.

The "feed-back model," one of the central concepts in the science of cybernetics espoused by Norbert Weiner[963] in 1948, and the "information-theory," utilized by the human factors engineer in studying man-machine relationships, are two recent theories of this type. These conceptual frameworks were initially grounded in studies of communication theory. Diagrammed, these two theories might be combined as follows:

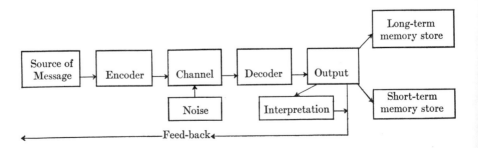

The boxes may represent either the components of an electronic sending-receiving system or the components of human-to-human or man-environment communication system. Motor learning may be graphically explained by reference to such a model. For example, as an individual learns a complex skill, such as shooting a free-throw in basketball, kinesthetic impulses are sent from the muscles, tendons, and joints performing a component of the movement and from the visual apparatus as the eyes observe the ball's pathway (or during the initial stages of the whole movement) and transmitted to the brain. These are transmitted by the nervous system (encoded) through various channels, the individual then interprets them (decodes), a meaning is attached to them—hit or missed? (output interpretation), and relative success and reasons for it are stored in the components indicated. Feed-back occurs as impulses are sent to the muscles which might govern subsequent muscular adjustments involved in the second three-throw.

Learning adjustments and modifications may thus be represented graphically. In addition to the concepts pictured, such ideas as long-term and short-term memory store have been utilized to evaluate the manner in which skills or concepts are retained over varying periods of time.

Numerous researchers have studied the implications of these various concepts. For example, the "channel" capacity of individuals has received considerable attention in an attempt to determine the volume of material which may be comprehended at one time, its nature, how many kinds of stimuli (vocal, movement, etc.) may be attended to, and what types of stimuli take precedence over others in an individual's "receiving channels."[116]

The psychological "noise" pictured refers to any type of block or impediment to communication. What kinds of blocks interfere most (emotional, physical, auditory, etc.)? Do the relative amounts of interference differ from individual to individual and from situation to situation? How may the sender discover the type of "noise" interfering with communication, and how may it be alleviated? These are some of the questions which have received experimental attention.

While some might object to the mechanistic and somewhat inhuman sound of these terms, they are useful as a concise means of explaining problems of communication, perception, and motor performance.

PERCEPTUAL-MOTOR LEARNING

Increased difficulty is encountered when attempting to differentiate between motor learning, perceptual-motor learning, and any other kind of learning. Similarly sharp distinctions become impossible to make between verbal learning and motor learning. Advocates of the theoretical models which follow often have voiced the opinion that differentiation between theories of skill learning and theories explaining learning in general differ in the main according to the type of response dealt with, rather than upon more basic issues.

The Memory Drum Theory of Neuro-Motor Reaction

General theories of personality purporting to explain general human functioning are first-level theories. At the second level are the learning theories reviewed on the previous pages. In addition, there are third-level theories which attempt to explain specific types of human functioning. Such a theory is the "memory drum theory" espoused by Franklin Henry.[442]

Using "computer terms," Henry made assumptions which are based upon the greater response delay which precedes the performance of more complex tasks. This phenomenon is interpreted to indicate that unconscious neural patterns acquired from past experience are stored in what may be thought of as a *memory storage drum*. The store is used when a movement skill is learned. The initial attempts to perform the new skill are awkward and carried out under conscious control if there has been no similar "program" previously recorded upon the drum. It is explained that, although some response delay is attributable to speed of nerve conduction, the minor "program" change necessary for a simple movement, once the "will to act" has been initiated, results in a shorter reaction time. A long complicated program of movements is more difficult to change and results in a delay of response to the complex task. Such a theory, it is believed, aids in explaining specificity of motor skill, as well as other phenomena related to motor learning.

The Progression-Regression Hypothesis

It has been assumed by some that skill acquisition rests upon the development, with practice, of the individual's ability to perceive and to act upon increasingly subtle cues. This increased attention to the more finite components of the task, it has been hypothesized, enables more adequate error-minimizing techniques to be developed, while at the same time maximizing methods of attending to the positive components of the task.[333]

Learning of a motor skill is marked by a reduction in errors, with a simultaneous increase in some positive indices of performance. Errors of commission and/or omission appear with decreasing frequency as practice is engaged in. The progression-regression hypothesis is not a fully developed theory at the present time, but it does relate to some of the more recent findings relative to the acquisition of skill as higher levels of excellence are reached.

Descriptions of Motor Learning

The memory drum theory is focused upon motor behavior. Numerous writers have advanced theoretical explanations of motor functioning.

Many of these explanations are subjective, but their consideration should add depth to the study of learning of motor skills. Hilgard[453] has separated definitions of learning into two main types: (1) theoretical, concerning the essential conditions or processes which are believed necessary to enable learning to occur, and (2) factual, relating to observations of behavior in the physical world. The materials which follow may be classified as factual rather than theoretical statements.

Descriptions of motor learning are sometimes subjective descriptions of how individuals appear to have behaved when learning a motor act. Anderson[29] has described learning as "a progressive organization of behavior" based upon the opportunity to repeat experience for a sufficient amount of time. He holds, along with Thorndike and others, that locomotion is the basic skill learned from the infant's crawling and climbing behavior to the gross body movements of the adult. Elements within the skilled act are identified by Anderson as including speed (a time element), strength (an energy element), and coordination (a quality element).

Sells,[801] refers to a "plasticity" quality necessary for the learning of a motor skill. This concept, similar to Tolman's concept of "creative instability," infers that individuals who learn best are those who easily may change persisting movement characteristics.

Kingsley[529] has described skilled performance as "purposive action" and identified four acquisition stages: (1) instruction, or receiving external and internal cues, (2) formulation of the task, or gaining task understanding, (3) progress toward goal, or practice, and (4) completion. It is held that during learning movements are revised, and abbreviated and unnecessary components ("fractionations") dropped out of the action. When learned, it is held that the skilled act is less likely to become disturbed by emotions and will be accompanied by fewer accessory responses (*i.e.,* words).

The Continuous Versus the Discontinuous Nature of Skill Acquisition

There has been a considerable amount of investigation and speculation as to whether the acquisition of skill may be considered to be a continuous process, or whether it might be considered as fragmented into various identifiable components. The question arrived at determines not only the theoretical construct most amenable to use, but also the practical methods which will elicit the most improvement in skill.

It is becoming increasingly clear upon inspection of the experimental literature that the learning process can be fragmented into several components, indicating several phases in skill acquisition. Initially the learner seeks to discover the task components which are similar to or different from those he has known in the past. During this initial stage various perceptual components of the act are important as well as the performer's ability to acquire directions relative to the task (his short-term memory) and similar cognitive attributes. Following the initial preparatory phase of learning, such factors as their ability to handle the various input information become important. For example, if the movement is rapid and continuous, the performer's ability to monitor kinesthetic input feed-in during the initial portion of the movement(s) influences the quality of subsequent performance. During this stage of learning the individual begins to organize discrete portions of the task into progressively larger components, as his perceptual-motor systems become increasingly capable of not only perceiving larger amounts of information, but become able to respond more qualitatively, evidencing a smoothing of motoric behaviors, and a higher and higher level of integration.

The final stages of skill learning have received relatively little attention on the part of researchers. Apparently, however, the evidence is beginning to indicate that improvement in perceptual-motor functioning continues to higher levels than was believed possible in past years. Not only are marks achieved by superior athletes indicative of increasing excellence, but recent information from researchers has advanced that subtle changes in ocular movements, in respiratory adjustments, and in similar concomitants of performance take place in the latter stages of skill acquisition, which permit extremely high levels of achievement to be attained.[829]

It thus seems that if skill acquisition is observed, it would be judged continuous; but shifts in strategies, in response modifications, and in the manner in which task components are integrated enable us to identify discrete phases within the learning process. Further research is needed to identify the characteristics of these phases, in particular the unique components of the final levels of achievement.

Limits of Motor Learning

Dudycha[258] and Gagne and Fleishman[337] both point to the importance of the acquisition of unconscious habits, although Gagne indicates that these are probably more important during the latter stages of learning. Both consider capacity limits, divided by Dudycha into two types: (1) practical limits, or that with which the individual is satisfied, and (2) physiological limits, or the individual's highest possible achievement. The second type of limit is approached gradually. The factors determining physiological limitations include nature of the nervous system, bodily proportions, the physical equipment measuring workout (speed of the typewriter), working conditions (temperature, noise), methods of learning (similar to Seashore's work methods concept,[797] and aspirational level (motivation). Gagne and Fleishman explain that "we cannot expect human motor skills to have characteristics which exceed the capacity of the response mechanism itself."[337]

THE QUANTIFICATION OF LEARNING

The gradual acquisition of complex skill has been represented by numerical indices as well as graphic curves. Using performance measures recorded over a period of time, a "learning" score has been arrived at by (1) subtracting the first score from the last, (2) dividing the number of trials into the total improvement record, a measure of learning rate, (3) averaging some portion of the trials (usually after a few "warm-ups"), (4) determining the extent to which some hypothetical or actual performance *limit* is reached, or (5) various combinations of these methods.

To obtain a valid measure of learning is not simple. Problems arise because of several complexities in the learning situation: (1) Usually the unique properties of the task determine the most appropriate learning score computed; methods proposed for one type of task mistakenly may be applied to another. (2) The measure of learning must be accomplished indirectly through performance measures, susceptible to many variables in addition to practice. (3) Most learning is a function not simply of the number of trials but also of their spacing. (4) Most measures of successive performance scores represent only a portion of the actual learning process. It is usually hypothesized that the first trial is really an initial performance level not affected by past experiences, an assumption which is seldom true. Previous experience in a similar or dissimilar task may facilitate or impede performance. Most measures represent only a portion of the learning taking place. Despite such problems, however, considerable thought and time have been spent in developing acceptable means for determining just *how much* skill an individual has acquired under various experimental conditions.

Although numerous investigations have dealt with objectifying verbal or cognitive learning tasks, several studies have been directed specifically toward quantifying the learning of motor skill. In 1955, McCraw[633] studied the validity of several possible measures of learning, including: (1) averaging all the scores, the first and last, (2) finding the difference between the initial raw score and the final raw score, (3) summing up the highest or best trials and subtracting a sum of the initial trials, and (4) dividing the actual gain from the initial to the final trial by the possible gain from the initial to the highest possible score. Agreeing with other scholars, McCraw found that using the same raw data a wide variety of "learning" scores might be obtained, depending upon the method employed. He concluded that the most valid learning score might be obtained by any of the following formulas:

(1) Adding all the scores

(2) $\dfrac{\text{Sum of highest successive trials (minus) sum of first trials}}{\text{Highest possible score (minus) sum of lowest scores}}$

(3) $\dfrac{\text{Sum of highest trials (minus) sum of first trials}}{\text{Highest possible score (minus) sum of first trials}}$

(4) $\dfrac{\text{Sum of all trials (minus) sum of first trials}}{\text{Highest possible score (minus) sum of first trials}}$

The latter three formulas are termed "Per cent of Possible Gain Methods."

Learning Curves

In addition to using a single numerical index, the ubiquitous *learning curve* is frequently employed as a measure of learning. This graphic representation of the acquisition of a task may involve several types: (1) the decreasing amount of time necessary to perform a task, (2) some measure of accuracy, as ability to hit a target, (3) a decrease in the number of errors committed when learning a task, (4) the percentage of success per trial, as compared to a real or hypothetical performance limit, or (5) a combination of two or more of the above measures. Ehrlich,[274] studying the accuracy of a fencing thrust as a motor skill involving total body skill and accuracy, recommends that curves should be constructed by analyzing performance from three points of view: (1) initial states, (2) rate of learning, and (3) maximal end points.

Learning curves represent the successive scores of an individual as he learns a task or of group means. Such graphs are helpful to illustrate "reminiscence," the effect of spacing upon improvement, "transfer," the influence of other tasks upon the task studied, a comparison of "whole vs. part" practice, or other practice variables.

At times reference has been made in the literature to a "typically" shaped motor learning curve, generally assumed to consist of one which indicates a gradual decrease in the amount of learning after initial quick improvement. In reality, however, motor learning curves assume a variety of shapes depending upon the nature of the task, the type of practice conditions imposed, and characteristics of the experimental situation or of the learner. Thus, while at times they might assume

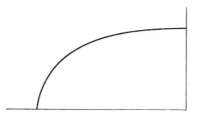

Fig. 5

the shape shown above (Fig. 5), others are characterized by initial slow improvement, with a gradual increase in the amount of learning from trial to trial. Thus curve is characteristic when the task is difficult or when the attempts of a feeble-minded subject or child's learning efforts are graphed (Fig. 6).

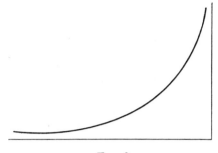

FIG. 6

General shape of the curve may depend upon the measure used, motivation, or upon facilitating or distracting conditions. In addition, the amount of task analysis required, as determined by task complexity, has an influence upon the shape of the learning curve. Many complex tasks might involve an error curve which would decline, while a curve based upon the number of successful trials might move in the opposite direction. Superimposed, these two curves may appear as shown in Figure 7.

While the general shape of curves often differs, several general characteristics of such graphs have been studied by various researchers. In general, motor learning curves are characterized by an initial stage of relatively rapid improvement. Melton[647] has termed this "the discovery stage" of learning. During this initial phase the individual acquires a general knowledge of task components and of the goal to be achieved. Following this initial portion, a second part has been termed the actual "performance" phase, during which improvement is generally not so rapid, but more stable and more likely to be retained.

Noticeable in most curves indicating skill acquisition are performance fluctuations. Investigators generally attribute these to motivational conditions, fatigue, or other such temporary factors. In addition, a plateau may appear at several stages in the learning process. A plateau has been defined as a period during which relatively little improvement has taken place. Plateaus in motor learning curves have been studied by several investigators. Some researchers have assumed that, if given enough trials, every motor learning curve will eventually evidence plateauing. Peterson,[725] however, found that a juggling task produced a learning curve which failed to evidence any plateauing. This is generally found to be true when a task is learned as a whole (Fig. 8).

18

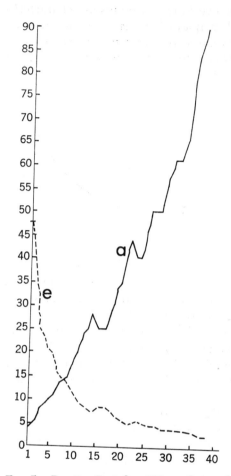

FIG. 7.   Practice Periods: 200 catches each.

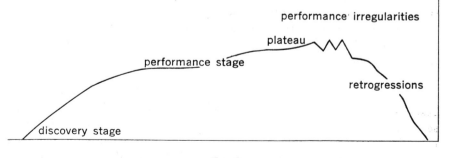

FIG. 8

It is usually stated that a plateau indicates a period during which parts of a task are combined into "wholes." While actual performance improvement may not be demonstrated, it is assumed that the individual is gradually assimilating task components and will suddenly evidence this by "breaking out" of the plateau effect. Such a simple explanation is not always valid, however. Kao,[510] undertaking an extensive study of plateaus in motor learning curves, concluded that when learning *simple skills* plateaus may be due to fatigue, a change of methods adopted by a subject, or a subtle change in the experimental environment (*i.e.*, shifting of the apparatus). When acquiring *complex skills*, Kao continued, plateaus result as individuals attempt to build complex patterns out of formerly independent ones. If success in an initial component leads to immediate task facilitation, however, probably no plateau would be evident. It was also advanced that when individuals continuously attend to the "whole" of the task no plateaus will be evident.

In addition to plateaus and performance irregularities, retrogression in skill is sometimes recorded during intermediate stages in the learning of a motor task. The reason for such performance decrements is sometimes attributed to the subject's attempts to exceed his psycho-physical limits.

Bahrick, Fitts and Briggs[42] have suggested that learning curve fluctuations are frequently artifacts produced as the task undergoes slight variations (*e.g.*, change of target size in an aiming or steadiness test). These researchers suggest that tasks which are scored on an all-or-none basis are particularly difficult to reduce to a valid learning curve.

Factorial Studies of the Learning Curve

Learning curves, as well as being linear, also have *thickness!* As has been seen, *a single performance measure* may be analyzed to determine the relative importance of various basic factors. Thus learning may be progressively analyzed (factorialized) to determine the relative importance of various basic qualities at several stages in the process of acquisition. Such studies are rare in the literature, and more are needed to provide a depth analysis of the learning process. An example of such an investigation was carried out by Fleishman and Hempel in 1954.[308] Scores were obtained at eight different stages of practice in a complex coordination test (making complex adjustments of an airplane stick and rudder in response to visual signal patterns). Their findings are summarized in Figure 9. As can be seen, the number of factors contributing to performance were more numerous during the initial stages and became fewer as learning continued. During the last four stages only three factors were present, while during the initial stages seven factors were apparent. There was also a shift in the "nature" of the factors. During the initial stages, "non-motor" or cognitive factors were more apparent (visualization of spatial relations, mechanical analysis, etc.).

From the fifth through the last stage, however, the factors of psycho-motor coordination, rate of movement, and a factor specific to the task predominated. Expressed as percentages during the early stages, "motor factors" contributed only about 29.5 per cent, while non-motor factors contributed to about 46.1 per cent of the task. Later in the learning process the motor factors contributed about 74.5 per cent, while non-motor factors accounted for only about 10.5 per cent.

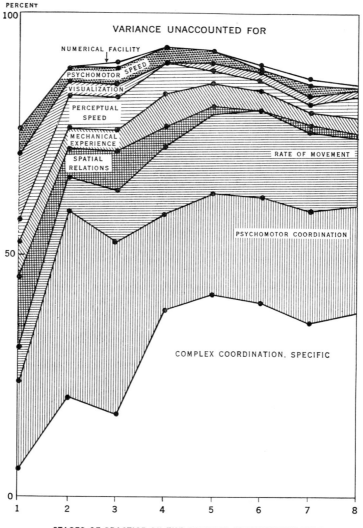

Fig. 9. Percentage of variance (shaded area) represented by each factor at different stages of practice on the Complex Coordination Test. (Fleishman and Hempel, courtesy of Psychometrika.)

Individual differences in learning may be affected by different factors during various stages of learning. For example, once the spatial relationships of a task are acquired, no further improvement may be possible or necessary, and other factors then assume increasing importance. The rise of the motor learning curve was considered by Fleishman and Hempel[308] to be the result of systematic transformations in particular combinations of abilities at various stages of practice. The task analyzed in this research was a basic skill needed to fly an airplane. It is believed, however, that generalities may be drawn from this research applicable to a wide variety of motor skills. The importance of correct verbalizing and of task analysis during the initial and later stages of learning appear to be statistically confirmed by these findings.

Investigations subsequent to this initial one by Fleishman and his colleagues have substantiated and elaborated upon these findings. An investigation in 1955[309] suggested that practice may exert unequal effect upon the numerous factors involved in the performance of reaction time test in response to a visual stimulus. The performance score at one point in the learning process, therefore appears to be a resultant of the changes in the unique combinations of abilities possessed by the performer at that point.

In a subsequent investigation[306] it was hypothesized that ideal training conditions, suited to the factorial changes in the task during learning, might facilitate final performance. Thus an investigation carried out in 1961 was based upon the premise that when it is known that a given ability may be important at a particular point in the practice schedule, verbal emphasis upon that ability at the correct time will enhance learning. The findings indicated that such an approach is a sound one, the experimental group subjected to this type of carefully placed verbal emphasis performed significantly better at the final stages of learning than two control groups receiving no such training. Such a program, of course, presupposed the skill under consideration has been previously subjected to a longitudinal factorial analysis. More recent studies by Fleishman[303] and by Fleishman and Rich[313] have continued to emphasize the fact that visual-spatial abilities are more important initially, and kinesthetic perception, and various movement attributes are more important in the latter stages of skill acquisition.

Formulizing Motor Learning Curves

Motor learning curves are frequently "smoothed" or reduced to some hypothetical mathematical formula. This is usually carried out to offer greater clarity to the learning phenomena studied or to facilitate prediction of performance scores in trials not recorded, or conversely, to predict at which trial certain performance levels may be reached. When carrying out such a mathematical operation, however, several assumptions usually must be made: (1) that there is an initial trial before which no learning has occurred, (2) that there is a fixed rate of learning evidenced, and (3) that, when contrasting two curves, the same parts of the learning process are comparable. The smoothing of learning curves, in addition, obliterates irregularities which in themselves might be worthy of study. Plateaus, retrogressions, and other irregularities are passed over when a learning curve is smoothed. Recent comparisons of the shape of learning curves derived from the practice of a number of perceptual-motor skills indicate that their shapes are remarkably similar.[514] The shape of a motor learning curve involving a sorting task, for example, is similar in conformation to that obtained when a pursuit-rotor is practiced for a period of time.

The result of this similarity has been to encourage several investigators to attempt to determine the extent to which performance at the initial stages of learning correlates with performance during the latter stages of the learning of the same skill. The results of these experimenters are inconclusive, but in general the closer the trials compared are within the learning schedule, the higher their intercorrelation. Walsh[919] found that prediction of the later learning of a ladder climbing task was tenuous if based upon knowing the initial scores posted.

Forgetting

In addition to "learning curves," "forgetting" curves have been investigated extensively. While numerous studies have been focused on verbal or cognitive tasks, little attention has been paid to the forgetting of motor tasks. In general, a "forgetting" curve is usually considered to be shaped as shown in Figure 10. It is characterized by initial rapid forgetting, which lessens as time passes.

Investigations concerned with the retention of motor skills generally obtain only a single performance measure after a period of prolonged inactivity, rather than studying successive performance drop-offs. Research in this area probably has been discouraged by the comparatively long period over which motor habits seem to endure.

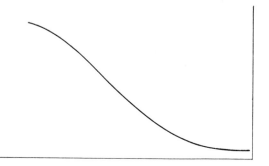

Fig. 10

MOTOR EDUCABILITY

Motor educability has been defined previously as the general ability to learn a number of tasks quickly and accurately. It refers to the ability of an individual to accommodate to the requirements of several kinds of motor tasks. If such a factor exists, one should be able to identify persons who might be predicted to learn a wide variety of motor skills with a minimum of time and/or effort. Motor educability might, therefore, be termed general motor intelligence.

If we find individuals who seem to *perform* a number of skills well, it would logically follow that these same individuals might also *learn* a variety of movements quickly. The close relationship between performance and learning has been previously discussed (p. 215). Such does not seem to be the case, however, as much of the experimental evidence argues against the existence of a general motor learning factor.

For years, Brace[104] carried out studies which utilized a stunt-type test as a measure of general motor ability. He incurred little success when attempting to discover a relationship between such general indices and the ability to learn motor skills. Gire and Espenschade[370] also failed to identify a general motor educability factor. In an elaborate study using several batteries of performance tests, no significant relationships were established between its scores and the ability to learn different sports skills.

Generally, such studies conclude that even combinations of strength test scores provide only a fair index of ability to learn *simple* gross motor skills. A comprehensive factor involved in the learning of *complex* tasks seems more difficult to isolate.

Cratty,[190] in an attempt to show a relationship between the ability to learn two similar spatial patterns of different sizes, failed to find significant correlation between learning proficiencies. He concluded, however, that comparison of skills which depend upon the same kinds of sensory information or which involve similar movement patterns might eventually lead to the identification of general learning factors.

The disturbing observation continues to be made, however, that some individuals seem able to learn quickly any skill to which they are exposed. At present, the subject is a controversial one. There is an indication, however, that these quick learners are highly motivated, possess above average strength, are able to analyze quickly and accurately the mechanics of a task, and are relatively free from excess tension which might impede performance. The isolation and identification of a single general motor educability factor, however, seems to be a tenuous experimental undertaking.

The motor educability question is related to the specificity vs. generality argument concerning motor performance and to the validity of various learning and transfer theories. Further reference to this question is found throughout the book, specifically in the sections concerned with performance and transfer.

Student References

Books

1. HILGARD, ERNEST R.: *Theories of Learning*, 2nd Ed., New York, Appleton-Century-Crofts, Inc., 1956.
2. MELTON, ARTHUR W.: *Categories of Human Learning*, New York, Academic Press, Inc., 1964.
3. MILLER, GEORGE A., GALANTER, EUGENE and PRIBHAM, KARL H.: *Plans and the Structure of Behavior*, New York, Henry Holt & Co., Inc., 1960.
4. RAGSDALE, C. E.: *The Psychology of Motor Learning*, Ann Arbor, Edward Brothers Press, Inc., 1930.
5. SMITH, K. U.: *Cybernetic Principles of Learning and Educational Design*, New York, Holt, Rinehart & Winston, 1965.
6. BILODEAU, EDWARD A.: *Acquisition of Skill*, Academic Press, New York, 1966.

Articles

1. BILODEAU, EDWARD A. and BILODEAU, INA McD.: "Motor skills learning," *Annual Review of Psychology*, pp. 243-280, Palo Alto, Calif., 1961.
2. HENRY, FRANKLIN: "Increase in speed of movement by motivation and by transfer of motivated improvement," *Res. Quart.*, 22, May 1951.
3. KAO, DJI-LIH: "Plateaus and the curve of learning in motor skill," *Psychological Monographs*, 49, 1-81, 1937.
4. McCRAW, L. W.: "Comparative analysis of methods of scoring tests of motor learning," *Res. Quart.*, 26, 440-453, 1955.

Chapter 17

Practice Factors, Learning and Retention

As defined in the previous chapter, *learning* is a rather permanent change brought about through practice. In this chapter we will review some of the ways in which various conditions influence retention. Problems arise when comparing and evaluating research findings. Many different types of skills have been investigated, from various theoretical points of view. In addition, many of the practice variables have not been subject to rigid control. For example, when studying massed vs. distributed practice, the majority of the investigators failed to control adequately the subjects' activities during rest periods.

Further problems are caused by the various definitions of "learning proficiency" and the number of ways in which retention is evaluated. Confusion also results from the performance measures utilized. Some experimenters are concerned with accurate performance, others with speed, and in other investigations, tasks involving the elimination of errors have been utilized. In any case, a review of the following studies has led to the conclusion that the current literature is inadequate. Numerous questions remain unanswered, and it is hoped that the ensuing discussion will not only summarize current knowledge but also stimulate the student to give consideration to undertaking research in this area.

RETENTION

Early Studies

Early studies focused primarily upon the retention of verbal materials. The classic work of Ebbinghaus,[269] as well as the studies of Luh[603] and Boreas,[96] indicated that for verbal material the majority of forgetting occurred during the few hours immediately after initial practice had been discontinued, with a negatively accelerated curve describing the forgetting process after the initial few hours. Later research involving verbal tasks identified other factors which seemed to affect retention. These included the method of measurement; the amount of original learning; the type, pleasantness, and amount of task; the degree of task complexity; the initial set of the learner; and the distribution of initial practice.

Swift[869,871] published studies from 1905 to 1910 concerned with the ability to keep two balls in the air simultaneously with one hand. He was one of the first investigators to report an interest in the retention of motor skill. In both investigations Swift found that, although some forgetting had occurred over periods of one and six years, respectively, relearning was rapid. He also found that in the final learning sessions the limiting factors seemed related to fatigue rather than to neuro-muscular integration. Using himself as a subject in a 1906 experiment, Swift reported that he had retained a considerable amount of typing skill over a two-year period and that relearning in 10 practice periods equalled 45 practice periods in the initial practice session two years before. Both Hill[455] in 1914, using a mirror drawing task, and Batson[59] in 1916, using ball tossing, also found that little loss of skill had occurred and rapid relearning took place, despite a period of no practice ranging from nine months to three years.

Recent Research on Retention

Hill[457] reported in 1957 on retention of typing skill, which is believed to be representative of the longest interval between original learning and relearning. He tested himself at twenty-five-year intervals, after original learning in 1907. It was found that retention was quite marked, with about 50 per cent retention of the first twenty-five years (in 1932) and about 25 per cent retention at the end of fifty years (in 1957).

Bell,[69] in 1950, using a pursuit motor task, produced findings that large amounts of retention existed up to one year after the initial learning took place and that relearning to the original criterion occurred far more rapidly than originally took place. Purdy and Lockhart[740] also demonstrated that gross motor skills are not readily forgotten and that rapid relearning takes place after an interval of one year without practice.

Both the early and more recent research suggest that motor skill seems remarkably resistant to extinction. In the following pages, some of the parameters which may contribute to retention are reviewed. The type of task, degree of original learning, and the nature of interpolated activities between initial learning and final tests of retention, massing vs. distributing practice and whole vs. part practice, will be the primary variables discussed.

VERBAL-MOTOR COMPARISONS, TASK ORGANIZATION, AND RETENTION

It was originally contended, because of the remarkable retention of motor material, that verbal skills were more likely to be forgotten than were motor skills.[610] Several studies were carried out to determine to what extent this generalization was true. McGeogh and Melton[639] in 1929, comparing the retention of maze tasks and lists of nonsense syllables, found no difference. Freeman and Abernathy,[323] in 1930, felt that motor acts were better retained perhaps because some degree of overlearning had taken place. They compared a typing task and a letter-for-numbers substitution task. Again, no retention differences were found at the end of two weeks, but with eight weeks of no practice, the motor task (typing) seemed to be retained best.

McGeogh[636] concluded that, since an early check on retention (after two weeks) revealed that motor materials were remembered best and after eight weeks verbal materials were retained best, verbal vs. motor retention was probably dependent upon a temporal variable. However, Freeman and Abernathy, replicating McGeogh's experiment, again found superior retention for motor activity. McGeogh suggested that over-practice reinforced motor skills more effectively than it did verbal skills.

In 1933, Waters and Poole[930] compared mental and finger mazes with similar degrees of difficulty to test McGeogh's overlearning hypothesis. In general, it was found that, when amount of practice was the same, no differences in retention occurred. Van Tilborg,[908] again attempting to control for difficulty by comparing a verbal-choice point "maze" (i.e., presenting sets of words in pairs, one of which was "right" and which allowed the individual to continue through the list) and a finger maze of comparable complexity, found no retention differences. This supported his hypothesis that difficulty was the primary factor.

Research in 1944 by Leavitt and Schlosberg[572] suggested that, since motor skills (e.g., typing and the like) represent tasks of a more inte-grated nature, they are more resistant to forgetting than are verbal skills (e.g., nonsense syllables), which are relatively more discrete. In short, they suggested that *task organization* was the most important factor in accounting for retention differences between motor skills and verbal tasks. Naylor and Briggs,[690] reviewing the research in this area, suggested that retention of an *arbitrary sequence,* either verbal or motor, was more difficult than were patterns of responses which involve meaningful patterns. They further indicated that differences between motor and verbal retention were due to difficulty and organiza-tional differences, rather than to the fact that one type of task primarily involved observable movement and the other either overt or covert verbalization.

A study by Ammons et al.[24] in 1958 and a report by Hufford and Adams reported by Naylor and Briggs[690] support the contention that task organization is an imperative variable when determining the amount of retention with other variables held constant. In general, it is found that a continuous task (e.g., tracking) is more resistant to extinction than one which involves discrete responses involving manipulations of paired switches and the like. Gagne and Fleishman[337] also suggested that human activities most resistant to forgetting are motor skills which are continuous, such as walking, swimming, and skating, as opposed to those consisting of separated movements.

Degree of Original Learning and Retention

It is a usual assumption that the higher the level of initial learning the more retention will occur. One of the first to test this hypothesis was Krueger[545] in 1930. Eight finger mazes were utilized and 3 degrees of initial learning were imposed on 3 groups (100, 150, and 200 per cent). Thus, if perfect performance was 6 trials without error, 150 per cent consisted of one and one-half times the original criterion, while 200 per cent was twice the original learning criterion. In general, it was found that the greatest per cent of retention occurred with between 100 and 150 per cent overlearning, and, although greater retention was evidenced after 200 per cent overlearning than after 150 per cent, there was not a direct relationship between overlearning and retention. Fleishman and Parker,[312] studying the retention of a tracking task over periods of one, five, nine, and fourteen months, also suggested that the most important factor was the level of initial learning.

Subsequent studies by Bell,[69] in 1950, and Rubin and Rabson,[769] in 1941, also suggest that, while original learning may facilitate retention to a degree, with increased amounts of learning, a point is reached which yields no extra returns. Although Purdy and Lockhart[740] suggest that initial performance in gross motor skills (balancing, throwing, and coordination movements) is a "valuable index" to future performance, there seems to be an optimal amount of overlearning in motor tasks which, if exceeded, does not produce proportionally more retention.

The Effect of Interpolated Activities Upon Retention

Several investigations have been concerned with the control of rest interval activity between the trials of serial memory tasks involving words. Generally, the findings indicate that the effect of the rest interval activity upon the primary task is a function of the intensity and type of the rest interval activity, of the instructions accompanying such activity with regard to mental rehearsal, and of the relationship between the rest interval activity and the primary task.

Mental Rehearsal. Sackett,[778] in 1934, found that the greater the amount of imaginary rehearsal, the greater the retention in a finger maze skill. Subsequent investigations by Egstrom,[273] involving ball hitting, Vandell, Davis, and Clugston,[905] involving dart throwing, Twining,[900] studying ring tossing, and Clark,[160] using a basketball foul shot, found that thinking through a movement was helpful. In no case, however, has mental practice, by itself, been demonstrated to be more efficient than physical practice, especially when muscular endurance is required to perform the task.[518] Although Start[851] found that the intelligence of the individuals engaged in mental rehearsal may not modify the effect upon motor learning, another investigation suggests that the nature of the task may be an important modifier.

In a study by Cratty and Densmore,[217] it was suggested that mental rehearsal may be more facilitating in a task which remains in a stable visual field than one that does not. No difference was found between groups whose time was occupied in simple noninterfering mental and motor tasks and a group that was permitted mentally to rehearse a locomotor maze task performed while blindfolded.

Similarity and Intensity of the Interpolated Activity. A discussion of this question involves the principle of transfer. However, it has been found that highly similar, as well as markedly different tasks will cause the least interference with the primary task, while tasks of moderate similarity will frequently cause a large degree of interference. This has been referred to as the Skaggs-Robinson hypothesis.

In general, research indicates that not only the similarity but also the intensity of the interpolated activity may be an important factor. Muller and Pilzecker[681] suggest that there is a continued neural discharge after activity of either a specific reflex-arc nature or of a generalized patterning function which might be inhibited if interpolated activity is sufficiently intense to interfere with the muscular and/or organic "set" produced by the original task learned.

THE NATURE OF WHOLE VS. PART PRACTICE

One of the questions with which experimenters have been concerned over the years has been the relative influence upon learning efficiency of practicing the *whole* of a task as opposed to first practicing its *parts*. Basically, it seems to be a question of the relative validity of a gestaltic theory as opposed to S-R theories of learning. Experimentally, the question has been approached from two standpoints: (1) an analysis of task performance efficiency using several criteria and (2) a study of the perceptual process, generally attempting to determine the amount an individual may perceive of a given task at a single exposure. The discussion within this section is mainly concerned with task analysis as viewed in performance measures.

Several combinations of whole-part practice conditions have been investigated. In addition to practicing the entire task, as opposed to practicing all of its parts separately, the *progressive-part method* has also been studied. This latter technique consists of first practicing the initial two parts of a task, combining these into a whole, learning a third part, and then chaining this to the first two, adding a fourth section, and so on. This process is then continued until the entire task seems mastered. In addition to these programs, the picture is made more complex by the several kinds of motor tasks that have been studied. Card-sorting, typewriting, and stylus mazes seem the favored manual tasks, while the gross motor skills investigated have included basketball skills and various gymnastic activities.

Accurate interpretation of the research in this area requires the formulation of common definitions for the terms "whole" and "economy of learning." For, according to Seagoe,[792] often what is really measured is the extent to which an individual is able to concentrate upon a task or the length of a subject's memory span, rather than the main problem in question.

The relative influence of various methods upon what kinds of "economy of learning" is a second crucial question. Does economy mean elimination of errors, increase in speed or rate of learning, improvement of accuracy, or just what? Studies by Koch[537] and Barton,[57] for example, indicate that the assessment of the best methods depends upon the definitions of economy. The *part method* sometimes aids in quickly reducing errors, while the *whole method* usually results in more rapid learning to a given criterion.

It also seems that the relative efficiency of one method or a second depends upon the nature of the task and upon the characteristics of the learner.[746,792] One investigator points out that high intelligence, advanced age, and/or a task of closely related sequences favor the *whole method.* When practice is massed and the material is difficult, the *part* or *progressive-part* method is usually found to be best. Other investigations indicate that retardates usually learn best by the part method,[461] while another researcher found that younger subjects learned best if the task was divided into component parts. Barton summarized this viewpoint by stating that to make "the units too large is to overwhelm the learner."

In general, a part method has been found to be wasteful of time, if the whole method suffices.[698] This finding has been attributed to the time that seems to be required when connecting the various parts

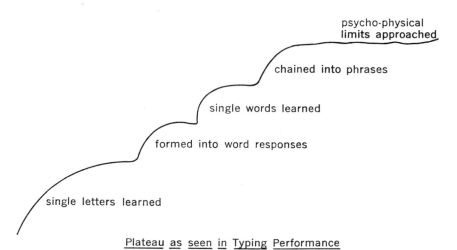

Plateau as seen in Typing Performance

FIG. 11

of a task and/or breaking up previously formed associations between parts. This may usually be seen in the plateau effect shown in learning curves. For example, when learning to type, progress is retarded as the learners change from single letter responses to movement patterns involving an entire word, and later to phrases. Similar plateaus are seen in the progressive performance measures of gross motor skills as time is required to chain parts together. No such time loss is experienced if the task is learned as a whole.

Further illustration of the relationship between the "best" method to use and the task complexity is found in Cross' study of basketball skills.[225] He reported that to learn simple unitary movements (e.g., passing and catching) the whole method proved best. In movements of greater complexity (e.g., stop-pivot-and-shoot), however, quicker progress was obtained with a progressive-part approach. Briggs and Naylor,[113] utilizing a tracking task, also suggested that the relative efficiency of whole vs. part training is a function of task complexity and the task organization. *Complexity* is defined as the ability to process information, while *organization* relates to establishing relationships between various task components.

The basic problem, therefore, seems to be recognizing the characteristics of motor "wholes." Seagoe[792] has helpfully synthesized concepts of "wholeness" into three statements: (1) It should be isolated and autonomous, an integrated unity. (2) It must have "form" quality. (3) It must be more than the sum of the parts; it must be a rational structure within itself. Such criteria might be considered subjective, but when it is considered that a kip on the hi-bar has been found to be best learned by the whole method,[806] while a four-part stylus maze task is best learned by the progressive-part method,[719] Seagoe's criteria become clearer.

The findings of a study completed in 1958 by Niemeyer[698] point to a second hypothesis which may clarify when the whole or the part method of teaching may be most effective. It was concluded that, when acquiring skills which involve complex interactions with an opponent (e.g., badminton and volleyball), the part method provides a sounder foundation. When learning movements which require no such interaction, on the other hand, the whole method seems superior. Although it was found that the whole method seemed to result in a better understanding of team interactions during the final stages of learning, more accurate performance was recorded when the skills were broken down into components during the early stages of acquisition.

Niemeyer's research[698] clearly demonstrated that learning to swim was carried out with far more efficiency when the whole method was used. This is due perhaps to the fact that when learning a whole movement less time is later needed to integrate the parts. Those taught the stroke as a unit were able to swim sooner, farther, faster, and with better form than those taught by the part method. Group differences were particularly striking when comparing the mean distances at the completion of the study. Those taught the whole stroke averaged 845 yards, while the group first learning the stroke by component parts averaged only 442 yards.

The task, therefore, seems to be to determine initially the characteristics and capacities of the learner and then to analyze the nature of the task. Quickest learning is generally obtained by practicing the "whole." If subsequent evaluation of performance suggests that the portions of the task selected, or a task as an entirety proved too large and/or complex for acquisition, the progressive-part method would then seem to hold the most promise.

Whole vs. Part Learning and Retention

Relatively few studies have dealt with the effect of initial whole vs. part learning upon long-term retention. Exceptions have been studies by Rubin-Rabson,[767] using piano playing as a task, and by Briggs and Waters,[114] who reported findings concerning the learning and retention of a complex tracking task in 1958.

Rubin-Rabson first studied the effect of practicing on the piano with only one hand vs. two-handed practice upon the retention of the same composition. The retention interval was fourteen days and final performance was with two hands. No significant differences were found between the two groups when re-tested. In a second study, three groups were utilized, and all subjects practiced with two hands. One group practiced the composition as a whole, a second practiced the piece in two parts, while a third practiced the composition in four segments. Again, after a fourteen-day period of no practice, no significant differences were noted among the three experimental groups.[768,769]

Although Briggs and Waters[114] found that initial whole practice facilitated retention of a tracking task, retention period was so short (twenty-four hours) that relatively little significance may be attached to their findings. It would thus seem that other variables, such as degree of initial learning and the type of task, are more influential upon retention than whether the task has been initially learned in parts or as a whole.

MASSING VS. DISTRIBUTING PRACTICE

A frequently investigated problem has been the relative efficiency of massing vs. distributing practice when learning various verbal or motor tasks. "Efficiency" usually refers to the level of final performance attained or the amount of retention evidenced at the completion of the learning program after a period of interpolated rest. Performance improvement due to the introduction of rest intervals has been termed "reminiscence."

The influence of many combinations of massing and/or spacing practice upon learning have been studied, including: (1) massing of practice with no rest intervals, (2) spacing of practice with rest intervals of a fixed duration, (3) initial massing of practice and gradually increasing the length of the rest intervals, (4) initial spacing and progressive massing or decreasing the length of rest intervals, (5) initial massing with irregularly introduced rests, or the reverse, and (6) initial spacing with irregularly introduced periods of massed practice. The complexity of the problem becomes apparent when it is realized that the distribution or massing of trials *within a single practice session* may also be varied according to these numerous schedules.

A number of tasks have been investigated in connection with the "reminiscence" effect. Initially the concern of the investigators was with verbal or rote learning tasks. Examples are the classic studies of Ebbinghaus[269] and Lyon,[606] based upon the retention of nonsense syllables.

While tasks of this nature continued to be investigated,[280,474] fine motor skills seemed to become a more popular evaluative tool, possibly because of the ease with which such performance is scored. Typical of these later studies are the investigations of Ammons,[77] Reynolds and Bilodeau,[752] and Snoddy,[840] using pursuit-rotors; Cook[173] and Pechstein,[720] using stylus mazes, and Lorge,[595] who used mirror-star tracing. Investigations of gross motor skills have appeared less frequently in the literature, although Harmon et al.,[419] using billiard playing, Lashley[562] and Young[987] using archery ability, Knapp and Dixon[533] studying juggling skill, and Neimeyer[698] using volleyball and badminton, are representative of this latter category.

The findings dealing with reminiscence are, at times, somewhat conflicting. Initially, the early investigators flatly concluded that spacing was more desirable than massing of practice, especially when verbal skills were involved.[269,606] According to more recent studies, distributed practice has been found to be effective also in a variety of tasks. Improvement of performance in a pursuit-rotor task,[22] juggling,[533] inverted alphabet printing,[508,818] and archery skill[987] was found to be benefited by the distribution of practice. In 1964, for example, Koonce, Davis and others[543] found that reminiscence in a pursuit-rotor task occurred after rest intervals of ten minutes, one, seven, thirty-five, seventy, one hundred and seventy-five, three hundred and sixty-five, and seven hundred and thirty days.

Less frequent are the findings which advocate the efficiency of massed practice. Both Pechstein[720] and Cook[773] found massing to be the most effective method of learning small stylus mazes and advanced skills in volleyball. Young[987] found that badminton was best learned when practice was massed, although Niemeyer found the opposite to be true of badminton skill.[698] In most cases the contention is that the mass-

19

ing of practice results in greater learning due to the fact that each performance strikes the forgetting curve of the previous performance at a higher level.

Changes of Learning Schedule

Numerous studies have investigated the effectiveness of various combinations of massing and spacing during the learning process. Tsai,[898] investigating mirror drawing, Harmon et al.,[418] studying billiard playing, Norris,[704] using a pursuit-rotor, and Niemeyer,[698] studying three sports skills, found that initial massing with subsequent spacing of practice produced the highest performance levels. These findings are usually attributed to a "warm-up" effect, or to the providing of a "foundation of understanding." Harmon has termed this initial massing with the introduction of gradually prolonged rests the "additive" method.

Lashley,[562] among others, found that early spacing with the later massing of trials proved to be most effective. This is generally attributed to the fact that once initial success is achieved in the task, such factors as fatigue or boredom, which might interfere in a massed practice situation, are somewhat negated. More willingness to work as the result of task-mastery is the hypothesis extended.

Zeaman and Kaufman[992] produced findings which indicate that fluctuating from a massed vs. distributed learning schedule may affect individual differences. Subjects performing an inverted alphabet writing task retained their starting differences when spaced practice conditions were retained, but lost their relative rankings when massed practice was introduced. It is interesting to note, however, that, when spaced practice was again resumed, the original skill differences became apparent.

A series of interesting studies were conducted at Columbia University several years ago. They involved irregularly introduced massing or spacing of practice in the learning situation. Using mirror-star tracing as a task, Gentry[349] found that when rests were suddenly introduced into a massed learning environment, more learning resulted. Conversely, Lorge[595] found that when trials were massed late in a spaced learning situation, performance dropped to a level achieved by a second group who had engaged only in massed practice. Extending the findings of his colleagues, Epstein[280] concluded that retention seemed more related to performance achieved than to the type of practice engaged in.

Generally less reminiscence is evidenced during the latter stages of the learning process, despite the arrangement of practice periods prior to reaching the limits of learning.[489]

Optimum Rest

Kimble[525] investigated the optimal amount of rest desirable between trials of pursuit-rotor tasks. Travis,[896] studying a gross tracking skill, found that twenty minutes was better than five minutes and also superior to longer time intervals up to one hundred and twenty hours. Kimble came to a similar conclusion, finding that the optimal rest interval was ten minutes. Ammons[22] also found an intermediate amount of rest was best when learning a pursuit rotor task. Several experimenters have found that best improvement is achieved when a day's rest is received.

It is interesting to note that Travis found that the performance of a gross motor skill (standing and attempting to keep a pointer on target) was aided by twice the rest time than was apparently desirable when performing and learning a fine motor task. Investigations of the relationship between fine and gross motor performance as a function of spacing or massing of practice seem to be lacking at the present time.

Several investigations indicate the advantage of twenty-four-hour rests, as opposed to practice carried on within a single day. Riopelle,[755] among others, has pointed to the advantage of inter-day rest as opposed to intra-day rest in the improvement of performance. Although studies of this nature are common, there is some uncertainty as to whether improvement is due to the twenty-four-hour rest, the sleep obtained, or to a combination of conditions.

Most studies of the reminiscence effect do not specify the number of trials in a particular practice session or at least have not attempted to deal with this important variable. The research by Hilgard, dealing with pursuit-rotor performance, is an exception, however.[452] While he found that the massing of practice within a single session proved initially most desirable, the spacing of trials in a single session became more effective later in the learning process. Plutchik and Petti[734] found that improvement in a pursuit-rotor task was more a function of the *relationship* between the time taken to perform the task and the rest between trials, rather than being dependent simply upon the length of the rest period. No significant differences were found in the mean rate of learning between work-rest ratios of forty to twenty seconds, thirty to sixty seconds, one to two minutes, two to four minutes, and five to two and one-half minutes. The findings suggest that there is an optimum work-rest ratio necessary for best performance and learning for a variety of tasks.

Reminiscence and Whole vs. Part Learning

Pechstein, in 1921, following up his investigation of the effect of massing in learning small stylus mazes, studied reminiscence as it related to whole vs. part learning of a complex maze task. Several interesting conclusions were forthcoming: (1) If the problem is short, massing is best. (2) Connecting the units of a complex task is most economical when practice is massed. Thus, to learn a complex skill, break it into parts and learn by massing practice. (3) Practice of the whole of a complex problem may strain the organism's capacity to analyze and to eliminate unnecessary task components. Pechstein termed this phenomenon the principle of "elimination."[720]

Pechstein also found that the habitual acquisition (the principle of "mechanization") of a complex task was facilitated by using the part method and massing practice. Such practice, it was felt, facilitated the connecting of the various parts of the task at the time the organism was ready to make such connections.

Theories of Reminiscence

The interpretation and synthesis of reminiscence studies is often difficult because of the number of variables which frequently are not controlled. For example, no control is usually exerted over what subjects do during rest intervals. Are they mentally rehearsing or reviewing the task? How are they being taught? How complex is the material being presented? What kinds of material are being learned, verbal, motor, or a combination?

It is usually found that more improvement will result as rest intervals are introduced. Several theories have been formulated to explain this phenomenon. Among them is the belief that intervals within the practice session result in more forgetting of the incorrect than of the correct responses.[114,266] Other experimenters have concluded that spacing of practice seems to reduce fatigue which may be building up in the learning situation.

Snoddy,[840] following twenty years of experimentation with the pursuit-rotor, formulated a theory of primary and secondary processes in mental growth. The initial improvement evidenced in learning curves was felt to be caused by the spacing of practice and was termed "primary growth." "Secondary growth," coming later, was felt to be the result of massed practice.

Hilgard and Marquis,[454] rejecting Snoddy's theory, proposed a more conventional explanation to describe the reminiscence effect. They concluded that with an overnight rest, forgetting is incomplete and that there is a residual gain from the previous day. "Learning," they believed, accounted for the relatively permanent growth base in the learning curve, "forgetting" for temporary losses.

Hull[477] viewed learning as the acquiring of "reaction potential," while at the same time "inhibiting" elements are building up. He felt that with distributed practice, inhibitory processes would largely disappear. Thus, he concluded, more improvement should result when practice periods are spaced. Adams[9] reported a detailed summary of the relationship of Hullian theory to the effects of massing and/or distributing the practice of motor skills.

Several authors have rejected the hypothesis that improvement takes place because of *rest intervals*. Webb,[933] finding that no difference was obtained in massing and distributing of practice on a pursuit-rotor, concluded that the *method used* to perform the task was of paramount importance in achieving improvement. Others feel that reminiscence is more closely related to the performance levels attained prior to rest. Kimble[527] attributed improvement after intervals of rest to motivational factors ("reminiscence after twenty-four hours is largely ego-centered").

Eysenck[290] has suggested that reminiscence is a function of drive. His subjects with high levels of drive (produced by suggesting that their scores were critical for their acceptance to engineering school) evidenced higher reminiscence scores during the initial stages of learning while response inhibition ($_sI_r$) inhibited their improvement because of rest during the latter stages of learning a pursuit-rotor task. On the other hand, subjects who were already assured of acceptance to engineering training evidenced less response inhibition during the latter performance trials.

Ammons,[27] among others, derived mathematical formulas to describe the optimal length of rest intervals to best learn a pursuit-rotor task. Goodenough and Brian,[382] on the other hand, seemed to view the interpolation of rest intervals as an art rather than a science and advocated appropriate interruptions when undesirable habits appear to be retarding progress. They concluded that the efficiency of massing or distributing practice is not based upon absolutes.

Additional Research Needed

A survey of the literature reveals that the question of whether massed or distributed practice is most productive of learning remains largely unanswered. Fleishman and Parker,[312] for example, found that initially re-learning was facilitated by distributing practice, but that within a short period of time there proved to be no difference in the amount of re-learning possible under massed or distributed conditions. Snoddy,[840] found that spacing increased accuracy while massing practice increased speed. These findings are largely confined to fine motor skills, however, and should be extended to determine whether this is true of gross motor skill. More research also seems needed concerning the spacing of trials and massing of trials within a single practice session. Research in this area has been briefly reviewed, but much additional investigation appears to be called for.

More extensive investigation of the nature of the task as affected by various practice conditions would appear fruitful. Are there differences between fine and gross motor learning with respect to reminiscence? Does the nature of the sensory cues depended upon when learning the task influence the effect of spacing practice? What is the role of fatigue, motivation, and other such variables upon reminiscence? What are the influences of a variety of work-rest ratios upon reminiscence in a variety of perceptual-motor tasks? These are only some of the problems needing clarification.

The existent research, however, justifies several generalizations: (1) The amount of spacing of practice seems related to the type of task and to the stage of learning reached. (2) Initial massing of practice seems the most desirable means of acquiring a basis from which to proceed. Considering Fleishman's research concerning the multitude of non-motor factors present during initial stages of learning motor tasks, it is plain that such massing must be intelligently applied and be accompanied by knowledge of the tasks. It is also noted that tasks which are largely motor (*e.g.*, nonvisual maze tracing) seem best learned by massing practice, while those requiring visual-motor coordination (*e.g.*, juggling and pursuit-rotors) seem most favorably affected by spacing practice. Such a generalization might certainly be questioned, however, when applied to gross motor skills because of fatigue during performance.

Research indicates that the optimal rest time is specific to the nature of the task. Thus, in the absence of exact formulas for the multitude of tasks possible in physical education and in allied fields, one might well follow the course of action advocated by Goodenough and Brian[382] initially employ mass practice after first analyzing the task to determine its requirements. If, upon subsequent evaluation of performance, improvement seems to diminish or plateaus result, rest intervals can be introduced and their effect upon progress studied.

The amount of reminiscence evidenced at a given point in the learning of a given skill depends simply upon the interest of the performer in the skill rather than upon more subtle factors. If the task is interesting, massing practice will produce best results. If the performer is not challenged by the task, it is too difficult, or he is otherwise repelled by it, distributing practice will lessen the effects of these unpleasant feelings and produce the best learning.

Massing vs. Distributing Practice and Retention

Relatively few studies have been carried out relating the degree to which initial practice has been massed and/or distributed to the amount of long-term retention evidenced. In 1952, Reynolds and Bilodeau,[752] using a pursuit-rotor and a rudder control task, found that no differences in retention scores were recorded between groups receiving various degrees of massed vs. distributed practice in the initial learning bouts. Retention testing was held ten weeks after original learning, and it was concluded that, for this period of time, distributed practice effects had disappeared.

In 1954, Adams and Reynolds,[6] using a rotary-pursuit task, found that whether practice was massed or distributed had no permanent *learning effects*, that fluctuations were noted only in momentary *performance* increments. Two groups of subjects were used in this study, working under both massed and distributed practice conditions.

Lewis and Lowe,[580] using a two-dimensional motor skill task, found a massed practice group retained best. Jahnke and Duncan,[491] on the other hand, using a pursuit-rotor apparatus, found that subjects who had participated in initial learning bouts under distributed practice conditions retained the higher skill levels after a period of no practice which was comparable to that used by Lewis and Lowe.[580] While the practice conditions and retention intervals were comparable in these two studies, other variables were not. The tasks were dissimilar as was the amount of original learning. Thus, no clear-cut statement may be made concerning the relative efficiency of massing vs. distributing practice as related to long-term retention. It appears that other factors, the integrated nature of the task, the length of the retention period, and the amount of original learning, are more important variables.

SERIAL-ORDER, LEARNING, AND RETENTION

The location of the practiced action within a series of movements influences learning and retention. In the case of humans, it has usually been demonstrated that in serial tasks involving chained-movements, the initial movements are learned first, next to be acquired are the final portions, and last to be learned are the middle parts. The learning of nonsense syllables has long demonstrated this same phenomenon. Research by Hicks and Carr,[451] as well as by Cratty,[914] indicates that the generalization holds true as humans learn locomotor mazes, whether of a static right-angle pattern or of rounded S-shaped curves. Animal studies, on the other hand, generally indicate that the final portions of a series of movements (e.g., a maze) are learned first. This has been attributed to the strong motivating effects of the terminal reward usually employed in such investigations.

In human learning, however, the end and beginning of the series seem to have a delineating effect which marks off these portions and makes them easier to learn. In addition, a "load" of material acquired near the beginning of a series can become so great that the learner seems to reach a limit to the amount he can "carry," thus making it more difficult to recall material near the middle portions.

Whether the differences in animal and human learning with respect to serial-order phenomena are due to motivating conditions or the complexity of the organism seems unclear at this time. Research is also lacking concerning whether materials of a discrete nature presented throughout a practice period, or during a school year, also follow a recency-primacy pattern.

SUMMARY

Although it is usually suggested that skilled movements are more resistant to forgetting than is written material, inspection of the research reveals that the internal consistency of the task (motor or verbal) is the more effective variable. Thus, nonsense syllables, as well as movements which are unique and discrete, are more quickly forgotten than are movements which are related to some logical task and which flow together into a patterned whole.

Although the nature of the task dictates whether whole, part, or progressive-part practice is more efficient, in general it is suggested that for quickest acquisition material be assimilated in as large a "whole" as the learner's perceptual span permits. Spacing practice also seems to facilitate learning of motor skills when boredom or fatigue begins to retard performance.

Retention is influenced primarily by the degree to which a task has been learned originally. Tasks which have been overlearned (to a point) are more resistant to forgetting than are tasks which have barely been acquired. Movements at the initial and final parts of a series are more quickly learned than those near the middle. Thus, the most important variables to be considered when studying the retention of skilled movements are not the methods by which the task was originally learned but the integrated nature of the task, the length of the retention period, its order in a series, and the amount of original learning which had taken place.

Student References

Articles

1. FLEISHMAN, EDWIN A. and PARKER, JAMES F., JR.: "Factors in the retention and relearning of perceptual-motor skill," *J. Exp. Psych.*, September 1962 v. 64 no. 3 p. 215-226.
2. HILL, L. B.: "A second quarter century of delayed recall or relearning at eighty," *J. Educational Psych.*, 48, 65-68, 1957.
3. KRUEGER, W. C. F.: "Further studies in overlearning," *J. Exper. Psych.*, 13, 152-63, 1957.
4. NAYLOR, JAMES C. and BRIGGS, GEORGE E.: "Long-term retention of learned skills. A review of the literature," August 1961, Behavioral Sciences Laboratory, Wright-Patterson Air Force Base, Ohio.
5. PECHSTEIN, LOUIS A.: "Alleged elements of waste in learning a motor problem by the 'part' method," *J. Educational Psych.*, 8, 303-310, 1917.
6. PURDY, BONNIE J. and LOCKHART, AILEEN: "Retention and relearning of gross motor skills after long periods of no practice," *Res. Quart.*, 33, p. 3, 1962.
7. SEAGOE, MAY V.: "Qualitative wholes: A re-evaluation of the whole part problem," *J. Educational Psych.*, 27, 537-545, 1936.
8. SWIFT, E. J.: "Relearning a skillful act: An experimental study in neuro-muscular memory," *Psych. Bull.*, 7, 17-19, 1910.

Chapter 18

Transfer

Two factors basic to human learning are said to be the ability to discriminate and the ability to generalize. The transfer concept is closely related to the latter quality and involves the tendency to draw from past experience when learning a new task. To define *transfer* merely as generalization, however, is similar to stating that green is greenness and white, whiteness. It is felt that for clarity, *transfer* is best explained as *the effect that the practice of one task has upon the learning or performance of a second.*

The basketball mentor strives to construct practice tasks that will be transferable to the game situation. The physical therapist is concerned with the re-education of an impaired limb as an adjacent member is exercised. The physical educator and industrial psychologist are interested in facilitating the learning of complex skills and in devising test batteries which might predict proficiency in a variety of tasks. An understanding of transfer is important to the athletic coach, the physical educator, the industrial psychologist, and the therapist.

In addition to the obvious "how to do it better" approach to the learning of skills, a review of the research dealing with transfer sometimes aids in the identification of basic task factors. If transfer is caused by the presence of identical elements in two tasks, identification of these elements usually results in a deeper understanding of movement constituents. Investigation of transfer also helps to clarify the generality and specificity question discussed in Chapter 14.

The extent to which transfer occurs among various mental and motor tasks has been at the core of educational theory for the past one hundred years. Those advocating a formal doctrine of education felt that general habits, including the ability to think and reason, transferred from such school subjects as Latin and algebra to many tasks. At the turn of the century, however, many educational psychologists, upon finding only slight transfer from one school subject to another, suggested that human functioning was highly specific. The controversy continues, and the extent to which practice of one task facilitates a second frequently rests upon the kind of evidence the experimenter is willing to consider, as well as the kinds of tasks under consideration.

The transfer concept may be studied in several contexts. Transfer may be negative, have no influence, or be positive in quality. Practice of an initial task may facilitate, have no significant influence, or impede the learning of a second.

Some investigators have insisted that all adult learning and performance results from transfer from childhood experiences. McGeogh and Irion,[638] for example, have suggested that after "small amounts of learning early in the life of the individual, every instance of learning is a result of transfer." Hebb[432] points out that, when little or no "transfer" occurs when comparing adult skills, it is probably due to the fact that transfer from the individual's past experiences "must have been complete before the experiments began." In contrast are those researchers who contend that, because of the limited extent to which skilled movements are seen to transfer in studies using mature subjects, motor performance and learning are highly dependent upon specific conditions connected with the immediate task.

Upon further consideration of motor skills research, several other classification systems become apparent. On the one hand are investigations dealing with cross-education, or the bilateral and unilateral transfer of skill and/or strength in the individual. These studies investigate the extent to which skill and strength are transferred from limb-to-limb (hand-to-hand, hand-to-foot, foot-to-hand). A second category deals with the influence of the performance and practice of one complex skill upon the proficiency of a second. In this second group are studies which explore the influence of verbal pre-training upon a motor task, the transfer of task components to the completed act, the transfer of task principles, and the transfer of skills containing similar or different spatial dimensions, force requirements, and/or time intervals.

Following a brief historical overview of the problem, research on cross-education will be discussed together with investigations of transfer between tasks. The influence of practice schedule and task complexity upon transfer is also discussed within this section. The chapter concludes with a summary, including questions which remain to be answered concerning the transfer phenomena.

AN HISTORICAL LOOK AT TRANSFER

As pointed out by Wieg,[962] interest in the problem of transfer between limbs dates back to the middle of the nineteenth century. Weber, in the United States, and Fechner, in Germany, both found that training of distance discrimination transferred from the trained hand to the idle one. In 1899, Woodworth[981] discovered that the ability to draw straight lines was transferrable between limbs. In 1892, Bryant reported the same phenomenon when measuring the tapping ability of children at various ages. He also found that cross fatigue was independent of general body fatigue.[123] Scripture,[790] working at the Yale Psychological Laboratory at the turn of the century, also found that transfer of skill occurred between limbs of the body. This was found to be true when studying a tapping exercise, and he also discovered the phenomenon when investigating the ability to thrust a needle into a small hole. Transfer studies concerned with the cross-education effect continued during the years and utilized stylus mazes,[175] adding machine tasks, mirror target practice,[106] and the like.

The first studies concerned with transfer between tasks mainly seemed based upon mental problems. While prior to 1900 educators assumed that such general qualities as attention to a task and the ability to reason transferred between various school subjects, Thorndike and Woodworth,[883] in their classic study published in 1901, declared the opposite to be true. After studying a number of tasks they concluded that human functioning (both mental and motor) was specific. They felt that it was incorrect to be concerned with general qualities, such as sense discrimination, attention, memory, observation, accuracy, and quickness, which were purported to underlie a number of tasks. Rather they felt that an individual's mind works in great detail, adapting itself to the "special data of the situation."

Although subsequent studies have purported to examine transfer between various "motor" tasks, in reality most of the transfer studies utilize tasks which rely heavily upon verbal-cognitive functions. Various tracking studies by Lincoln and Smith,[586] rotary pursuit tasks by Namikas and Archer[688] and others, as well as various paired association tasks, encourage the subject verbally to rehearse elements which might result in transfer. Studies concerned with "pure" motor acts are less frequent, although those by Woodward,[980] Cratty,[197] Henry,[443] Lindeberg,[589] and Nelson[692] point in this direction.

THEORIES OF TRANSFER

Numerous theories have been devised to explain transfer of skill. While the identical elements theory and the general factors theory are the most popular, several others become apparent upon reviewing the literature. A third category might include statements which accept both a general and specific explanation of transfer. A general gestaltic concept of "transposition" has also been proposed. In addition, various neurological explanations have been reported which attempt to explain transfer in anatomical terms. The concept of "nerve impulse diffusion" is representative of this latter classification.

General Elements Theory

The initial proponent of the general factors theory was Judd.[508] He concluded that general instructions were transferable, since he found individuals were aided in hitting a submerged target with an arrow when the principle of refraction of light was explained to them. Judd felt that motor accuracy was due to unconscious transfer from previous tasks to an individual's present movement needs and came about as a result of the utilization of neurological pathways previously established for earlier tasks.

Several studies reported in the intervening years seem to substantiate the general elements theory first proposed by Judd. In 1921, Norcross,[703] studying adding machine skill, concluded that transfer was due to emotional factors, mental readiness for the task, ability to concentrate on the task, freedom from distractions, and other general conditions. Woodward,[980] studying the transfer of training in two industrial skills, felt that, although the transfer found might have been due to the presence of identical spatial requirements in the two tasks, it was more likely due to a similarity in the general work situations.

Harlow, in his classic investigation of "learning sets," concluded that both children and primates evidenced the ability to begin at successively higher levels when problems of a single classification were presented to them. Both species seemed to be learning how to learn, and the author suggested that his data indicated that his subjects "can gradually learn insight."[413]

Seymour,[803] presenting a synthesis of transfer literature in 1955, suggested that transfer is merely evidence that individuals learn to select the most appropriate muscle groups to be used, resulting, for example, in less "fumbling" when performing industrial tasks. He felt that improvement was generally due to improving general methods rather than to transfer of specifics. Seymour concluded his synthesis with the suggestion that experiments be conducted which investigate general principles of transfer, rather than task minutia. In addition, Seymour felt that the study of individual differences in the ability to transfer experience should hold promise for the future.

Denny and Reisman,[248] studying the role of anxiety in transfer, presented findings which suggest that general tension might impede transfer of skill. Individuals scoring high on Taylor's Manifest Anxiety Scale, when attempting to transfer skill, had more marked initial feelings of failure when the task changed and did poorly in subsequent attempts at the changed task. Individuals who were not anxious, on the other hand, were found to adapt more readily to a change of task and to benefit more from the previous task practice.

In 1952, Lewis and Smith[581] presented a summary of the prevalent arguments for a general factors theory of motor transfer. After finding that transfer was not impeded when specific stimuli and responses of a task were modified, they proposed a theory which attempted to explain the acquisition of proficiency in complex motor tasks and the simultaneous negative and positive transfer effects sometimes seen. Lewis and Smith felt that five constructs were important in summarizing their

argument:[581] (1) *dexterity,* understanding the general task requirements, (2) *facilitating,* the tendency to respond to general unchanging
features of a task, (3) *skill,* the ability to modify one's responses and to
predict changes in the task situation while performing, (4) *interference,*
the tendency, due to past experience, to make inappropriate responses
to any part of the task situation, and (5) *inhibition,* the tendency to
suppress irrelevant or inappropriate responses. *Performance potential,*
it was concluded, was a function of all of the tendencies to make appropriate responses or to inhibit inappropriate ones, minus some function
of all tendencies to make inappropriate ones.

Identical Elements Theory

More numerous are the studies which point out that transfer is possible
only when elements of one task correspond exactly to those of the second.
Generally, these elements are considered to consist of similar stimulus
conditions or responses which are identical. So, while the generalist
speaks of common conditions resulting in transfer, the researcher advocating the identical elements theory is concerned with small bits of
the tasks in the form of discrete stimuli or responses which are similar,
rather than with patterns or meanings.

Baker and Wylie,[46] in 1950, and Namikas and Archer,[688] in 1960,
reported findings that upheld the identical elements theory. Both, utilizing rotary pursuit tasks, found that greatest transfer occurred when
the revolutions of their devices were similar. Individuals seemed to
program their "memory drums" specifically for the task practiced, following a target at 60 r.p.m. rather than at 70 or 50 r.p.m.

Lincoln,[585] studying tracking ability, and Smith and Von Trebra,[832]
investigating the ability to manipulate knobs and to travel manually
from one knob to another, and Gagne et al.,[335] studying the ability to
press buttons when presented with light stimuli, all point to the specificity of skill and hold that transfer is due to similarity in responses or
stimuli conditions between two variations of the same task.

In general, such researchers theorize that a "gradient of generalization" exists with relation to stimulus or to response and that transfer
will occur to the extent that similarities between either exist. In some
cases it is said that subjects generalize from stimulus to stimulus or
recognize similarities in the elements which cue or trigger the movements
of the task. In this context, the S-R specificist holds that *stimulus generalization* has caused the transfer. In other cases, it is felt that a similarity
in responses facilitated transfer, that the subject, usually on the conscious
level, recognized the similarity in the movement responses required of
him when performing the two tasks. In this latter case it is said that
response generalization has taken place.

Gestaltic Theory

In opposition to those advocating specificity of transfer and slightly modified from the position taken by most generalists who attempt to explain transfer in neurological terms, stand the classic Gestalt learning theorists who hold that transfer occurs when a pattern of dynamic relationships is discovered to exist in two learning situations. "Transposition" is said to take place if the practice of one task facilitates the learning of a second.

"Transposition" may occur due to the presence of common patterns, configurations, or relationships. One learns, it is believed, from previous task experience through understandings, not through the discovery of piecemeal stimuli or discrete responses common to two situations. It is felt that through this type of understanding one is able to transfer his experience to a wider range of situations, rather than to the limited ones possible in stimuli-response terms.

Cratty[204] published a study in 1961 which utilized gestaltic terms to explain transfer. Studying the effect of small pattern practice upon large pattern learning (using maze tasks of varying sizes), he found that blindfolded practicing of a similar small pattern facilitated large pattern learning, and that practice in a reverse small pattern impeded large pattern learning. Negative and positive transfer occurred, depending upon pattern relationships. The subjects seemed to learn the tasks as patterned wholes and seemed unaware of the relationships involved, due to the irregular shape of the maze pathways and the emphasis upon speed in performance. Cratty concluded that explanation of the negative and positive transfer found was best accomplished in gestaltic terms.

Two-Factor Theories

In addition to theories which point to general neurological factors, those which support an identical elements theory, and those which utilize gestaltic terms, several investigators suggest that transfer may occur due to a combination of factors both general and specific. This theory suggests that individuals not only transfer such generalities as "learning-how-to-learn" and "general work methods," but also learn new tasks through the acquisition of stimulus and/or response patterns.

This theory was advanced by Munn[682] in 1932 as he studied the bilateral transfer of mirror-tracing. He concluded that the formulation of method as well as discrete movements of the opposite hand probably caused transfer. Duncan,[262] in 1952, echoed this view when, studying transfer in a lever-positioning skill, he concluded that "learning-how-to-learn," as well as "response generalization," had facilitated transfer. Wieg,[962] studying bilateral transfer of adults and children when learning cul-de-sac mazes, also felt that attention to the task as well as attention to discrete cues facilitated transfer from one maze task to another.

Norcross,[703] in 1921, studying the ability to utilize an adding machine, felt that various emotional factors, readiness for the task as well as task specifics, influenced transfer. Swift,[872] studying the ability to keep two balls in the air with one hand, concluded that alterations in the central nervous system as well as the ability to comprehend and to meet a situation caused the bilateral transfer discovered. Meredith,[653] reporting research in 1941, also took an eclectic approach when explaining transfer. He felt that transfer depends upon an individual's awareness of the usable common elements, verbalization of the task, and factors unique to the task.

From a theoretical standpoint, then, transfer may be explained as depending upon (1) general factors underlying several tasks, (2) pathways on the nervous system, (3) the existence of identical elements (usually stimuli-response elements) common to two tasks, (4) the "transposition" of meanings, understanding, or configurations from one task to a second, and (5) a combination of factors both general and specific. It would seem that the last explanation holds the most promise at the present time. Studies relating to tasks which can be analyzed in discrete elements (e g, paired serial learning tasks and light to lever position) generally support the identical elements theory, while studies of more complex and integrated tasks support a generalized or gestaltic approach. The careful student, however, seems to attribute most frequently the influence of one complex task upon the performance and learning of a second to several kinds of factors, those accompanying the general experimental environment as well as conditions unique to the tasks compared.

BILATERAL TRANSFER OF SKILL

Initial studies concerning the transfer phenomenon came about when it was observed that the performance of a skill with one hand seemed to "teach" the same skill to the other hand. Such transfer from hand-to-hand is termed "bilateral" transfer. Although bilateral transfer has been studied from several standpoints and many kinds of motor and perceptual-motor tasks have been employed, much remains to be learned. Reviews of research concerning cross-transfer were prepared by Wieg[962] in 1932 and Bray[106] in 1928. A review of the research on bilateral transfer of skill was written by Ammons[24] in 1958.

Most of the skills studied to determine the nature and conditions of cross-education of skill have involved fine motor tasks or perceptual motor skills. Wieg's[962] cul-de-sac maze tasks learned without sight, and Cook's[176] small irregular patterned mazes are examples. One of the few studies in the literature dealing with a gross motor skill is that of swift,[872] completed in 1903, which studied the transfer of juggling skill from hand-to-hand (keeping two balls in the air with one hand). The task used, however, seems heavily dependent upon cognitive and verbal elements.

In general, the research indicates that transfer from hand-to-hand of a skilled act, to some degree, always occurs. It is usually taken to indicate that skilled performance is a function of *central* rather than *peripheral* processes in the nervous system. In early studies in this area by Woodworth[981] and by Bray,[106] a motor task observed by the performer in a mirror was utilized. Woodworth[981] used mirror-star tracing; Bray utilized target spotting with a pencil while viewing the act from a mirror.[106] Both found that transfer not only occurred from hand-to-hand, but also from hand-to-foot and from foot-to-foot and from feet-to-hands. Cook also found that transfer between all four limbs of the body occurred when learning a maze task.[176] Eberhard published an investigation in recent years which makes a valuable contribution to our knowledge of transfer; specifically it pointed to the importance of the visual processes in the learning of visual-motor skills. It was found that as much bilateral transfer occurred in a one-handed manipulative task as was derived by the subjects when they simply *watched* another individual perform the task first![270]

Researchers concerned with cross-education of skilled performance have given many reasons for the occurrence of the phenomena. Ammons,[24] summarizing studies in this area, suggests that the following are the usual rationale given for bilateral transfer: cues from verbal self-instruction, visual cues, relaxing effects of practicing a skill, general muscular tension accompanying the skill, body position and posture, movements of the entire body, eye movements, head movement, complex perceptual adjustments, formulating principles of efficiency, familiarity with the general nature of the task, neural structure, past learning of highly similar skills, fatigue effects, consistency and stability of approach, subliminal practice of the skill by the ostensibly idle limbs, solutions to problems in the handling of equipment, emotional adjustments, and feelings of confidence or boredom.

The questions seem to be, what kinds of practice conditions and tasks best facilitate transfer? And more important, will learning of a skill with one hand be facilitated by ambidextrous practice during the learning process? Few attempts seem to have been made to answer these questions, although Bray suggests, in a mirror-target hitting task, that cross-education was present only during the initial trials, with later ones showing no such transfer effects.[106] In addition, Allen[15] suggests that alternate practice from hand-to-hand of a mirror-drawing task produced higher efficiency than massed practice with the same hand prior to attempting the skill with the second limb.

Studies have also shown that the effects of motivation further becloud the amount of bilateral transfer observed. Ammons felt that the lowering of proficiency in a rotary pursuit task by high school girls in the upper grades was probably due to motivation. He further suggested that with a high level of motivation a poorly transferable task would be frustrating and would probably produce extreme variability of performance. Likewise, a poorly motivated group might not exhibit the transfer expected due to a lack of attention to the details of the task or some other such factor.[24]

There is some conjecture, however, as to whether more transfer occurs from the dominant to the non-dominant hand, or whether the reverse is true, and whether such transfer is due to the dominance factor, or be due to the general level of limb proficiency. In general, it would seem that both factors are operative. Swift suggests that, in juggling a ball, the transfer from right to left hand was less when the proficiency of the left hand was lower.[872] The same was found to be true by Briggs and Brodgen[112] using a pursuit task.

This suggests that the amount of transfer occurring is mainly a function of the proficiency of the limb *from* which or *to* which the transfer occurs. Wieg,[962] for example, found that for adults, transfer of a maze skill was greater than for children. Cook's[176] studies also suggest that transfer is determined by the proficiency of the first limb trained.

The use of research findings concerning the transfer phenomenon may be twofold: (1) Some experimental evidence may be used to study the effects of brain damage and of other injury to the central nervous system. Freeman utilized bilateral transfer to pinpoint neurological functioning.[322] (2) Transfer research may be utilized to identify the common components of two tasks or to identify discrete elements present in the learning of a new task.

Ammons[24] suggested that a "reference" skill, the components of which have been identified, might be used in studying factors in a second task. Greater objectivity needs to be achieved in pinpointing common factors that appear to be related to positive transfer between skills, however, before the use of such "reference" skills can be applied with confidence to ordinary skill development.

Cross-Transfer and Physical Education

What implications do the findings on transfer from hand-to-hand have for the physical educator? Most so-called gross motor tasks such as ball throwing, involve fine adjustments. The finite adjustments of fingers, for example, are necessary when releasing a ball in a throwing act. It would seem that practice with both hands, the dominant and the non-dominant, might facilitate the learning of many such tasks by the preferred hand. If findings concerning the effects of fatigue upon accuracy are valid, it would seem that one might practice longer, and with more positive results, by utilizing the non-dominant hand while resting the dominant one. If skill is partially a function of the central nervous system, practice at the cortical level might continue, while localized muscular fatigue in a particular limb might impede continued practice with the single body member. Investigations of these concepts are at present absent in the literature.

Further research is needed to identify (1) the kinds of tasks which seem to transfer most effectively, (2) the reasons for the occurrence of bilateral transfer, and (3) at what point practice with the non-preferred limb should be introduced for best results. In addition, the important variable of motivation in relation to amount of transfer needs further investigation, as does the transfer of skills from hand-to-foot and from feet-to-feet. Soccer skills, for example, involve extensive use of the lower extremities. From a practical standpoint, coaches of this sport might be interested in the extent to which the feet acquire movements first learned by the upper limbs and the extent to which left-footed kicking practice facilitates right-leg proficiency.

VERBAL-MOTOR TRANSFER

Transfer from hand-to-hand (or cross-transfer) is sometimes found to be facilitated by verbal self-instruction, by solution of special task problems, or through the formulation of principles relative to two tasks. Consequently, it would seem important to examine the extent to which verbal pre-training transfers to the performance of a skilled motor act.

Most of the tasks used in studies in this area have consisted of paired-serial skills. An example is seen in a study by Gagne et al.,[336] who used a panel of switches cued by visual signals. Verbal rehearsal of the correct pairings between a visual signal and a switch was practiced. The extent to which verbal pre-training transferred to the motor act was studied and taken as the amount of speed achieved in the final visual-motor act. A level positioning skill used by Battig[60] and the pairing of lights to switches studied by Baker et al.[46] are typical examples of the types of skill which seem best adaptable to verbal pre-training.

In most cases, a complex motor task involving discrete stimuli-response elements, either alone or in series, is facilitated by verbal rehearsal of the pairings desired. Practicing a verbal formula (e.g., "red light means number one switch" or "initial positioning of a lever," "blue light means switch number three,") seems to transfer to the motor act. Subjects who received this type of training performed at a higher level than did those who received no such training.

There seems, however, to be an optimal amount of pre-verbal practice. Baker,[46] for example, found that small amounts of pre-verbal practice had no effect, and it was only when larger amounts were introduced that the light-to-switch skill was facilitated. Underwood,[902] on the other hand, found that after a certain amount of verbal pre-training later improvement was not noted.

Verbal pre-training seems to facilitate a motor act that is easily translated to a word description. In addition to the kinds of paired serial tasks already described, McAllister[624] found that verbal pre-training facilitated a task in which the subjects were required to move a rod to various star points upon being confronted with colored light stimuli. Pre-training, using word formulas, seemed most helpful in reducing errors, rather than in improving speed in tasks of this nature.

The literature deals mainly with the effect of verbal pre-training in connection with paired association acts. Motor acts involving fast or irregular movement patterns either have not been studied or are so difficult to reduce to a word formula that the results have been negative or simply have not lent themselves to verbal pre-training.

It would seem that the baseball coach, requiring accurate placement of the ball in discrete game situations, might rely upon verbal pre-training. (Instruction such as, "With two outs and a man on first, a ball hit to the short stop should be relayed to second base," might facilitate the motor act.) On the other hand, it appears doubtful that an excessive amount of verbal pre-training in an irregular and continuous movement pattern, as is required in a tennis serve, would facilitate learning. In some cases, it is suggested that an excessive amount of verbal pre-training might result in impaired performance, as the performer attempts to slow down a ballistic pattern to correspond to the time needed to translate the movement into a word formula.

Although further research is needed in this area, it appears accurate to assume that paired-associative type tasks will probably be facilitated by a moderate amount of verbal pre-training, while movements of an irregular or rapid nature probably will not be greatly aided by the same type of pre-task verbalizing.

TASK-TO-TASK TRANSFER

Studies of transfer from one motor or spatial-motor task to another, using mature subjects, usually point to the specificity of motor skill. Lindeberg[587] studied the transfer of "coordination" exercises to sports activities and found none. Nelson,[692] in another study of gross motor activities, indicated that the deliberate teaching of principles for three pairs of sports skills produced negative effects. This may have resulted from incorrect statements or misunderstanding of the principles. For example, when transfer between tennis and badminton is compared, although the stimuli present are similar (i.e., both involve hitting an object with a racket), the responses required are quite different. Badminton requires wrist action, while tennis requires movement of the entire arm. Slight transfer was found, however, between the initial learning of a tennis skill and a badminton skill.

Langdon and Yates[555] found little transfer among various manual skills closely approximating industrial tasks. Namikas *et al.*[680] and Lordahl and Archer,[560] on studying the transfer effect between various conditions surrounding pursuit motor performance, found that transfer to the same speed was highest, while Lordahl found that when the radius of the pursuit rotors was the same the transfer was greatest. As Namikas *et al.* pointed out, individuals seemed to learn a specific set of motor components.[688]

Transfer from the Simple to the Complex

Should one expect more transfer from a complex task to a simple one, or might the reverse be expected? Does the learning of a simple task facilitate the learning of a more complex one? The experimental evidence seems contradictory.

Lawrence,[569] using a discrimination task with animal subjects, found that transfer was greatest if learning occurred from the simple to the complex. Gagne, Baker, and Foster,[335] using human subjects on a similar task (hitting switches in response to light cues), found the reverse to be true in that the most difficult kinds of discrimination seem to transfer best to the simpler components of the task. Lewis, Smitt, and McAllister,[624] using a two-handed coordination task, found that transfer from a difficult to an easy task may be greater as the initial task requires more facilitation of the correct responses and inhibition of the incorrect ones. A simple skill, on the other hand, might be performed without extensive learning, thus reducing or eliminating the amount of transfer found.

Seymour[803] found that his subjects seemed to fumble less when learning the whole of an industrial task because more perception of the correct and appropriate muscle groups was required. He also found that positive transfer from a part of an extremely complex task to the whole was also noted in his experimental findings. Lordahl and Archer found that more positive transfer was noted from simple to the complex than occurred in the reverse direction. Using a pursuit rotor task, greater transfer was found when the r.p.m.'s were increased from 40 to 60 than was noted when the initial learning occurred at 80 r.p.m., and the secondary task involving practicing with the rotor at 60 r.p.m.

Holding[462] concluded that transfer is not simply a function of the easy-difficult dichotomy, but is influenced by other factors. Mukherjee also states that transfer is a direct function of initial ability attained rather than being dependent upon the difficulty-to-easy argument.[680]

Thus, it would seem that whether more transfer might be expected from the simple to the complex, or in the reverse direction, is a function of the task and experimental conditions. The question is further confounded when an attempt is made to objectify and equate "simple" and "complex" with "easy" and "difficult." For example, Seymour[803] found

that the whole of the task (the apparently complex aspect of performance) was actually easily performed because of its integrated nature.
One might therefore conclude that for practical purposes most transfer
can be expected to occur from the complex to the simple. The ability
to master a difficult skill will certainly facilitate a less complex component. The problem is to select a complex skill for which the simple one
is really a component and which will not prove too difficult in initial
mastery. If transfer is desired in the opposite direction (from simple to
complex), again intelligent selection of the initial, simple skill must be
made. Too simple a beginning would probably result in little transfer,
unless considerable overlearning takes place.

Transfer of Motor Habits over a Time Interval

In the absence of studies using human subjects, we must turn to a
series of articles completed from 1936 to 1946 by M. E. Bunch[126] and
others, who investigated negative and positive transfer of animal maze
habits as influenced by time intervals between learning bouts. In general,
it was found that the longer the time interval, the less positive transfer
was noted between tasks.

Bunch's findings concerning negative transfer, however, are more
complex. In general, it was found that at first, if the interval between
practice and re-test was not too great, negative transfer effects appear
which are similar to those noted as related to positive transfer (i.e., a
gradually decreasing function of the time interval). However, past
a certain point in time, negative effects disappear and positive transfer
becomes evident, which in turn finally declines gradually toward a
zero effect as the time interval is prolonged still more. As a result of
this finding, Bunch concluded that whether one habit is antagonistic
to another is a function of the interval between initial acquisition of the
two habits, rather than because of the relationship between task components.

Although it is often difficult to generalize from animal studies, it is
believed that these findings suggest research which might prove helpful
in understanding the transfer effect in humans over a time interval.

Motivation, Fatigue, and Transfer

As has been suggested, practice conditions and factors which influence
skill transfer are numerous. Several astute researchers have attributed
transfer to both negative and positive variables, other than improved
neuromuscular efficiency or learning. Motivation may be a factor in
negative or positive transfer. Familiarity with general work methods
which facilitate the learning of various types of tasks will cause positive
transfer, as will becoming accustomed to a set of experimental conditions or to the general experimental environment.

Henry[441] and, later, Fairclough[291] reported findings which indicated that positive and negative transfer might be caused by motivating or inhibiting circumstances in the experimental environment rather than by the nature of the tasks studied. When experimental subjects were stimulated by sound or shocks on their slower trials, reaction time showed a larger and more significant transfer than did movement time. When the shock and sound were omitted from the experimental conditions, transfer of training failed to occur. Thus, the transfer found under the experimental conditions was attributed to motivation by both of the experimenters. It is interesting to note that no significant differences were found between the transfer effects of a sound (a non-punitive type of reminder) and the shock (more punitive).

Transfer and Massed Practice

Negative transfer will occur between two tasks regardless of their relationships if too much massed practice is introduced in the experimental conditions. Nystrom et al.,[705] using a keyboard task, Reynolds et al.[752] and Kimble,[525] using a rotary pursuit task, found that extensive massing of initial practice produced negative transfer.

A clear-cut example of the inhibiting effect of massed practice is described by Hall,[407] using a mirror-tracing task. He found that negative transfer occurred when the mirror was placed in various positions relative to the subject. He hypothesized that it might have been attributed to fatigue resulting from the massing of tasks with little rest interval between each positioning of the mirror. A follow-up investigation allowed more time between trials (between thirty seconds and five minutes between sets of 10 trials) and positive transfer occurred.

Transfer and Amount of Initial Learning

Transfer may also be influenced by the amount of learning accomplished on the initial task. Generally, if slight learning has occurred, little transfer will occur, whereas if extensive learning has taken place on the initial task and it is dissimilar, negative transfer will usually take place. Duncan underscored this as he concluded, following the study of a lever-moving task into radially placed slots, that positive transfer was a function of both first task learning and task similarities.[262]

Theoretical Viewpoints of Negative Transfer

For effective learning and teaching, one must be as aware of factors which result in negative transfer as of conditions which contribute to positive transfer. The attempt, of course, is generally made to produce a situation which will encourage the latter and discourage the former, although occasionally it is desirable to inhibit learning for various reasons.

A thorough consideration of the effects and implications of negative transfer phenomenon. Britt[115] found, upon reversing the situation, that when two activities differed to the maximum in content, meaning, form, method of execution, and environment negative transfer or inter-task inhibition occurred. As the degree of similarity of one or all of these factors was relatively increased, more negative transfer occurred. A certain point was eventually reached, however, at which increasing the degree of similarity resulted in more identity of the various factors by the performer. From this point on, the amount of negative transfer tended to decrease, until, at the upper limit, actual identity of all factors was reached and no inhibition occurred, with the exception of the effect of task repetition. Britt's theoretical explanation of negative transfer seems most in tune with the various experimental findings.[115]

Principles of Transfer

To summarize, some of the major principles of transfer derived from an inspection of the data include the following:

1. Transfer is greatest when the training conditions of two tasks are highly similar.
2. When the task requires the same response to a new but similar stimulus, positive transfer increases as the stimulus conditions become more alike.
3. When the task requires the learner to make a new or different response to the same stimuli, transfer tends to be negative and increases as the responses become less similar.
4. If the responses in the transfer task are different from those in the original task, then the more similar the stimuli the less the positive transfer.
5. Continued practice in learning a number of related tasks leads to increased facility in learning how to learn.
6. Transfer is greatest if greater effort is extended during the early part of a series of related tasks.
7. Insight occurs with more frequency as extensive practice is gained in a series of related tasks.
8. Transfer can occur as the result of "cognitive links" formed between two tasks.
9. The greater the amount of practice on the original task, the greater the transfer.
10. Time elapsing between the original and transfer tasks is not critical unless specific details must be remembered.
11. Transfer is greater if the performer understands general principles which are appropriate to two or more tasks.

Questions for Further Experimental Work

Although general laws may be formulated from the experimental evidence available, a survey of the literature on transfer will produce more questions than answers. Among these questions it is felt that the following are most important:

1. To what exact factors may transfer be attributed—transfer of learning, of experimental conditions, of work methods, of motivational (positive and negative) conditions, or what?

2. Is bilateral transfer of strength actually a neurological phenomenon, or, as recent students seem to feel, may it result from the tensing and stabilizing of one side of the body as the other side applies force in some strength task?

3. To what extent is transfer affected by general experimental environments, the subjects' feelings about the experimenter, the task, or the rewards for successful performance?

4. What is the relationship of mental rehearsal, or pre-task verbal training, to motor transfer? What kinds of motor tasks are facilitated or impeded by what kinds of verbal activity either preceding or interspaced with skill learning?

SUMMARY

A better understanding of the available information of motor skill transfer is important from a theoretical viewpoint in order that elements common to several motor tasks may be identified and applied to the teaching-learning situation. Interest in and research published about this question extends back to the middle 1800's, and, while the initial concern was with verbal-mental problems, it now extends to a variety of motor and perceptual-motor tasks.

Theories explaining transfer include the general elements theory, the specific factors theory (or identical elements theory), and theories which incorporate both general and specific factors, as well as gestaltic theories involving "transposition" concepts, referring to the presence of common patterns and the relationships between two tasks.

Extensive transfer of skill and strength can be demonstrated between hand-to-hand (cross-education) and hand-to-foot, while little task-to-task transfer is generally found. The cross-education effects are usually interpreted to indicate that skilled performance is a function of the central rather than peripheral process in the nervous system. The lack of extensive task-to-task transfer, in general, supports the identical elements theory of transfer.

Generally, transfer seems facilitated in paired-associative tasks by (1) verbal pre-training, (2) first learning a complex task and then learning a simpler one, (3) spaced practice, rather than massed, and (4) a high level of motivation, regardless of task interrelationships. Transfer is impeded (negative transfer occurs) when (1) the tasks are dissimilar, (2) a high level of learning is desired in the secondary task, and (3) fatigue is present. Skill transfer thus seems to be a function of inter-task similarity and a resultant of general motivating or inhibiting conditions in the total learning environment.

Student References

Books

1. AMMONS, ROBERT B.: "Le Mouvement," Current Psychological Issues edited by Georgene H. Seward and John P. Seward, New York, Henry Holt & Co., Inc., 1958.
2. ELLIS, HENRY: *The Transfer of Learning*, New York, The Macmillan Company, 1965.

Articles

1. BRUCE, R. W.: "Conditions of transfer of training," *J. Exper. Psych.*, *16*, 343-361, 1933.
2. CRATTY, BRYANT J.: "The influence of small-pattern practice upon large pattern learning," *Res. Quart.*, *33*, 4, 1960.
3. LINDEBURG, FRANKLIN A.: A study of the degree of transfer between quickening exercises and other coordinated movements," *Res. Quart.*, *20*, 180-195, 1949.
4. SEYMOUR, W. DOUGLAS: "Transfer of training in engineering skills," *Perceptual and Motor Skills*, *7*, 235-237, 1957.

Chapter 19

An Overview

IN this, the final chapter, a summary of the material in the body of the text is presented in four primary divisions: (1) movement considered *functionally* through a discussion of behavioral "loops," (2) movement considered *qualitatively,* in terms of several performance continuums, (3) areas of needed research, and (4) implications.

BEHAVIORAL LOOPS: MOVEMENT CONSIDERED FUNCTIONALLY

On reviewing the research upon which the material in the text is based, the existence of a number of interacting chains of events both in and external to the organism are clearly apparent. These mutually effective happenings initiate, sustain, and modify motor activity.

The concept of behavioral loops is not original. Advocates of the information theory as well as neurophysiologists, refer continually to the human "servo system." By this it is meant that the human being acts as a self-correcting mechanism, constantly adjusting to changes in his external and internal environment. Smith's[834] neurogeometric theory of motion also depends upon the concept that perception and motion are inseparable units of behavior. As used here, however, "a behavioral loop" is seen as a broader construct that includes a consideration of socio-cultural factors and perceptual and physiological events, interacting within and external to the organism.

The concept of a behavioral loop emphasizes that a measurable "bit" of motor performance does not somehow function independently but is dependent upon immediate and long-range functional loops composed of events external and internal to the organism. The following postulates are presented for consideration as basic concepts underlying the functioning of these dynamic chains.

1. Several loops operate simultaneously at various levels to sustain a single identifiable type of motor activity that occurs in a specific time period. For example, when throwing a baseball, the individual is dependent upon internal loops, or the mutual interactions among the cerebrum-cerebellum-reticular formations, for the smoothing and monitoring of the movement at the neurological level. A larger loop, involving sensory feed-back, relays the resultant "feel" of the throw back to the

central nervous system so that further modifications may take place. These might be termed internal loops. Externally, and operating simultaneously with the aforementioned internal loops, are visual-motor integrations which further serve to direct the throwing movement and to modify the intensity and placement of subsequent throws.

2. Some skilled activities are more dependent upon internal loops than upon external loops, and the relative dependence may change as the movement is learned or as the organism matures. For example, an adult, when writing his signature, is primarily dependent upon internal loops involving kinesthetic feed-back. The adult can replicate his own signature without the use of vision. The young child, on the other hand, learning to write his name for the first time, is greatly dependent upon an external visual-motor loop and becomes less dependent upon it only as he matures and acquires the necessary skill. Poulton[736] has termed activities primarily dependent upon internal loops as "closed skills," while those requiring external feed-back were named "open skills."

3. External and internal loops can function to modify performance immediately or over a considerable period of time. Skilled learning has been explained by Hebb[432] as consisting of the establishment and storage of functional, neurological loops (cell-linkages or phase cycles) which are called upon when it is desired to repeat some act. External loops may operate over long time periods. As the individual obtains continual feed-back from his environment in the form of social approval or disapproval of his efforts, he gradually forms a "self" construct which modifies his subsequent movement behavior and determines whether he will even attempt new skills. It is suggested that long-term loops operate to offer feed-back of performance and the social implications of success or failure.

4. The relative dependence upon external loops may be reduced as learning occurs. For example, the automatization of a motor act generally requires less dependence upon visual feed-back in the latter stages of skill acquisition.

5. Learning a new act, or eliciting a performance modification, consists of "breaking in" on an established loop with an affective event, cue, or stimulus. The result is the establishment of another loop, either in addition to or taking the place of the previous one. For example, some word cue, type of motive, or demonstration may be introduced in an established loop to encourage some modification of performance. It is usually the purpose of the teacher or coach to introduce some affective type of interfering stimulus or perceptual event causing change to occur. The research suggests, however, that there is an optimal amount of interference (*i.e.*, word cues) which may be introduced. Too strong an interfering event may serve to break down some of the underlying external loops important to the performance of the movement desired.

6. Performance or learning difficulties occur as a loop is broken up by some interfering stress, without replacing it with some new functional loop. For example, if the instruction proves stressful, it may not contribute to the establishment of a new loop but rather might serve to break down an existing one. As a result, learning difficulties may occur. Some type of stressful event may break down the normal internal monitoring loops in the nervous system as well as various functioning external loops. In contrast, the removal of some stressful event may aid in recalling some suppressed loop to a functional relationship, thus facilitating performance.

7. Retention of a skilled act involves the "calling-up" of a relatively stable loop and its re-performance. Repetition and overlearning seem to contribute to the stabilizing and strengthening of such a behavioral loop.

8. External loops may be termed *complete* or *adjusted*. Complete loops are interacting chains of events primarily dependent on an individual's own actions and perceptions (*e.g.*, hitting a tennis ball against a wall). The adjusted loop depends, however, upon relatively unpredictable interpersonal events for its functional completion. Playing tennis with another person involves a loop of this nature; for, however the ball is hit by the performer, constant adjustments need to be made to the unpredictable actions of the opponent when returning the missile.

9. One might also refer to loops which involve the presence of two or more people vs. those in which a single person is interacting with a portion of his environment which does not react to him with verbal behavior and gestures. One is constantly forming and breaking up various social loops as he encounters and otherwise interacts with people in his immediate environment. The quality and nature of these human interactions form a potent source of stress and reward, as was pointed out in Chapter 9 dealing with social motives. People perform for and react to the approval and disapproval of others in a more intense way than if they are merely hitting a ball against a wall in the absence of competitors, onlookers, and/or teammates.

CONTINUUMS: MOVEMENT BEHAVIOR CONSIDERED QUALITATIVELY

Because of the complexity of the human organism, an identifiable "bit" of movement behavior might be considered on several continuums, scales which describe various *qualitative* differences between motor acts. Among these are the verbal-motor, the perceptual-motor, fine-gross, and simple-complex continuums. As learning takes place, a motor act may shift from one portion to another on the same continuum. At the same time, a single motor act can be described as residing on different portions of several scales.

The Verbal-Motor Continuum

Types of movement behavior may be classified in accordance with the extent to which word cues, either internal or received from an external source, contribute to or support performance. It is usually found that irregular rapid movements require fewer words. Activities that are relatively slow and composed of discrete movements, on the other hand, are better accompanied by word descriptions. The extent to which an activity is compatible with verbalization depends also upon prior learning as well as the maturational level of the performer. Younger children seem less likely to depend upon verbal cues and more upon imitation and kinesthetic "feel" of the movement. During initial learning stages, verbalization plays a more important role than during the latter stages.

Perceptual-Motor Continuum

Activities may also be classified according to the extent to which they are perceptually "loaded," as opposed to consisting of responses to relatively simple stimuli. Here again, the perceptual loading, or the extent to which judgments or meanings need to be formulated prior to the motor output, vary as the task is learned. Usually less complex judgments are needed during the latter stages of task acquisition.

Tasks in which a simple key pressing or switch turning response is required in response to light or word cues, while sometimes termed *motor,* seem actually heavily laden with perceptual factors. One of the problems when reviewing studies of motor skills is selecting those that seem to use "true motor activities" as evaluative tasks. Many of the so-called motor skill investigations have utilized tasks that are largely cognitive or perceptual in nature with the motor component of the task a relatively simple, unchanging, and minor portion of the behavior measured.

Force-Accuracy Continuum

Quantitatively, motor performance also may be considered as including or requiring varying amounts of force as contrasted to accuracy. Some researchers feel that motor activity is primarily a force-speed phenomenon, while others emphasize spatial accuracy as basic. It is believed that force, spatial accuracy, and temporal factors (speed and/or rhythm) are all vital components of motor activity. The problem becomes one of analyzing the specifics of the task under consideration in order to determine which kinds of factors are important.

Visual-Motor Continuum

The classification of a task according to the extent to which visual cues are utilized in its performance also is important. This again can be a function of the stage of learning involved, with the initial portion of the learning process usually more dependent upon visual cues than the latter. It is often found that visual cues override the kinesthetic or movement cues. More accuracy can usually be achieved, however, when available visual information is used.

Fine vs. Gross Continuum

Seashore et al.[794] have compared the performance of fine vs. gross motor skills. In general, such a classification depends upon the size of the muscle groups involved, the magnitude of space utilized for the movements, and the amount of force necessary to complete the movement. A three-way breakdown has been suggested by Karl Smith.[831] Included in the triad are movements which involve hand-finger manipulations, travel movements of the limbs, and locomotor activities. Rather than discrete categories, however, a continuum might be constructed on which activities are arranged according to the amount of space utilized in their execution. At the present time, however, no exact classification system has been evolved, and most writers continue to use a two-way system.

At the finite level are finger movements, tapping activities, and steadiness tests, movements which at times seem related to the physiological tremor rate of the individual. Gross motor skills have included arm movements, dynamic balance activities, and the like. Cratty[190] has referred to a large locomotor maze as a "gross motor skill." However, when comparing such a task to that involving the rotary pursuit apparatus, the need for a three-way classification becomes apparent.

The fine vs. gross continuum is closely related to the simple vs. complex continuum. This is because fine motor skills seem to be simpler than are gross motor activities which require stabilizing actions, the organization of a larger space field, and usually the total involvement of the performer.

Personal Equation vs. Optimum Effort

A "bit" of motoric behavior can be classified as to whether it is dependent upon some combination of an individual's personal equations (see Chapter 12) or whether it is dependent upon ability traits measured under conditions which encouraged maximum effort. In general, performance task scores in which it is attempted to manifest one's "best" will correlate more highly with various ability trait measures, while samplings of movement behavior in which there is no such stress imposed will be primarily a manifestation of various basic movement preferences on the part of the individual.

Simple-to-Complex Continuum

The point on the simple-to-complex continuum at which a skill might be placed is based upon a variety of conditions. It may depend upon the complexity of sensory information that is necessary or upon the complexity of the movement pattern required. In still another context, classification of the skill might rest upon the serial nature of the task or the stage of learning involved. For example, when learning to type, the initial portion of the process involves learning letter location and becomes more complex as total word and phrase responses are learned. Thus, the particular skill level at which the performer is functioning at the moment, in this case, would govern the point on a simple-to-complex continuum at which his motor activity might be located. The maturational level of the performer must also be taken into account in utilizing such a continuum. For example, skills simple for adults might be classified as complex when infants or children attempt to perform them.

The extent to which perceptual judgments are necessary to execution is an important criterion upon which to judge the simplicity or complexity of a skill. Direct motor acts cued by a single stimulus might be termed simple, while complicated movements requiring frequent modifications because of unexpected or uncontrollable cues would be labeled complex.

NEEDED RESEARCH

Some topics related to movement behavior and motor learning appear frequently in the literature, while others have received relatively little attention. It is believed that the following general problem areas are most in need of further investigation.

The Neurological and Biochemical Bases of Learning and Retention

Innumerable research programs suggest themselves upon a review of the material in Chapter 15. The influence of RNA and DNA upon learning, as well as the exact mechanisms involved, needs further investigation. Additionally, the relationship between various neuro-electrical measures and learning and retention are critically in need of further elucidation. Developmental studies in learning and retention as a function of the biochemical make-up as well as of the anatomical appearance of the human brain would be helpful. A continued effort should be made to elaborate upon various inter-species differences in brain structure and function at various points within the phylogenic scale.

Anthropology and the Human Action System

Examination of the parallel evolvement of man's abilities to utilize his hands to other indices of his social and intellectual development might reveal interesting insights into the manner in which movement characteristics contributed to the development of these other capacities. Evolutionary changes made via surgery on primates would be helpful in clarifying relationships between movement capacities and intellect.

For example, whether surgically altering the higher primate so that his hands were free for manipulation 100 per cent of the time was a question asked in the last decade, but apparently not as yet acted upon.

The Development of Motor Attributes in Infancy and Childhood

In the child development area, the problems which remain unexplored seem endless. For example, there are few studies dealing with the development of body awareness or kinesthetic maturation; nor do investigations exist which deal with the manner in which a child might gain a more stable concept of his physical self. The development of visual perception has received only cursory attention, while changes in the ability to move accurately with advancing age have been neglected in longitudinal investigations.

Verbal-Motor Relationships

Man is not only a moving organism but a verbal animal. The relationships between these two types of behavior, however, have received little attention. Except for comparative retention studies, there seems to have been little emphasis upon investigations in this area.

The Nature of Play, Manipulation, and Exploration

More objective studies seem needed in examining the parameters of play, manipulation, and exploration in children and adults. Although it is frequently suggested that children engage more in unstructured play than do adolescents, few objective studies have examined the intensity, emphasis, and duration of play and manipulative activities as a function of age. Restriction from movement as a motive to move also belongs in this general classification. Although studies utilizing animals have been carried out, I am unaware of investigations in which human subjects have participated.

Construction of a Tension-Performance Scale

Another fruitful area of investigation is the relation between tension level and optimum performance. Investigations in this area would require valid measures of tension, motivational or arousal-level, and classifications of tasks which might be performed best in various portions of such a scale.

Movement Panaceas?

Several clinicians have within recent years suggested that a variety of perceptual, cognitive, and emotional problems evidenced by children and adults can be ameliorated through practicing various kinds of perceptual-motor tasks. It has been suggested that by recapitulating various locomotor sequences, visual and auditory perception, together with speech, may be improved.[245] Many of these theories have resulted in practices which are proving helpful to atypical children; on the other hand, a considerable amount of experimental data is needed to further refine their use, and to suggest the scope as well as the limitations of the programs proposed.[756]

Longitudinal Studies of Learning and Retention

Studies of long-term retention of motor skills are needed. As Naylor and Briggs[689] have pointed out, such research begins to assume important practical implications when man attempts to conquer space and must retain various kinds of instrument behavior in the confines of a space ship over extended periods of time.

Studies in Kinesthetics

Much information is needed concerning the nature and function of kinesthetic sensations. Among the problems are whether there are specific or general factors involved (although Scott[787] has published research in this area) and the manner in which kinesthetic sensations integrate with vestibular, visual, and pressure cues to form a total perception of movement. Investigations of the nature of kinesthetic after-effects at the finite and gross levels might also provide added knowledge. Experimental induction of a kinesthetic illusion, an after-effect, in essence involves creating a short-term perception. It is believed that research in which an attempt is made to control some of the variables contributing to this kind of temporary distortion might shed light on the nature of kinesthetic perception.

IMPLICATIONS

It is believed that the following implications are important as a basis for understanding the general and specific factors which contribute to movement "output." These "threads" are found in several research areas concerned with motor performance and learning. They are important for the teacher who attempts to modify the movement behavior of others, as well as for the performer who wishes to gain more complete knowledge about his personal action patterns.

The Importance of Socio-Cultural Factors

Motor performance levels are usually affected by the social implications of the immediate situation, as well as by the over-all cultural context in which the action takes place. As the individual learns a skill, he is concerned with not only task specifics but how the culture expects one of his age, sex, and background to perform. Thus, the performer is continually sensitive to the extent to which his performance level

21

either coincides or falls short of cultural expectations. As an example, the concept of "failure-anxiety" (Chapter 10, p. 163) suggests that a large portion of the apprehension experienced when one attempts to perform relatively hazardous movements may relate to the social consequences of failure.

Growth and development literature outlines several social-performance relationships. The cultural expectations related to the performance of boys, as opposed to the performance of girls, are exacting. These demands of the society tend to channel the type as well as the intensity of motor activities engaged in by the two sexes, particularly as they reach adolescence. Society also exerts an influence over the movement patterns of the very young. The vigorous total-body effort seen in the throwing behavior of two- and three-year-old boys, as opposed to the comparatively more restricted throw of girls at this age level, has been attributed to differing cultural expectations (Chapter 7, p. 122).

Within limits, the teacher may manipulate the social clime immediately connected with performance. For example, judiciously selected team captains may enhance group performance. However, if just the obvious and proximal social dimensions are dealt with, only a portion of the complex cultural picture is being accounted for. The individual attempting to change the performance of another should be aware not only of the manner in which the task fits into the immediate learning situation but also of the way in which the hoped for action pattern coincides with the performer's perceptions of himself in a total sociocultural context, composed of family demands, community expectations, and national goals.

Both General and Specific Factors Contribute to Performance

Another important principle apparent upon review of the literature on skilled learning is that, in addition to task specifics, motor performance is molded by a number of general conditions. A four-part theory was presented in Chapter 14, elaborating upon this concept. Although a single motor task may be analyzed in terms of specific components, such general conditions as motivational level, ability to interpret instructions, maturational level, the ability to vary force and tension, and similar qualities may contribute in a general way to performance of several kinds of motor skills.

While identification of general coordination of adults will generally meet with little success, general performance qualities of young children have at times been isolated. In addition, there seems to be a typical arousal level which an individual sustains through his day, which is probably influential in molding performance and learning.

A personality trait which might be labeled "need for achievement," "aspiration level" or "need for social approval" also appears to underlie the performance of a number of skills. Individuals who generally strive to succeed, whatever the nature of the task facing them, seem to score higher on motor skills tests.

An awareness of such general conditions underlying performance, however, does not negate the remarkable specificity of adult motor skill. The numerous studies cited in Chapter 14 point to the necessity for practicing the task at hand, rather than relying too heavily upon general conditions, inherent physical qualities, or transfer from past experience.

Arousal, Tension, Motivational Level, and Performance

The concept of an optimal level of "trying" on the part of the performer is needed to perform a motor task most efficiently (Chapter 8). An individual may evidence too much residual muscular tension for optimal performance or might be said to be too highly aroused or motivated to perform a desired movement successfully. On the other hand, the evidence also seems to indicate that motor performance might be impeded by a motivational state (or tension level) which is not high enough. The performance of simple direct movements, requiring moderate to large amounts of force, will usually suffer unless enough tension is summoned by the individual engaged in them.

The athletic coach, and others hoping to elicit outstanding performance from individuals, should be particularly sensitive to this concept. The instructor who attempts to make all the members of a team "mad" at their opposition is perhaps ignoring this principle. On the other hand, the athletic leader who attempts to encourage some, while relaxing others, upon noting the amount of tension already present in the individual and evaluating the requirements of the task, would be following a sounder course of action.

The Instructor and Motor Performance

Throughout the book an attempt has been made to describe conditions which contribute to individual variations in movement behavior, motor performance, and motor learning. It was felt that a simple presentation of principles, formulas, methods, or guide lines for action in the teaching-learning situation would have been naive. Rather, it has been the intent to provide for an appreciation of the complexity of the action patterns of man.

However, upon review of the preceding chapters, several broad implications related to formal instruction seem important to re-emphasize. Initially, it is believed that the primary lesson to be gained is that an instructor should introduce an optimal amount of formal guidance at opportune times within the learning process. Too much formal guidance as well as too little may prove equally undesirable. For example, if an instructor attempts to give immature learners an exact awareness of the multitude of principles underlying their performance, more confusion than enlightenment may be the result. The educator, it would seem, should take into account the maturity level of his students, their attention span, and the nature of the task, and then introduce formal guidance when it is felt appropriate.

In general, the literature indicates that the maximal amount of guidance should be offered during the initial part of the learning process, with care taken not to present an overabundance of verbage when rapidly executed movements are to be assimilated. During the final stages of learning the student might be allotted time to engage in unguided practice, with the instruction imposed only to correct errors.

A second major implication when studying the instructor-performance relationship is that the teacher, if he is to be effective, should be able to utilize well several kinds of sensory input. This assumption is based upon findings that individuals at various portions of their lives tend to change the type of sensory cues they may habitually depend upon when learning motor skills. In addition, for a given maturational level, learners often differ widely in the type or combination of learning cues which have the most meaning for them. It has also been found that prediction of the type of cues a learner may usually depend upon in a variety of performance situations is an extremely tenuous undertaking. In a given task, for example, some individuals may utilize word cues best and thus require a rather detailed verbal description of the movement. Others may learn best with a visual demonstration, while others may prefer to practice and to "feel" the movement kinesthetically. However, upon changing the nature of the task, these same individuals will report dependence upon different sensory cues, or combinations of cues.

In addition, the relative dependence upon various kinds of sensory input often changes as various portions of the learning process are reached. For example, the kinds of cues best utilized during the initial stages may hinder the student during the final stages of learning. Thus, to have the most desirable impact upon the learning situation in the absence of the means to evaluate the manner in which his students learn best, the instructor should cultivate the ability to communicate in several sensory modalities, through verbal instructions, visual demonstration, and manual guidance.

My primary purpose was to contribute to the development of two attitudes on the part of the student: (1) *sensitivity* and (2) *flexibility* in the teaching-learning situation. If one wishes to modify his motor attributes or those of another, he, first of all, must be *sensitive* to the numerous conditions which mold and channel performance. Secondly, cognizance of this multitude of factors should promote an attitude of *flexibility* on the part of the teacher. An instructor should be prepared and able to change the manner in which he approaches the instruction of a group or individual, rather than to adhere to preconceived guide lines. Consequently, it is hoped that the future teacher, upon considering the material in the preceding chapters will be able to analyze the situation, the learner, the task, and his own attributes with greater facility and thus be able to modify more effectively the movement behavior of those in his charge.

Underlying much of the material in the preceding chapters has been the inference that at certain levels performance and learning are not divisible into motor and mental components. However, it is hoped that the reader has not assumed that movement has been considered the key from which all aspects of behavior, mental, emotional, and social must stem. An attempt has been made, however, to point out that observable action is an imperative facet of human behavior, and through failure to understand movement behavior, one may glimpse only a portion of the totality of man.

Student References

Books

1. HEBB, D. O.:   The Organization of Behavior, New York, John Wiley & Sons, Inc., 1949.
2. McGeoch, J. A., and Irion, A. L..   The Psychology of Human Learning, 2nd ed., New York, Longmans, Green & Co., 1952.
3. SMITH, KARL U., and SMITH, WILLIAM M.:   Perception and Motion, Philadelphia, W. B. Saunders Co., 1962.
4. WOODWORTH, R. S.:   Dynamics of Behavior, New York, Henry Holt & Co., 1958.

Bibliography

1. Abbe, M.: The spatial effect upon the perception of time. *Jap J. Exp. Psych.,* 3, 1-52, 1936.
2. ————: Temporal effect upon the perception of time. *Jap. J. Exp. Psych.,* 4, 83-93, 1937.
3. Abbey, David S.: Age, proficiency and reminiscence in a complex perceptual-motor task. *Percept. & Mot. Skills, 14,* 51-57, 1962.
4. Abel, Lorraine B.: The effects of shift in motivation upon the learning of a sensory-motor task. *Arch. Psych.,* 29, 1-57, 1936.
5. Abercrombie, M. L. J. and Tyson, M. C.: Body Image and draw-a-man test in cerebral palsy. *Develop. Medicine and Child Neurology, 8,* 9-15, 1966.
6. Adams, Gary L.: Effect of eye dominance on baseball batting. *Res. Quart.,* 36, 3-9, 1965.
7. Adams, J. A.: Human tracking behavior. *Psych. Bull.,* 58:1, 55-79, 1961.
8. ————: The relationship between certain measures of ability and the acquisition of a psycho-motor criterion response. *J. Gen. Psych., 56,* 121-134, 1957.
9. ————: Some implications of Hull's theory for human motor performance. *J. Gen. Psych., 55,* 189-198, 1956.
10. Adams, J. A. and Reynolds, B.: Effect of shift in distribution of practice conditions following interpolated rest. *J. Exp. Psych., 47,* 32-36, 1954.
11. Adelson, Daniel: The relational influence of size on judgments of distance. *J. Gen. Psych., 69,* 319-333, 1963.
12. Adey, W. R.: Recent thoughts on the neuron model based on brain wave analysis. Paper given at Biomedical Engineering Symposium, San Diego, California, April 1961.
13. Adler, A.: *The Practice and Theory of Individual Psychology,* New York, Harcourt & Brace, 1927.
14. Ahrens, Shirley J.: Spatial dimensions of movement. Master's Thesis, University of California, Los Angeles, 1966.
15. Allen, R. M.: Factors in mirror drawing. *J. Ed. Psych., 39,* 216-226, 1948.
16. Allen, Sara: The effects of verbal reinforcement on children's performance as a function of type of task. *J. Exp. Child Psych., 13,* 57-73, 1965.
17. Allport, Gordon W.: *Personality, a Psychological Interpretation.* New York, Henry Holt & Co., 566, 588, 1937.
18. ————: *Social Psychology.* Boston, Houghton Mifflin Co., 1924.
19. ————: *Studies in Expressive Movement.* New York, The Macmillan Co., 1933.
20. Allport, Gordon W. and Pettigrew, T. F.: Cultural influence on the perception of movement: The trapezoid influence among Zulus. *J. Ab. & Soc. Psych.,* 65, 104-113, 324, 1957.
21. Ames, A., Jr.: Reconsideration of the origin and nature of perception. In Ratner, S. (Ed.) *Vision and Action.* New Bruswick, Rutgers University Press, 1953.
22. Ammons, R. B.: Acquisition of motor skill: III. Effects of initially distributed practice on rotary pursuit performance. *J. Exp. Psych., 40,* 777, 1950.
23. ————: Effects of pre-practice activities on rotary pursuit performance. *J. Exp. Psych., 41,* 187-191, 1951.
24. ————: *"Le Mouvement"* Current Psychological Issues, Georgene H. Seward and John P. Seward (Eds.), Henry Holt & Co., 1958.
25. Ammons, R. B., Alprin, S. I., and Ammons, C. H.: Rotary pursuit performance as related to age and sex of pre-adult subjects. *J. Exp. Psych., 49,* 127-133, 1955.

26. Ammons, R. B., Farr, R. G., Block, Edith, Neuman, Eva, Marion, Deny M., and Ammons, C. H.: Long-term retention of perceptual motor skills. *J. Exp. Psych.*, 55, 318-328, 1958.
27. Ammons, R. B. and Willig, Leslie: Acquisition of motor skills: IV. Effects of repeated periods of massed practice. *J. Exp. Psych.*, 51, 2, 1956.
28. Anastasiow, Nicholas J.: Success in school and boys' sex role patterns. *Child Dev.*, 33, 1053-1066, 1965.
29. Anderson, John E.: *The Psychology of Development and Personal Adjustment.* New York, Harper & Bros., 152, 1949.
30. Arps, G. F.: Work with knowledge of results vs. work without knowledge of results. *Psych. Monographs*, 28, 125, 1920.
31. Asch, Solomon: *Social Psychology.* Englewood Cliffs, N.J., Prentice-Hall, Inc., 1951.
32. Aschoff, J.: Circadian rhythms in man. *Science*, 148, 1427-1432, 1965.
33. Atkinson, John W.: *Motives in Fantasy, Action and Society.* Princeton, N.J., D. Van Nostrand Co., Inc., 1958.
34. Attneave, Fred and Arnoult, Malcolm D.: The quantitative study of shape and pattern perception. *Psych. Bull.*, 53, 452, 1956.
35. Aubert, H.: "Die Bewegungsempfindung." *Arch. Ges. Physiol.*, 39, 347-370, 1886.
36. Ausubel, D. P.: *Theory and Problems of Adolescent Development.* New York, Grune & Stratton, 1954.
37. Ausubel, D. P., Schiff, H. M., and Goldman, M.: Qualitative characteristics in the learning process associated with anxiety. *J. Ab. & Soc. Psych.*, 48, 537, 1953.
38. Bachman, John C.: Influence of age and sex on the amount and rate of learning two motor tasks. *Res. Quart.*, 37, 1966.
39. ————: Motor learning and performance as related to age and sex in two measures of balance coordination. *Res. Quart.*, 32, 123-137, 1961.
40. ————: Specificity vs. generality in learning and performing two large muscle motor tasks. *Res. Quart.*, 32, 3-11, 1961.
41. Bahrick, H. P.: Retention curves—facts or artifacts? *Psych. Bull.*, 61, 188-194, 1964.
42. Bahrick, H. P., Fitts, P. M., and Briggs, G. E.: Learning curves—facts or artifacts? *Psych. Bull.*, 54, 256-268, 1957.
43. Bakan, P., Meyers, Louis B., and Schoonard, James: Kinesthetic after-effects and length of inspection period. *Am. J. Psych.*, 75, 457-461, 1962.
44. Bakan, P. and Thompson, Richard: The effect of pre-inspection control measures on the size of kinesthetic after-effects. *Am. J. Psych.*, 75, 302-303, 1962.
45. Bakan, P. and Weiler, Ernest: Kinesthetic after effect and mode of exposure to the inspection stimulus. *J. Exp. Psych.*, 65, 319-320, 1963.
46. Baker, K. E. and Wylie, Ruth C.: Transfer of verbal training to a motor task. *J. Exp. Psych.*, 40, 623, 1950.
47. Baker, Lawrence M.: *General Experimental Psychology.* New York, Oxford University Press, 1960.
48. Baker, Robert F.: The effects of anxiety and stress on gross motor performance. Doctoral dissertation, University of California, Los Angeles, 1961.
49. Bannister, H. and Blackburn, J. H.: An eye factor affecting proficiency at ball games. *Brit. J. Psych.*, 21, 382-384, 1931.
50. Barber, Theodore X.: Physiological effects of 'hypnosis'," *Psych. Bull.*, 58, 390-419, 1961.
51. Barch, Abram M.: Bi-lateral transfer of warm-up in rotary pursuit. *Percept. & Mot. Skills*, 17, 723-726, 1963.
52. Bardach, J. L.: Effects of situational anxiety at different stages of practice. *J. Exp. Psych.*, 59, 420-424, 1960.
53. Bartley, S. Howard: The perception of size or distance based on tactile and kinesthetic data. *Psych. J.*, 36, 401-408, 1953.
54. ————: *Principles of Perception.* New York, Harper & Rowe, 1958.
55. Bartley, S. Howard and Chute, Eloise: *Fatigue and Impairment in Man.* New York, McGraw-Hill Book Co., 1947.

56. Barton, J. W.: Comprehensive units in learning typewriting. *Psych. Monographs, 35*, 164, 1926.
57. ————: Smaller versus larger units in learning the maze. *J. Exp. Psych., 4*, 418-429, 1921.
58. Basowitz, H., Persky, H., Korchin, S. J., and Grinker, R. R.: *Anxiety and Stress, an Interdisciplinary Study of a Life Situation.* New York, McGraw-Hill Book Co., 1955.
59. Batson, W. H.: Acquisition of skill. *Psych. Monographs, 21*, 91, 1916.
60. Battig, W. F.: Transfer from verbal pretraining to motor performance a function of motor task complexity. *J. Exp. Psych., 51*, 371-378, 1956.
61. Battig, W. F., Nagel, E. H., Voss, J. F., and Brogden, W. J.: Transfer and retention of bidimensional compensatory tracking after extended practice. *Am. J. Psych., 70*, 75-80, 1957.
62. Bayley, Nancy: The development of motor abilities, during the first three years. Monographs for the society for research in child development. Washington, D.C., 1935.
63. ————: A study of the crying of infants during mental and physical tests. *J. Genet. Psych., 40*, 306-329, 1932.
64. Bayton, J. A. and Conley, H. W.: Duration of success background and the effect of failure upon performance. *J. Gen. Psych., 56*, 179-185, 1957.
65. Beach, Frank A.: Current concepts of play in animals. *Am. Nat., 79*, 523-541, 1945.
66. Beam, J. C.: Serial learning and conditioning under real life stress. *J. Ab. & Soc. Psych., 51*, 543-551, 1955.
67. Beardslee, David C. and Wertheimer, Michael: *Readings in Perception.* Princeton, N.J., D. Van Nostrand Co., Inc., 1958.
68. Beasley, John W. and Mendelson, Jack H.: Effects of visual deprivation on nucleic acid levels in rat brain cortex. *Recent Advances in Biol. Psychiatry, 7*, 101, 1966.
69. Bell, H. M.: Retention of pursuit rotor skill after one year. *J. Exp. Psych., 40*, 648-649, 1950.
70. Bendig, A. W.: Factor analytic scales of need achievement. *J. Gen. Psych., 90*, 59-67, 1964.
71. Benson, David: Effects of concomitant learning in relaxation and swimming on swimming improvement. Unpublished study, University of California, Los Angeles, 1958.
72. Benton, Arthur L.: *Right-Left Discrimination and Finger Localization,* New York, Paul B. Hoeber, Inc., 1959, p. 14.
73. Benton, J. A. and Whyte, E. C.: Personality dynamics during successful failure sequence. *J. Ab. & Soc. Psych., 45*, 583-591, 1950.
74. Bentson, T. B. and Summerskill, John: Relation of personal success in intercollegiate athletics to certain aspects of personal adjustment. *Res. Quart., 26*, 8-14, 1955.
75. Berg, Irwin A. and Bass, Bernard M.: *Conformity and Deviation.* New York, Harper & Bros., 1961.
76. Bergès, J. and Lezine, I.: *The Imitation of Gestures.* Suffolk, The Lavenham Press Ltd., 1963.
77. Berkeley, G.: An essay toward a new theory of vision, in B. Rand (Ed.) *Classical Psychologists.* Boston, Houghton Mifflin Co., 1912.
78. Berlyne, D. E.: *Conflict, Arousal and Curiosity.* New York, McGraw-Hill Book Co., 1960.
79. Berman, Arthur: The relation of time estimation to satiation. *J. Exp. Psych., 25*, 281-293, 1939.
80. Berridge, Harold L.: An experiment in the psychology of competition. *Res. Quart., 35*, 37-42, 1935.
81. Bielianskas, Vytantas: Recent advances in the psychology of masculinity and femininity. *Psych. J., 60*, 255-263, 1965.
82. Bills, A. G.: The influence of muscular tension on the efficiency of mental work. *Am. J. Psych., 38*, 226-251, 1927.

83. Bills, A. G. and Brown, C.: The quantitative set. *J. Exp. Psych., 12,* 301-323, 1929.
84. Bilodeau, E. A.: Motor performance as affected by magnitude and direction of error contained in knowledge of results. *J. Psych., 50,* 103-113, 1955.
85. Bilodeau, E. A. and Bilodeau, Ina McD.: Motor skills learning. *Ann. Rev. Psych., 42,* 243-280, 1961.
86. ————: Variable frequency of knowledge of results and the learning of a simple skill. *J. Exp. Psych., 55,* 379-383, 1958.
87. Bilodeau, E. A., Bilodeau, I. McD., and Schumsky, D. A.: Some effects of introducing and withdrawing knowledge of results early and late in practice. *J. Exp. Psych., 58,* 142-144, 1959.
88. Bilodeau, E. A., Jones, Marshall B., and Long, Michael C.: Long-term memory as a function of retention time and repeated recalling. *J. Exp. Psych., 67,* 303-309, 1964.
89. Bilodeau, E. A. and Levy, C. Michael: Long-term memory as a function of retention time and other conditions of learning. *Psych. Rev., 71,* 27-41, 1964.
90. Bilodeau, I. McD.: Performance of an effortful task with variation in duration of prior practice and anticipated duration of present practice. *J. Exp. Psych., 46,* 146, 1953.
91. Bindra, Dalbir: *Motivation, a Systematic Reinterpretation,* New York, The Ronald Press, 1951.
92. Bladen, S. R.: An extensive experiment in motor learning and re-learning. *J. Ed. Psych., 15,* 313-315, 1924.
93. Blane, Howard T.: Space perception among unilaterally paralyzed children and adolescents. *J. Exp. Psych., 63,* 244-247, 1958.
94. Blick, Kenneth S. and Bilodeau, E. A.: Interpolated activity and the learning of a simple skill. *J. Exp. Psych.,* 65:5, 515-519, 1963.
95. Bogoras, W.: *The Chukchee.* New York, G. E. Stechert & Co., 1909.
96. Boreas, Th.: Experimental studies on memory: II. The rate of forgetting. *Praktika de l'Academie d' Athenes, 5,* 382, 1930.
97. Boring, Edwin C.: *A History of Experimental Psychology.* 2nd ed. New York, Appleton-Century-Crofts, 1950.
98. ————: *Sensation and Perception in Experimental Psychology.* New York, Appleton-Century-Crofts, 1942.
99. Bourne, Lyle B., Jr., Kepros, Peter G., and Beier, Ernest G.: Effect of post inspection delay upon kinesthetic figural after-effects. *J. Gen. Psych., 68,* 37-42, 1963.
100. Bourne, L. E.: An evaluation of the effect of induced tension on performance. *J. Exp. Psych., 49,* 418-422, 1955.
101. Bowditch, H. P. and Southard, W. F.: A comparison of sight and touch. *J. Physiol., 3,* 232-254, 1882.
102. Bowers, Louis: Effects of autosuggested muscle contraction on muscular strength and size. *Res. Quart., 37,* 302-312, 1966.
103. Brace, C. L. and Montagu, M. F.: *Man's Evolution,* New York, The Macmillan Co., 1965.
104. Brace, David K.: *Measuring Motor Ability, A Scale of Motor Ability Tests.* New York, A. S. Barnes Co., 1926.
105. ————: Studies in the rate of learning gross bodily motor skills. *Res. Quart., 12,* 181-185, 1941.
106. Bray, Charles W.: Transfer of learning. *J. Exp. Psych., 11,* 443-467, 1928.
107. Breckenridge, Marian E. and Vincent, E. Lee: *Child Development, Physical and Psychologic Growth Through the School Years.* Philadelphia, W. B. Saunders Co., 1955.
108. Brengelmann, J. C.: Abnormal and personality correlates of certainty. *J. Ment. Sci., 105,* 142-162, 1959.
109. ————: Expressive movements and abnormal behaviour. Ch. III: *Handbook of Abnormal Psychology,* H. J. Eysenck (Ed.). New York, Basic Books, Inc., 87, 1961.
110. Bridges, K. M. B.: Emotional development in early infancy. *Child Dev., 3,* 324-341, 1932.

111. Briesen, Hans V.: A discussion of stress and exhaustion as a primary as well as a contributing etiologic factor in organic neurological disease. The Military Surgeon, 5, 101, 1947.
112. Briggs, G. E. and Brogden, W. J.: The effect of component practice on performance of a level-positionary skill. *J. Exp. Psych.*, 48, 375-380, 1954.
113. Briggs, G. E. and Naylor, J. C.: The relative efficiency of several training methods as a function of transfer of task complexity. *J. Exp. Psych.*, 64, 505, 512, 1962.
114. Briggs, G. E. and Waters, L. K.: Training and transfer as a function of component interaction. *J. Exp. Psych.*, 56, 492-500, 1958.
115. Britt, S. H.: Retroactive inhibition—a review of the literature. *Psych. Bull.*, 32, 381, 1935.
116. Broadbent, D. E.: *Perception and Communication.* London, Pergamon Press, 338, 1958.
117. Brodbeck, A. J. and Irwin, O. C.: The speech behavior of infants without families. *Child Dev.*, 17, 145-156, 1946.
118. Brown, J. S., Knauft, E. B., and Rosenbaum, G.: The accuracy of positioning reactions as a function of direction and extent. Office of Naval Research N5 ori-57, 1947.
119. Brown, Robert H.: Visual sensitivity to differences in velocity. *Psych. Bull.*, 58, 89, March 1961.
120. Brown, V.: Thresholds for visual movement. *Psych. Forsch.*, 14, 249-268, 1931.
121. Brozek, J. and Taylor, H. L.: Tests of motor functions in investigations on fitness. *Am. J. Psych.*, 67, 590-611, 1954.
122. Bruner, J. S. and Goodman, C. C.: Value and need as organizing factors in perception. *J. Ab. & Soc. Psych.*, 42, 33-44, 1947.
123. Bryant, W. L.: On the development of voluntary motor ability. *Am. J. Psych.*, 123-204, 1892.
124. Buhler, Charlotte, as quoted in Young, Re Smiling. *Motivation and Emotion.* New York, John Wiley & Sons, 1961.
125. Bunch, M. E.: Retroactive inhibition or facilitation from interpolated learning as a function of time. *J. Comp. Psych.*, 39, 287-291, 1946.
126. ————: Transfer of training in the mastery of an antagonistic habit after varying intervals of time. *J. Comp. Psych.*, 28, 189-200, 1939.
127. Bunch, M. E. and Lang, E. S.: The amount of transfer of training from partial learning after varying intervals of time. *J. Comp. Psych.*, 27, 449-459, 1939.
128. Bunch, M. E. and McTeer, F. D.: The influence of punishment during learning upon retroactive inhibition. *J. Exp. Psych.*, 15, 473-495, 1932.
129. Bunch, M. E. and Rogers, M.: The relationship between transfer and the length of the interval separating the mastery of the two problems. *J. Comp. Psych.*, 21, 37-52, 1936.
130. Bures, J. and Buresora, O.: Cortical spreading depression as a memory disturbing factor. *J. Comp. & Physiol. Psych.*, 56, 268-272, 1963.
131. ————: The use of Leao's spreading depression in the study of interhemispheric transfer of memory traces. *J. Comp. & Physiol. Psych.*, 53, 558-563, 1960.
132. Bures, J., Buresora, O. and Fifkora, E.: Interhemispheric transfer of passive avoidance reaction. *J. Comp. & Physiol. Psych.*, 57, 326-330, 1964.
133. Buresora, O. and Bures, J.: Interhemispheric synthesis of memory traces. *J. Comp. & Physiol. Psych.*, 59, 211-214, 1965.
134. Burg, Albert and Halbert, Slade: Dynamic visual acuity as related to age, sex and static acuity. *J. Appl. Psych.*, 45, 111-116, 1961.
135. Burt, C.: *The Factors of the Mind.* London, University of London Press, 1956.
136. Buxton, E. E. and Humphreys, L. G.: The effect of practice upon intercorrelations of motor skills. *Science, 81*, 441-442, 1935.

137. Cameron, D. Even, Solyom, L., Smed, S., and Wainrib, B.: Effects of intra-venous administration of ribonucleic acid upon failure of memory for recent events in pre-senile and aged individuals. *Recent Advances in Biol. Psychiatry, 5,* 365-373, 1965.
138. Cameron, Paul and Wertheimer, Michael: Kinesthetic after-effects are in the hands, not in phenomenal space. *Percept. & Mot. Skills, 20,* 1131-1132, 1965.
139. Cannon, W. B.: *The Wisdom of the Body.* New York, W. W. Norton & Co., Inc., 1932.
140. Cantrell, Robert Paul: Body balance activity and perception. *Percept. & Mot. Skills, 17,* 431-437, 1963.
141. Carlson, Jean B.: Effect of amount and distribution of inspection time and length of delay interval on kinesthetic after-effect. *J. Exp. Psych., 66,* 377-382, 1963.
142. Carpenter, Aileen: The measurement of general motor capacity and general motor ability in the first three grades. *Res. Quart., 13,* 444-465, 1942.
143. ————: Tests of motor educability for the first three grades. *Child Dev., 11,* 293-299, 1940.
144. Carr, H. A.: The influence of visual guidance in maze learning. *J. Exp. Psych., 4,* 399-417, 1921.
145. Carter, L. F.: Maze learning with a differential proprioceptive cue. *J. Exp. Psych., 19,* 758-762, 1936.
146. Carter, L. F., Haythorn, W., and Howell, Margaret: A further investigation of the criteria of leadership. *J. Ab. & Soc. Psych., 46,* 589-595, 1951.
147. Carter, L. F. and Nixon, Mary: An investigation of the relationship between four criteria of leadership ability for three different tasks. *J. Psych., 27,* 245-261, 1949.
148. Castaneda, A.: Effects of stress on complex learning and performance. *J. Exp. Psych., 52,* 9-12, 1956.
149. Castaneda, A. and Palmero, David S.: Psychomotor performance as a function of amount of training and stress. *J. Exp. Psych., 50,* 175-179, 1955.
150. Cattell, Raymond B.: The nature and measurement of anxiety. *Sc. Am., 206,* 96-104, 1963.
151. Caudill, W.: Effects of social and cultural systems in reactions to stress. *Soc. Sc. Res. Council,* pamphlet, 1958.
152. Chan, Dolly: An apparatus for the measurement of tactile activity. *Am. J. Psych., 77,* 489, 1964.
153. Chapanis, Alphonse: Knowledge of performance as an incentive in repetitive monotonous tasks. *J. Appl. Psych., 48,* 263-267, 1964.
154. Chase, Wilton P.: The role of kinesthesis in ideation maze learning. *J. Exp. Psych., 17,* 424-438, 1934.
155. Chernikoff, R. and Taylor, F. V.: *Reaction Time to Kinesthetic Stimulation Resulting from Sudden Arm Displacement.* Washington, D.C.: Naval Research Laboratory, NRL Report 3887, November 19, 1951.
156. Church, Russell M.: The effects of competition on reaction time and palmar skin conductance. *J. Ab. & Soc. Psych., 65,* 32-40, 1962.
157. Church, Russell M. and Camp, D. S.: Change in reaction time as a function of knowledge of results. *Am. J. Psych., 77,* 102-106, March 1965.
158. Churchill, A. V.: Visual-kinesthetic localization. *Am. J. Psych., 78,* 496-498, 1965.
159. Clark, K. B.: Some factors influencing the remembering of prose materials. *Arch. Psych., 32,* 253, 1940.
160. Clark, L. Verdelle: Effect of mental practice on the development of a certain motor skill. *Res. Quart., 31,* 560-568, 1960.
161. Clarke, A. D. B. and Blakemore, C. B.: Age and perceptual-motor transfer in imbeciles. *Br. J. Psych., 52,* 125-131, 1961.
162. Clarke, A. D. B. and Cookson, Margaret: Perceptual-motor transfer in imbeciles: A second series of experiments. *Brit. J. Psych., 53,* 321-330, 1962.
163. Cleghorn, T. E. and Darcus, H. D.: The sensibility to passive movement of the human elbow joint. *Quart. J. Exp. Psych., 4,* 66-77, 1952.

164. Clifton, Marguerite A. and Smith, Hope M.: Viewing oneself performing selected motor skills in motion pictures and its effect upon the expressed consciousness of self in performance. *Res. Quart., 33,* 369-375, 1962.

165. Coan, Richard W.: Factors in movement perception. *J. Consult. Psych., 28,* 394-402, 1964.

166. Cohen, John and Dearnally, E. J.: Skill and judgment of footballers in attempting to score goals. *Brit. J. Psych., 53,* 1962.

167. Cohen, Paul: Relationship of performance in two maze tasks. Unpublished Master's Thesis, University of California, Los Angeles, 1963.

168. Coleman, James S.: *The Adolescent Society.* New York, The Free Press of Glencoe, 1961.

169. Comalli, Peter E., Jr., Wagner, Seymour, and Wemer, Heinz: Effect of muscular involvement on size perception. *Percept. & Motor Skills, 9,* 116, 1959.

170. Comrey, Andrew: Group performance in a manual dexterity task. *J. Appl. Psych., 37,* 207, 1953.

171. Comrey, Andrew and Deskin, Gerald: Group manual dexterity in women. *J. Appl. Psych., 38,* 178, 1954.

172. ————: Further results on group manual dexterity in men. *J. Appl. Psych., 38,* 116, 1954.

173. Cook, Thomas W.: Factors in massed and distributed practice. *J. Exp. Psych., 34,* 325-334, 1934.

174. ————: Mirror position and negative transfer. *J. Exp. Psych., 29,* 155-160, 1941.

175. ————: Studies in cross-education. Mirror tracing the star-shaped maze. *J. Exp. Psych., 16,* 146-147, 1933.

176. ————; Studies in cross-education. Further experiments in mirror tracing the star-shaped maze. *J. Exp. Psych., 16,* 679-700, 1933.

177. ————: Studies in cross education. Kinesthetic learning of an irregular pattern. *J. Exp. Psych., 17,* 745-751, 1934.

178. Corah, N. L.: Attention and kinesthetic figural after-effect. *Am. J. Psych., 74,* 629-630, 1961.

179. Corder, Owens: Effects of physical education on the intellectual, physical, and social development of educable mentally retarded boys. *Except. Children, 43,* 357-364, February 1966.

180. Cortes, John B. and Gatte, Florence M.: Physique and self-description of temperament. *J. Consult. Psych., 29,* 429-432, 1965.

181. Costello, C. G., Herrera, Beatriz, and Holland, H. C.: The role of the interpolated stimulus in producing kinesthetic figural after-effects. *Am. J. Psych., 76,* 670-674, 1963.

182. Courts, F. A.: Relations between muscular tension and performance. *Psych. Bull., 39,* 347-367, 1942.

183. Coville, Francis H.: The learning of motor skills as influenced by knowledge of mechanical principles. *J. Ed. Psych., 48,* 321-327, 1957.

184. Cowan, Edwina A. and Pratt, Bertha M.: The hurdle jump as a developmental diagnostic test of motor coordination for children from three to twelve years of age. *Child Dev., 5,* 107-121, 1934.

185. Cox, F. N.: Some effects of test anxiety and presence or absence of other persons on boys' performance on a repetitive motor task. *J. Exp. Child Psych., 3,* 100-112, 1965.

186. Craddock, Ray A. and Stern, Michael R.: Effect of pre- and post-stress upon height of drawings in a perceptual-motor task. *Percept. & Mot. Skills, 17,* 283-285, 1963.

187. Crafts, L. W. and Gilbert, R. W.: The effect of knowledge of results on maze learning and retention. *J. Ed. Psych., 26,* 177-187, 1935.

188. Cratty, Bryant J.: A comparison of fathers and sons in physical ability. *Res. Quart., 31,* 12-15, 1960.

189. ————: A comparison of selected pre-teaching competencies of transfer and non-transfer students. *The Jr. College J., 31:2,* 78-81, 1960.

190. ————: A comparison of the learning of a fine motor skill to learning a similar gross motor task, based upon kinesthetic cues. *Res. Quart., 33,* 212-221, 1962.

191. ————: An investigation of motor educability. *Percept. & Mot. Skills, 13,* 179-181, 1961.

192. ————: Assessing the accuracy of gross human movement. Proceedings 65th Annual College Physical Education Association, 1961-62.

193. ————: Assessing movement accuracy with a fluid-patterned locomotor maze. *Percept. & Mot. Skills, 13,* 162, 1961.

194. ————: The assessment of teacher sensitivity. *Calif. J. Ed. Res., 13,* 2, 1962.

195. ————: Athletic and physical experiences of fathers and sons who participated in physical fitness testing at Pomona College, 1925-1959. *Calif. J. Ed. Res., 10,* 1959.

196. ————: A three level theory of perceptual-motor behavior. *Quest VI,* 3-10, May 1966.

197. ————: Characteristics of human learning in a locomotor maze. *Calif. J. Ed. Res., 14,* 36-42, January 1963.

198. ————: Comparison of verbal-motor performance and learning in serial memory tasks. *Res. Quart., 34,* 431-439, December 1964.

199. ————: *Developmental Sequences of Perceptual-Motor Tasks.* Manuscript submitted, 1967.

200. ————: Effects of intra-maze delay upon learning. *Percept. & Mot. Skills, 15,* 14, March 1962.

201. ————: The evolution of the human action system. *Quest, VI,* 1965.

202. ————: Figural after-effects resulting from gross action patterns: Part II. Perceptual alterations of veer by interpolated movement experience. *Res. Quart., 36,* 22-28, March 1965.

203. ————: Figural after-effects resulting from gross action patterns: Part III. The amount of exposure to the inspection task and the duration of the after-effects. *Res. Quart., 36,* 4, October 1965.

204. ————: The influence of small-pattern practice upon large pattern learning. *Res. Quart., 33,* 523-535, 1962.

205. ————: Motor Learning. In *The Science and Medicine of Exercise and Sport,* Warren Johnson (Ed.). New York, The Macmillan Co., 1965.

206. ————: On the Threshold. Merck Sharpe and Dohme Lecture at the Texas Institute of Child Psychiatry, Houston, Texas, December 1965.

207. ————: The perception of gradient and the veering tendency while walking without vision. *Res. Bull.,* The American Foundation for the Blind, October 1965.

208. ————: Perception of inclined plane while walking without vision. *Percept. & Mot. Skills, 22,* 547-556, 1966.

209. ————: The perceptual-motor attributes of mentally retarded children and youth. Monograph, Mental Retardation Services Board of Los Angeles County, August 1966.

210. ————: Perceptual thresholds of non-visual locomotion. Monograph, Part I, Department of Physical Education, University of California, Los Angeles, August 1965.

211. ————: Personality and individual variations in gross movement behavior. Paper presented to the So. Sec. of the Calif. Assn. for Physical Education, 1961.

212. ————: The psychological bases of physical activity. *J. Health, Phys. Ed., & Recreation, 7,* 71-72, 1965.

213. ————: *Psychology and Physical Activity.* Englewood Cliffs, N.J., Prentice-Hall, Inc. (in press), 1968.

214. ————: Recency vs. primacy in a complex gross motor task. *Res. Quart., 34,* 3-8, 1963.

215. ————: *Social Dimensions of Physical Activity.* Englewood Cliffs, N.J., Prentice-Hall, Inc., 1967.

216. ————: The veering tendency and the perception of gradient. *The New Outlook for the Blind,* August 1965.

217. Cratty, Bryant J. and Densmore, Ann E.: Activity during rest and learning a gross movement task. *Percept. & Mot. Skills, 17,* 250, 1963.

218. Cratty, Bryant J. and Eachus, T.: Correlates of personality and motor performance in two maze tasks. Paper presented at Nat. College Physical Assn., 1961.
219. Cratty, Bryant J. and Hutton, Robert S.: Figural after-effects, resulting from gross action patterns. *Res. Quart.*, 35, 147-160, 1964.
220. Cratty, Bryant J. and Sage, Jack N.: The effects of primary and secondary group interaction upon improvement in a complex movement task. Unpublished study, University of California, Los Angeles, 1963.
221. ———: Spirokinesis. *Res. Quart.*, 37, 4, December 1966.
222. Cratty, Bryant J. and Williams, Harriet G.: Accuracy of facing movements executed without vision. *Percept. & Mot. Skills*, 23, 1231-1238, 1966.
223. ———: Perceptual thresholds of non-visual locomotion. Monograph, Part II, Department of Physical Education, University of California, Los Angeles, 1966.
224. Cron, G. W. and Pronko, N. H.: Development of the sense of balance in school children. *J. Ed. Res.*, 51, 33-37, 1957.
225. Cross, Thomas J.: A comparison of the whole method the minor game method, and the whole part method of teaching basketball to ninth-grade boys. *Res. Quart.*, 8, 49-54, 1937.
226. Crutcher, R.: An experimental study of persistence. *J. Appl. Psych.*, 18, 409-417, 1934.
227. Cumbee, Frances: A factorial analysis of motor coordination. *Res. Quart.*, 25, 412-420, 1954.
228. Cumbee, F. Z., Meyer, M., and Peterson, G.: Factorial analysis of motor coordination variables for third and fourth grade girls. *Res. Quart*, 28, 100-108, 1957.
229. Cunningham, B. V.: An experiment in measuring gross motor development of infants and young children. *J. Ed. Psych.*, 18, 43-54, 1927.
230. Cushing, Frank H.: Manual concepts. *Am. Anthropologist*, 5, 289-317, 1892.
231. Daniel, R. S.: The distribution of muscular action potentials during maze learning. *J. Exp. Psych.*, 24, 621-629, 1939.
232. Dart, Raymond A.: *Adventures With the Missing Link.* New York, Viking Press, 1959.
233. Darwin, Chas. R.: *The Descent of Man, and Selection in Relation to Sex.* London, John Murray, 1875.
234. ———: *The Expression of Emotions in Man and Animals.* New York, Appleton, 1872.
235. Daughtrey, Greyson: The effects of kinesiological teaching on the performance of Junior High School boys. *Res. Quart.*, 16, 26-33, 1945.
236. Daval, Stephen H., Hastings, Mary Lynn, and Klein, Deborah A.: Effect of age, sex, and speed of rotation on rotary pursuit performance by young children. *Percept. & Mot. Skills*, 21, 351-357, 1965.
237. Davidson, M. and McInnes, Parnell R.: The distribution of personality traits in 7-year-old children. *Br. J. Ed. Psych.*, 27, 48-61, 1957.
238. Davis, R. C.: Methods of measuring muscular tension. *Psych. Bull.*, 39, 329-346, 1942.
239. ———: The relation of certain muscle action potentials to 'mental work.' Indiana University Publication, Science Series, 5, 1937.
240. ———: Set and muscular tension. Indiana University Publication, Science Series, 10, 1940.
241. Davis, R. C. and Payne, B.: The role of muscular tension in the comparison of lifted weights. *J. Exp. Psych.*, 27, 227-242, 1940.
242. Dawson, Wm. W. and Edwards, R. W.: Motor development of retarded children. *Percept. & Mot. Skills*, 21, 223-226, 1965.
243. Dayton, Glenn O., Jr., Jones, Margaret H., Steele, Barry, and Rose, Marvin: Developmental study of coordinated eye movements in the human infant. *Arch. Ophthalmology*, 71, 871-875.
244. Dearnally, E. J.: Estimates of endurance under risky conditions. *J. Gen. Psych.*, 68, 243-250, 1963.

245. Delacato, Carl H.: *The Diagnosis and Treatment of Speech and Reading Problems.* Springfield, Charles C Thomas, 1963.
246. Dember, Wm. N.: *The Psychology of Perception.* New York, Henry Holt & Co., 1960.
247. Dember, Wm. N. and Earl, R. W.: Analysis of exploratory, manipulatory and curiosity behaviors. *Psych. Rev., 64,* 91-96, 1957.
248. Denny, M. Ray and Reisman, John M.: Negative transfer as a function of manifest anxiety. *Percept. & Mot. Skills, 6,* 73-75, 1956.
249. Dillon, Donald J.: Measurement of perceived body size. *Percept. & Mot. Skills, 14,* 191-196, 1962.
250. Dinner, Bruce, Wapner, S., McFarland, J., and Werner, Heinz: Rhythmic activity and the perception of time. *Am. J. Psych., 76,* 287, 292, 1963.
251. Domey, Richard G., Duckworth, James E., and Morandi, Anthony J.: Taxonomies and correlates of physique. *Psych. Bull., 62,* 411-426, 1964.
252. Dore, Leon L. and Hilgard, E. R.: Spaced practice and the maturation hypothesis. *J. Psych., 4,* 245-259, 1937.
253. Doty, Barbara and Doty, Larry A.: Effect of age and chlorpromazine on memory consolidation. *J. Comp. & Physiol. Psych., 57,* 331-334, 1964.
254. Dowling, Robert M.: Visual recognition threshold and concurrent motor activity. *Percept. & Mot. Skills, 20,* 1141-1146, 1965.
255. Downey, June E.: *The Will-Temperament and Its Testing.* Yonkers-on-Hudson, New York, World Book Co., 339, 1923.
256. Draper, Wm. R.: Sensory stimulation and Rhesus monkey activity. *Percept. & Mot. Skills, 21,* 319-322, 1965.
257. Drazin, D. H.: Effects of foreperiod, foreperiod variability, and probability of stimulus occurrence on simple reaction time. *J. Exp. Psych., 62,* 43-45, 1961.
258. Dudycha, George J.: *Learn More with Less Effort.* New York, Harper & Bros., 240, 1957.
259. Duffy, E.: *Activation and Behavior.* New York, John Wiley & Sons, Inc., 1962.
260. —————: Muscular tension as related to physique and behavior. *Child Dev., 3,* 200-206, 1932.
261. —————: The psychological significance of the concept of "arousal" or activation. *Psych. Rev., 64,* 265-275, 1957.
262. Duncan, C. P.: Transfer in motor learning as a function of 1st task learning and inter-task similarity. *J. Exp. Psych., 45,* 1-11, 1953.
263. Dunlap, K.: Rhythm and time. *Psych. Bull., 8,* 230-242, 1911 . . . *9,* 197-199, 1914 . . . *11,* 169-171, 1916 . . . *13,* 206-208, 1918.
264. Dusenbury, Delwin and Knower, Franklin H.: Experimental studies of the symbolism of action and voice. *Quart. J. Speech, 24,* 424-435, 1938.
265. Dusenbury, Lois: A study of the effects of training in ball throwing by children ages three to seven. *Res. Quart., 23,* 9-14, 1952.
266. Easley, Howard: The curve of forgetting and the distribution of practice. *J. Ed. Psych., 28,* 474-478, 1937.
267. Eason, Robert G.: Effect of level of activation on the quality and efficiency of performance of verbal and motor tasks. *Percept. & Mot. Skills, 16,* 525-543, 1963.
268. —————: Relation between effort, tension level, skill and performance efficiency in a perceptual-motor task. *Percept. & Mot. Skills, 16,* 297-317, 1963.
269. Ebbinghaus, Herman: Memory: A contribution to experimental psychology. Bureau of Publications, Teachers College, Columbia University, 1913.
270. Eberhard, Ulrich: Transfer of training related to finger dexterity. *Percept. & Mot. Skills, 17,* 274, 1963.
271. Eckert, Helen M.: Linear relationships of isometric strength to propulsive force, angular velocity, and angular acceleration in the standing broad jump. *Res. Quart., 35,* 298-306, 1964.
272. Efron, David: *Gesture and Environment.* London, King's Crown Press, 1941, 155.

273. Egstrom, Glen: The effects of an emphasis on conceptualizing techniques upon the early learning of a gross motor skill. Doctoral dissertation, University of Southern California, Los Angeles, 1961.
274. Ehrlich, Gerald: A method of constructing learning curves for a motor skill involving total body skill and accuracy. *J. Appl. Psych.*, 27, 494-503, 1943.
275. Eiduson, Samuel, Eiduson, B. T., Geller, Edward, and Yuwiler, Arthur: *Biochemistry and Behavior.* Princeton, N.J., D. Van Nostrand Publishers, 1964.
276. Eisenberg, P. and Reichline, P. B.: Judging expressive movements II. Judgment of dominance feeling from motion pictures of gait. *J. Soc. Psych.*, 10, 345-357, 1939.
277. Ekman, Paul: Body position, facial expression and verbal behavior during interviews. *J. Ab. & Soc. Psych.*, 68, 295-301, 1964.
278. Elkine, D.: De l'orientation de l'enfant d'age schdaire daus les relations temporales. *Journal de Psych.*, 25, 425-429, 1928.
279. Ellis, Henry: *The Transfer of Learning.* New York, The Macmillan Company, 1965.
280. Epstein, B.: *Immediate and Retention Effects of Interpolated Rest Periods on Learning Performance.* Teachers' College Contributions to Education, 949, 1949.
281. Epstein, Wm.: Experimental investigations of the genesis of visual space-perception. *Psych. Bull.*, 61, 115-118, 1964.
282. Epstein, Wm., Pash, John, and Coney, Albert: The current status of the size-distance hypothesis. *Psych. Bull.*, 58, 491-514, 1961.
283. Eriksen, C. W., Lazarus, R. S., and Strange, J. R.: Psychological stress and its personality correlates. *J. Personal.*, 20, 277-286, 1952.
284. Espenschade, Anna: Motor performance in adolescence. Society for Research in Child Development, 5, Serial No. 24, No. 1. National Research Council, Washington, D.C., 1940.
285. Eysenck, H. J.: *The Dynamics of Anxiety and Hysteria.* London, Routledge and Kegan Paul, 1957.
286. ————: *Handbook of Abnormal Psychology.* New York, Basic Books, Inc., 1961.
287. ————: Involuntary rest pauses in tapping as a function of drive and personality. *Percept. & Mot. Skills*, 18, 173-174, 1964.
288. ————: On the dual function of consolidation. *Percept. & Mot. Skills*, 22, 273-274, 1966.
289. ————: *The Structure of Human Personality.* London: Methune, 1953.
290. Eysenck, H. J. and Maxwell, A. E.: Reminiscence as a function of drive. *Br. J. Psych.*, 58, 43-52, 1961.
291. Fairclough, Richard H., Jr.: Transfer of motivated improvement in speed of reaction and movement. *Res. Quart.*, 23, 1, 1952.
292. Farber, I. E. and Spence, K. W.: Conditioning and extinction as a function of anxiety. *J. Exp. Psych.*, 45, 116-119, 1953.
293. Fechner, G. T.: *Elemente der Psychophysik*, II. 311-313, 1860.
294. Fenz, Walter D. and Epstein, S.: Manifest anxiety: Unifactoral or multifactoral composition. *Percept. & Mot. Skills*, 20, 773-780, 1965.
295. Fisher, Seymour: Body sensation and perception of projective stimuli. *J. Consult. Psych.*, 29, 135-138, 1965.
296. ————: Power orientation and concept of self-height in men. Preliminary note, *Percept. & Mot. Skills*, 18, 732, 1964.
297. Fisher, Seymour and Cleveland, Sidney E.: *Body Image and Personality.* New York, D. Van Nostrand Publishers, Inc., 389.
298. Fitts, Paul M.: The information capacity of the human motor system in controlling amplitude of movement. *J. Exp. Psych.*, 47, 381-391, 1954.
299. ————: Perceptual-motor skill learning. In *Categories of Human Learning*, Arthur W. Melton (Ed.), New York, Academic Press, Inc., 1964.
300. Fitts, P. M., Bahrick, H. P., and Noble, M. E.: *Skilled Performance.* New York, John Wiley & Sons, Inc., 1961.

301. Fitts, P. M. and Crammell, C.: Location discrimination II. Accuracy of reaching movements to 24 different areas, USAF Air Material Command Technical Report 5833, 1950.
302. Fleishman, Edwin A.: A comparative study of aptitude patterns in unskilled and skilled psychomotor performances, *J. Appl. Psych., 41,* 54-63, 1957.
303. ————: Component and total task relations at different stages of learning a complex tracking task. *Percept. & Mot. Skills, 20,* 1305-1311, 1965.
304. ————: The dimensions of physical fitness—the nationwide normative and developmental study of basic tests, Technical Report No. 4, The Office of Naval Research, Department of Industrial Administration and Department of Psychology, Yale University, New Haven, Conn., August 1962.
305. ————: Perception of body position in the absence of visual cues. *J. Exp. Psych., 46,* 261-270, 1953.
306. ————: A relationship between incentive motivation and ability level in psychomotor performance. *J. Exp. Psych., 56,* 78-81, 1958.
307. Fleishman, Edwin A. and Ellison, Gaylor D.: A factor analysis of fine manipulative tests. *J. Appl. Psych., 46,* 96-105, 1962.
308. Fleishman, Edwin A. and Hempel, Walter E., Jr.: Changes in factor structure of a complex psychomotor test as a function of practice. *Psychometrike, 19,* 239-252, 1954.
309. ————: The relation between abilities and improvement with practice in a visual discrimination reaction task. *J. Exp. Psych., 49,* 301-312, 1955.
310. ————: Factorial analysis of complex psychomotor performance and related skills. *J. Appl. Psych., 40,* 2, 1956.
311. Fleishman, Edwin A., Kremer, Elmar J., and Shoup, Guy W.: The dimensions of physical fitness—A factor analysis of strength tests. Technical Report No. 2, The Office of Naval Research, Department of Industrial Administration and Department of Psychology, Yale University, New Haven, Conn., August 1961.
312. Fleishman, Edwin A. and Parker, J. F., Jr.: Factors in the retention and relearning of perceptual-motor skills. *J. Exp. Psych., 64,* 215-226, 1962.
313. Fleishman, Edwin A. and Rich, Simon: Role of kinesthetic and spatial-visual abilities in perceptual-motor learning. *J. Exp. Psych., 66,* 6-11, 1963.
314. Fleishman, Edwin A., Thomas, Paul, and Munroe, Philip: The dimensions of physical fitness—A factor analysis of speed flexibility, balance and coordination tests. Technical Report No. 3, The Office of Naval Research, Department of Industrial Administration and Department of Psychology, Yale University, New Haven, Conn., September 1961.
315. Flourens, M. J. P.: *Experiences Sur le Systeme Nerveaux,* 1825.
316. Fowler, Harry: *Curiosity and Exploratory Behavior.* New York, The Macmillan Company, 1965.
317. Frank, L. K.: *Society as the Patient.* New Brunswick, N.J., Rutgers University Press, 1949.
318. ————: Tactile communication. In *Explorations in Communication,* Edmund Carpenter and Marshall McLuhan (Eds.), Boston, Beacon Press, 4-11, 1964.
319. Freeman, G. L.: Facilitative and inhibitory effects of muscular tension upon performance. *Am. J. Psych., 45,* 17-52, 1933.
320. ————: The optimal locus of 'anticipatory tensions' in muscular work. *J. Exp. Psych., 21,* 554-564, 1937.
321. ————: The optimal muscular tensions for various performances. *Am. J. Psych., 51,* 146-150, 1938.
322. ————: Studies in the psycho-physiology of transfer: I. The problem of identical elements. *J. Exp. Psych., 2,* 521, 1937.
323. Freeman, F. N. and Abernathy, E. M.: Comparative retention of typewriting and of substitution with analogous material. *J. Ed. Psych., 21,* 639-647, 1930.
324. ————: New evidence of the superior retention of typewriting to that of substitution. *J. Ed. Psych., 23,* 331-334, 1932.
325. Freeman, R. B., Jr.: Figural after-effects: Displacement or contrast? *Am. J. Psych., 77,* 607-613, 1964.

326. French, J. D.: The reticular formation. *J. Neurosurgery, XV,* 97-115, 1958.
327. Freud, Sigmund: In Hall, Calvin S. and Lindquey, Gardner, *Theories of Personality.* New York, John Wiley & Sons, Inc., 1957.
328. Frijda, Nico H.: Facial expression and situational cues: a control. *Acta Psych. Amst., 18,* 239-244, 1961.
329. Frischeisen-Kohler, L.: The personal tempo and its inheritance. *Character & Personal., 1,* 301-313, 1933.
330. Fromm, Erich: *Man for Himself.* New York, Rinehart & Co., 112, 1947.
331. Fruchter, B.: *Introduction to Factor Analysis.* Princeton, N.J., D. Van Nostrand Publishers, Inc., 1954.
332. Fuchs, Alfred H.: Perceptual-motor skill learning. *J. Exp. Psych., 42,* 177-182, 1962.
333. ————: The progression-regression hypothesis in perceptual-motor skill learning. *J. Exp. Psych., 63,* 177-182, 1962.
334. Funkenstein, Daniel H., King, Stanley J., and Drolette, Margaret E.: *Mastery of Stress.* Cambridge, Harvard University Press, 1957.
335. Gagne, R. M., Baker, Katherine E., and Foster, Harriet: On the relation between similarity and transfer of training in the learning of discriminative motor tasks. *Psych. Rev., 57,* 2, 1950.
336. ————: Transfer of discrimination training to a motor task. *J. Exp. Psych., 40,* 314, 1950.
337. Gagne, R. M. and Fleishman, E. A.: *Psychology and Human Performance.* New York, Henry Holt & Co., 493, 1959.
338. Gaito, John: DNA and RNA as memory molecules. *Psych. Rev., 70,* 471-480, 1963.
339. Gaito, John and Zavala, Albert: Neurochemistry and learning. *Psych. Bull., 61,* 45-62, 1964.
340. Galambos, R.: Changing concepts of the learning mechanism. In *Brain Mechanisms and Learning,* Fessard, Gerard, Konorski, and Delafresnaye (Eds.), Springfield, Charles C Thomas, 231-242, 1961.
341. ————: Glia, neurons, and information storage. In *Macro-Molecular Specificity and Biological Memory.* F. Schmitt (Ed.), Cambridge, Mass., The MIT Press, 52-54, 1962.
342. Ganz, L. and Day, R. H.: An analysis of the satiation fatigue mechanism of figural after-effects. *Am. J. Psych., 78,* 345-361, 1965.
343. Gardner, R. Allan: Immediate and residual figural after-effects in kinesthesis. *Am. J. Psych., 74,* 457-461, 1961.
344. Garfiel, Evelyn: The measurement of motor ability. *Arch. Psych., 9,* 1-47, 1923.
345. Garvey, W. D. and Mitnick, L. L.: An analysis of tracking behavior in terms of lead-lag errors. *J. Exp. Psych., 53,* 373-378, 1957.
346. Gates, G.: The effects of an audience upon performance. *J. Ab. & Soc. Psych., 18,* 334-344, 1924.
347. Gellhorn, E.: Motion and emotion: The role of proprioception in the physiology and pathology of the emotions. *Psych. Rev., 71,* 457-472, 1964.
348. Cemelli, A.: The visual perception of objective motion and subjective movement. *Psych. Rev., 61,* 304-314, 1954.
349. Gentry, John Robert: Immediate effects of interpolated rest periods on learning performance. Teachers College Contributions to Education, 799, 1940.
350. George, F. H.: Errors of visual recognition. *J. Exp. Psych., 43,* 202-206, 1952.
351. Gesell, Arnold: *Studies in Child Development.* New York, Harper & Bros., 1948.
352. ————: *Vision.* New York, Paul B. Hoeber, Inc., 1949.
353. ————: *Wolf Child and Human Child.* New York, Harper & Bros., 1941, 107.
354. Gesell, Arnold and Amatruda, Catherine S.: *Developmental Diagnosis.* New York, Paul B. Hoeber, Inc., 1960.

355. Gesell, Arnold and Ilg, F. L.: *The Child from Five to Ten*. New York, Harper & Bros., 227-237, 1946.
356. Gesell, Arnold and Thompson, Helen: *Infant Behavior, Its Genesis and Growth*. New York, McGraw-Hill Book Co., 1934.
357. Getman, Jerold W. and Kane, Elmer: The physiology of readiness. The Program to Accelerate School Success, Minneapolis, Minn.
358. Ghent, Lila: Developmental changes in tactile thresholds on dominant and non-dominant sides. *J. Comp. & Physiol. Psych.*, 54, 670-673, 1961.
359. Ghisselli, E.: Changes in neuromuscular tension accompanying the performance of a learning problem involving constant choice of time, *J. Exp. Psych.*, 19, 91-98, 1936.
360. Gibson, H. B.: The spiral maze: A psychomotor test with implications for the study of delinquency. *Br. J. Psych.*, 55, 219-225, 1964.
361. Gibson, J. J.: Adaptation, after-effect and contrast in the perception of curved lines. *J. Exp. Psych.*, 16, 1-33, 1933.
362. —————: *The Perception of the Visual World*. Boston, Houghton-Mifflin Co., 1950.
363. —————: Observations on active touch. *Psych. Rev.*, 69, 477-491, 1962.
364. —————: The useful dimensions of sensitivity. *Am. Psychologist*, 18, 178-195, 1963.
365. Gibson, J. J., Gibson, E. J., Smith, O. W., and Flock, H.: Motion parallax in perceived depth. *J. Exp. Psych.*, 58, 40-51, 1959.
366. Giesecke, Minnie: The genesis of hand preference. Study No. 2. Committee on Child Development, University of Chicago, Monographs for the Society for Research in Child Development No. 5, National Research Council, Washington, D.C., 1935.
367. Gilinsky, Alberta S.: The effect of growth on the perception of visual space. Paper presented to the Eastern Psych. Assn., New York, April 1960.
368. Gilliland, A. R., Hofeld, Jerry, and Eckstrand, Cordon: Studies in time perception. *Psych. Bull.*, 43, 162-176, 1946.
369. Ginzberg, Eli, Anderson, James K., Ginsberg, S. W., and Merma, John L.: *Patterns of Performance*. New York, Columbia University Press, 1959.
370. Gire, Eugenia and Espenschade, Anna: Relation between measures of motor educability and learning of specific motor skills. *Res. Quart.*, 13, 41-56, 1942.
371. Glaser, R. (Ed.): *Training Research and Education*. Pittsburgh, University of Pittsburgh Press, 137-175, 1962.
372. Glassow, Ruth B. and Kruse, Pauline: Motor performance of girls age six to 14 years. *Res. Quart.*, 31, 426-433, 1960.
373. Glickman, Stephen E.: Perseverative neural processes and consolidation of the memory trace. *Psych. Bull.*, 58, 218-233, 1961.
374. Goldfarb, W.: The effects of early institutional care on adolescent personality. *J. Exp. Ed.*, 12, 106-129, 1943.
375. Goldscheider, A.: Physiologie des Muskelsinnes: Gesammelte. *Abhandlungen* II, 1898.
376. Goldstein, Ins B.: Role of muscle tension in personality theory. *Psych. Bull.*, 61, 413-425, 1964.
377. Goldstein, Jacob and Weiner, Chas.: On some relations between the perception of depth and of movement. *J. Psych.*, 55, 3-23, 1963.
378. Goldstein, Kurt: The organism, a holistic approach to biology. In *Pathological Data in Man*. New York, American Book Co., 1939.
379. Goldstone, S., Bond, Wm. K., and Lohamon, Wm. T.: Intersensory comparisons of temporal judgments. *J. Exp. Psych.*, 57, 243-248, 1959.
380. Goodenough, F. L.: The expression of emotions in infancy. *Child Dev.*, 2, 96-101, 1931.
381. —————: Interrelationships in the behavior of young children. *Child Dev.*, 1, 29-48, 1930.
382. Goodenough, F. L. and Brian, C. R.: Certain factors underlying the acquisition of motor skills by pre-school youngsters. *J. Exp. Psych.*, 12, 127-155, 1929.

383. Goodenough, F. L. and Smart, R. C.: Interrelationships of motor abilities in young children. *Child Dev., 6,* 141-153, 1935.
384. Gopalaswami, M.: Economy in motor learning. *Br. J. Psych., 15,* 226-236, 1925.
385. ————: Intelligence in motor learning. *Br. J. Psych., 14,* 274-290, 1924.
386. Gordon, K.: Group judgments in the field of lifted weights. *J. Exp. Psych., 7,* 398-400, 1924.
387. Gordon, Malcolm W., Deanin, Grace G., Leonhardt, Harry, and Gwynn, Robert: RNA and memory: A negative experiment. *Am. J. Psychiatry, 43,* 1174-1177, 1966.
388. Gordon, Richard E., Gorton, Katherine K., and Gunther, Max: *The Split Level Trap.* New York, B. Geis Assn., Random House Distributors.
389. Gottlieb, Gilbert and Wilson, Ian: Cerebral dominance: Temporary description of verbal memory by unilateral electroconvulsive shock treatment. *J. Comp. & Physiol. Psych., 60,* 368-375, 1965.
390. Gottsdanker, Robert, Frich, James W., and Lockhard, Robert B.: Identifying the acceleration of visual targets. *Br. J. Psych., 52,* 1, 31-42, 1961.
391. Graham, C. H., Baker, K. E., Hecht, M., and Lloyd, V. V.: Factors: Thresholds for monocular movement parallax. *J. Exp. Psych., 38,* 205-223, 1948.
392. Graybiel, Ashton, Jokl, Ernst, and Trapp, Claude: Russian studies of vision in relation to physical activity and sports. *Res. Quart., 26,* 480-485, 1955.
393. Green, Richard and Money, John: Effeminacy in pre-pubertal boys. Summary of eleven cases and recommendations for case management. *Pediatrics, 27,* 2, 1961.
394. Greenspoon, Joel and Foreman, Sally: Effect of delay of knowledge of results on learning a motor task. *J. Exp. Psych., 51,* 226-228, 1956.
395. Greenwald, Anthony G.: Skill and motivation as separate components of performance. *Percept. & Mot. Skills, 20,* 239-246, 1965.
396. Grinker, R. R. and Spiegel, J. P.: *Men Under Stress.* Philadelphia, The Blakiston Co., 1945.
397. Groen, J. J. and Jongkees, L. B. W.: The threshold of angular acceleration perception. *J. Physiol., 107,* 1-7, 1948.
398. Groos, Karl: *The Play of Animals.* New York, D. Appleton & Co., 338, 1898.
399. Grossack, Martin M.: Some effects of cooperation and competition upon small group behavior. *J. Ab. & Soc. Psych., 49,* 341-348, 1954.
400. Guilford, J. P.: A system of psychomotor abilities. *Am. J. Psych., 71,* 164-174, 1958.
401. ———— (Ed.): *Printed Classification Tests.* A.A.F. Aviation Psych. Program Research Reports No. 5, Government Printing Office, Washington, D.C., 1947.
402. ————: The structure of intellect. *Psych. Bull., 53,* 267-293, 1956.
403. Gurnee, H.: Maze learning in the collective situation. *J. Psych., 3,* 437-443, 1937.
404. Gutherie, E. R.: *The Psychology of Learning.* New York, Harper & Bros., 91, 305, 1952.
405. Gutteridge, Mary V.: A study of motor achievements of young children. *Arch. Psych., 6,* 244, 1939.
406. Haith, Marshall M.: The response of the human newborn to visual movement. *J. Exp. Child Psych., 3,* 235-243, 1966.
407. Hall, B. E.: Transfer of training in mirror tracing. *J. Exp. Psych., 25,* 316-318, 1939.
408. Halverson, H. M.: The acquisition of skill in infancy. *J. Gen. Psych., 43,* 3-48, 1933.
409. ————: A further study of grasping. *J. Gen. Psych., 7,* 34-64, 1932.
410. ————: An experimental study of prehension in infants by means of systematic cinemo record. *Genetic Psych., 10,* 2, 1931.
411. Hansen, Frederick C.: Serial action as a basic measure of motor capacity. *Psych. Monographs, 31,* 320-382, 1922.
412. Harding, D. W.: Rhythmization and speed of work. *Br. J. Psych., 23,* 262-278, 1932.

413. Harlow, H. F.: The formation of learning sets. *Psych. Rev.*, 56, 51-65, 1949.
414. Harlow, Robert G.: Masculine inadequacy and compensatory development of physique. *J. Personal.*, 19, 312-323, 1951.
415. Harmon, Darell Boyd: *Notes on a Dynamic Theory of Vision*, Vol. 1, published by author, 1958.
416. ————: *Winter Haven Study of Perceptual Learning*. Winter Haven Lions Research Foundation, Inc., Winter Haven Lions Club, Winter Haven, Florida, 1962.
417. Harmon, H.: *Modern Factor Analysis*. Chicago, University of Chicago Press, 1960.
418. Harmon, John M. and Miller, Arthur G.: Time patterns in motor learning. *Res. Quart.*, 21, 182-187, 1950.
419. Haromian, Frank and Sugerman, Arthur: A comparison of Sheldon's and Parnell's methods for quantifying morphological differences. *Am. J. Phys. Anthro.*, 23, 135-142, 1965.
420. Harris, Chester W. and Libo, Maria R.: *Component, Image, and Factor Analysis of Tests of Intellect and of Motor Performance*. Cooperative Research Project No. S-192-64, University of Wisconsin, 1965.
421. Harris, Dorothy V.: Comparison of physical performance and psychological traits of college women with high and low fitness indices. *Percept. & Mot. Skills*, 17, 293-294, 1963.
422. Harris, Laurren: The effects of relative novelty on children's choice behavior. *J. Exp. Child Psych.*, 2, 297-305.
423. Harrison, R. and Dorcus, R.: Is rate of voluntary bodily movements unitary? *J. Gen. Psych.*, 18, 31-39, 1938.
424. Harrison, Virginia F.: Review of the neuromuscular bases for motor learning. *Res. Quart.*, 33, 59-69, 1938.
425. Hartman, Doris M.: The hurdle jump as a measure of the motor proficiency of young children. *Child Dev.*, 14, 201-211, 1943.
426. Harton, J. J.: The influence of the difficulty of activity on the estimation of time. *J. Exp. Psych.*, 23, 270-287, 1938.
427. Harways, H.: Judgments of distance in children and adults. *J. Exp. Psych.*, 65, 385-390, 1963.
428. Haskins, Mary Jane: Development of a response recognition training film in tennis. *Percept. & Mot. Skills*, 21, 207-211, 1965.
429. Hatfield, J. A.: *The Psychology of Power*. New York, The Macmillan Co., 1923.
430. Hebb, D. O.: Emotion in man and animal: An analysis of the intuitive processes of recognition. *Psych. Rev.*, 88-106, 1946.
431. ————: Man's frontal lobes. *Arch. Neurology & Psychiatry*, 54, 10-24, 1945.
432. ————: *The Organization of Behavior*. New York, John Wiley & Sons, Inc., 1949.
433. Heidler, Fritz: On perception, event structure, and psychological environment. *Psych. Issues*, 1, 3, Monograph 3. New York, International Universities Press, Inc., 1959.
434. Hellenbrandt, F. A., Schade, Moja, and Carns, Marie L.: Methods of evoking the tonic neck reflexes in normal human subjects. *Am. J. Phys. Med.*, 41, 90-137, 1962.
435. Hellenbrandt, F. A. and Waterland, Joan C.: Indirect learning. *Am. J. Phys. Medicine*, 41, 90-137, 1962.
436. ————: Expansion of motor patterning under exercise stress. *Am. J. Phys. Med.*, 41, 56-66, 1962.
437. Hellweg, Dolores A.: Effect of different stress situations on emotional response. Master's Dissertation, University of California, Los Angeles, 1960.
438. Helson, Harry (Ed.): *Theoretical Foundations of Psychology*. New York, D. Van Nostrand Publishers, Inc., Chapter 8, Perception, 349-385, 1951.
439. Hendrickson, G. and Schoreder, W. H.: Transfer of training in learning to hit a submerged target. *J. Ed. Psych.*, 32, 205-213, 1941.

440. Henry, Franklin: Dynamic kinesthetic perception and adjustment. *Res. Quart., 24,* 176, 1953.

441. ————: Increase in speed of movement by motivation and by transfer of motivated improvement. *Res. Quart., 22,* 219-288, 1951.

442. ————: Increased response latency for complicated movements and a "memory drum" theory of neuromotor reaction. *Res. Quart., 31,* 448-457, 1960.

443. ————: Interdependence of reaction and movement times and equivalence of sensory motivators of fast response. *Res. Quart., 23,* 43-53, 1952.

444. ————: Personality differences in athletes and physical education and aviation students. *Psych. Bull., 38,* 745-755, 1941.

445. Henry, Franklin and Smith, Leon E.: Simultaneous vs. separate bilateral muscular contractions in relation to neural overflow theory and neuromotor specificity. *Res. Quart., 32,* 42-46, 1961.

446. Henry, Franklin and Whitley, J. D.: Relationships between individual differences in strength, speed, and mass in an arm movement. *Res. Quart., 31,* 24-33, 1960.

447. Heriot, J. T. and Coleman, P. D.: The effect of electroconvulsive shock on retention of a modified 'one-trial' conditioned avoidance. *J. Comp. & Physiol. Psych., 55,* 1082-1084, 1962.

448. Hewes, Gordon W.: The anthropology of posture. *Sci. Am., 196,* 123-132, 1957.

449. Hicks, James Allen: The acquisition of motor skill in young children. *University of Iowa Studies in Child Welfare,* 4, No. f, University of Iowa Press, 1929.

450. Hicks, James Allen and Ralph, Dorothy W.: The effect of practice in tracing the porteus diamond maze. *Child Dev., 11,* 156-158, 1931.

451. Hicks, Vinnie C. and Carr, H. A.: Human reactions in a maze. *J. Animal Behavior, 2,* 98-125, 1912.

452. Hilgard, E. R.: The role of learning in perception. In R. R. Blake and G. V. Ramsey (Eds.), *Perception, an Approach to Personality.* New York, The Ronald Press, 95-120, 1951.

453. ————: *Theories of Learning.* New York, Appleton-Century-Crofts, Inc., 407, 1948.

454. Hilgard, E. R. and Marquis: *Conditioning and Learning,* 2nd ed., New York, Appleton-Century-Crofts, Inc., 1961.

455. Hill, D. S.: Minor studies in learning and relearning. *J. Ed. Psych., 5,* 375-386, 1914.

456. Hill, Kennedy T. and Stevenson, Harold W.: The effects of social reinforcement vs. nonreinforcement and sex of E on the performance of adolescent girls. *J. Personal., 33,* 30-45, 1965.

457. Hill, L. B.: A second quarter century of delayed recall or relearning at eighty. *J. Ed. Psych., 48,* 65-68, 1957.

458. Hill, S. R.: Studies on adrenocortical and psychological response to stress in man. *Arch. Int. Med., 97,* 269-298, 1956.

459. Hill, W. C. Osman: *Man As An Animal.* London, Hutchinson and Company, 1957.

460. Hill, W. F.: The effect of long confinement on voluntary wheel-running by rats. *J. Comp. Physiol. Psych., 51,* 770-773, 1958.

461. Hirsch, Wm.: Motor skill transfer by trainable mentally retarded and normal children. Doctoral dissertation, University of California, Los Angeles, May 1965.

462. Holding, D. H.: Transfer between difficult and easy tasks. *Br. J. Psych., 53:4,* 397-407, 1962.

463. Hollingworth, H. L.: Correlation of abilities as affected by practice. *J. Ed. Psych., 4,* 405-413, 1913.

464. Holtzman, W. H. and Bitterman, M. E.: A factorial study of adjustment to stress. *J. Ab. & Soc. Psych., 52,* 179, 1956.

465. Holway, Alfred H. and Hurvich, Leo M.: On the discrimination of mineral differences in weight. I. A theory of differential sensitivity. *J. Psych., 4,* 309-332, 1937.

466. Holzman, P. S. and Klein, G. S.: Cognitive system principles of leveling and sharpening; individual differences in assimilation effects in visual time error. *J. Psych., 37,* 105-122, 1954.

467. Honzik, C. H.: The role of kinesthesis in maze learning. *Science, 84,* 373, 1936.

468. Hood, Albert B.: A study of the relationship between physique and personality variables measured by MMPI. *J. Personal., 31,* 97-107, 1963.

469. Horney, Karen: In Hall, Calvin S. and Lindzey, Gardner, *Theories of Personality.* New York, John Wiley & Sons, Inc., 1957.

470. Howard, I. P. and Templeton, B.: *Human Spatial Orientation.* New York, John Wiley & Sons, Inc., 1966.

471. Howell, F. C. and Bourliere, F. (Eds.): *African Ecology and Human Evolution.* Viking Fund Publications in Anthropology, No. 36, 1963.

472. Howell, Maxwell L.: Influence of emotional tension to speed of reaction and movement. *Res. Quart., 24,* 22-32, 1953.

473. ————: Use of force-time graphs for performance analysis in facilitating motor learning. *Res. Quart., 27,* 12-22, 1956.

474. Howland, C. I.: Experimental studies in rote-learning theory: VI. Comparison of retention following learning to same criterion by massed and distributed practice. *J. Exp. Psych., 26,* 568-587, 1940.

475. Hubbard, and Seng, C. N.: Visual movements of batters. *Res. Quart., 25,* 42-57, 1954.

476. Huizinga, Johan: *Homo Ludens* (Man the Player). Boston, Beacon Press, 1950.

477. Hull, C. L.: *Principles of Behavior.* New York, Appleton-Century-Crofts, Inc., 1943.

478. Humphrey, James H.: Comparison of the use of active games and language workbook exercises as learning media in the development of language understandings with third-grade children. *Percept. & Mot. Skills, 21,* 23-26, 1965.

479. Hunt, Valerie: Cerebral palsied youngsters, and body-image problems. Unpublished report to the Faculty, University of California, Los Angeles, 1962.

480. Hutton, Robert S.: Kinesthetic after-effect produced by walking on a gradient. *Res. Quart., 37,* 368-374, 1966.

481. Hyden, H.: Biochemical changes in glial cells and nerve cells at varying activity. In Proceedings of the Fourth International Congress of Biochemistry: *Biochemistry of the Central Nervous System,* v. 3, London, Pergamon Press, 1959.

482. ————: Satellite cells in the nervous system. *Sci. Am., 205,* 62-70, 1961.

483. Icheiser, G.: Misunderstandings in human relations: A study in false social perception. *Am. J. Sociol., 55,* 2, 1949.

484. Ittelson, W. H.: *Visual Space Perception.* New York, Springer Publishing Co., Inc., 1960.

485. Ittelson, W. H. and Cantril, Hadley: *Perception, A Transactional Approach.* New York, Doubleday & Co., 1954.

486. Jacobson, Allen L.: Learning in flatworms and annelids. *Psych. Bull., 60,* 74-94, 1963.

487. Jacobson, Allen L., Fried, C., and Horowitz, S. D.: Planarians and memory: I. Transfer of learning by injection of ribonucleic acid. *Nature, 209,* 599-601, 1966.

488. Jacobson, Edmund: *Progressive Relaxation.* Chicago, The University of Chicago Press, 1938.

489. Jahnke, J. C.: Post-rest motor learning performance as a function of degree of learning. *J. Exp. Psych., 62:6,* 605-611, 1961.

490. ————: Retention in motor learning as a function of amount of practice and rest. *J. Exp. Psych., 55,* 270-273, 1958.

491. Jahnke, J. C. and Duncan, C. P.: Reminiscence and forgetting in motor learning after extended rest intervals. *J. Exp. Psych., 52,* 273-282, 1956.

492. Jenkins, L. M.: Comparative study of motor achievements of children five, six and seven years of age. New York: Teachers College, Columbia University Contributions to Education, 414, 1930.

493. Johannson, Gunnar: *Configurations in Event Perception.* Upsala, 1950.
494. Johnson, G. B.: Physical skills test for sectioning classes into homogeneous units. *Res. Quart., 3,* 128-136, 1932.
495. Johnson, Warren R. and Kramer, George F.: Effects of different types of hypnotic suggestions upon physical performance. *Res. Quart., 31,* 469-473, 1960.
496. Johnson, Warren R., Massey, Benjamin H., and Kramer, George F.: Effect of posthypnotic suggestions on all-out effort of short duration. *Res. Quart., 31,* 142-146, 1960.
497. Jones, Frank P. and Hanson, John A.: Note on the persistence of pattern in a gross body movement. *Percept. & Mot. Skills, 14,* 230, 1962.
498. —————: Time-space pattern in a gross body movement. *Percept. & Mot. Skills, 12,* 35-41, 1961.
499. Jones, Harold E.: The California adolescent growth study. *J. Ed. Res., 31,* 561-567, 1938.
500. —————: *Motor Performance and Growth.* A developmental study of static dynamometric strength. Berkeley, University of California Press, 182, 1949.
501. —————: Physical ability as a factor in social adjustment in adolescence. *J. Ed. Res., 40,* 287-301, 1946.
502. Jones, M. B.: Simplex theory. U.S. Naval School of Aviation Medicine Monograph Series 3, Pensacola, Florida, 1959.
503. Jones, Mary Cover: Psychological correlates of somatic development. *Child Dev., 33,* 899-911, 1965.
504. Jones, Stephen and Vroom, Victor H.: Division of labor and performance under cooperative and competitive conditions. *J. Ab. & Soc. Psych., 68,* 313-320, 1964.
505. Jones, Theresa Dowei. The development of certain motor skills and play activities in young children. New York: Bureau of Publications, Teachers College, Columbia University, 1939.
506. Jones, Wayne R. and Ellis, Norman R.: Inhibitory potential in rotary pursuit. acquisition by normal and defective subjects. *J. Exp. Psych., 63:6,* 534-537.
507. Judd, C. H.: Movement and consciousness. *Psych. Rev., 7,* 199-226, 1905.
508. —————: The relationship of special training to general intelligence. *Educ. Rev., 26,* 28-42, 1908.
509. Katz, D.: Gestalt laws of mental work. *Br. J. Psych., 39,* 175-183, 1949.
510. Kao, Dij-Lih: Plateaus and the curve of learning in motor skills. *Psych. Monographs, 49,* 1-81, 1937.
511. Kardiner, Abram and Spiegel, Herbert: *War Stress, and Neurotic Illness.* New York, Paul B. Hoeber, Inc., 1947.
512. Karlin, Lawrence and Mortimer, Rudolph G.: Effect of verbal, visual and auditory augmenting cues on learning a complex motor skill. *J. Exp. Psych., 65,* 75-79, 1963.
513. —————: Effects of visual and verbal cues on learning a motor skill. *J. Exp. Psych., 64,* 608-614, 1962.
514. Kaufman, Herbert, Smith, Jerome, and Zeaman, Daniel: Tests of generality of two empirical equations for motor learning. *Percept. & Mot. Skills, 15,* 91-100, 1962.
515. Kawasima, S.: The influence of time intervals upon the perception of arm motion. *Jap. J. Psych., 12,* 270-289, 1937.
516. Kelley, Richard and Stephens, Mark W.: Comparison of different patterns of social reinforcement in children's operant learning. *J. Comp. & Physiol. Psych., 57,* 294-296, 1964.
517. Kelley, T. L.: *Crossroads in the Mind of Man.* Stanford, California, 1928.
518. Kelsey, Ian Bruce: Effects of mental practice and physical practice upon muscular endurance. *Res. Quart., 32,* 47-54, 1961.
519. Kempe, J. E.: An experimental investigation of the relationship between certain personality characteristics and physiological responses to stress in a normal population. Unpublished doctoral dissertation, Michigan State University, 1956.

520. Kennedy, J. L. and Travis, R. C.: Prediction of speed of performance by muscle action potentials. *Science, 105,* 410-411, 1947.
521. Kephart, Newell C.: *The Slower Learner in the Classroom.* Columbus, Ohio, Charles E. Merrill Books, Inc.
522. Kershner, John R.: An investigation of the Doman-Delacato theory of neuro-psychology as it applies to trainable mentally retarded children in public schools. Bureau of Research Administration and Coordination Area of Research Administration and Coordination Area of Research and Development, Department of Public Instruction, Commonwealth of Pennsylvania, October 1966.
523. Kientzle, Mary J.: Learning curves, etc. *J. Exp. Psych., 36,* 187-211, 1946.
524. Kilpatrick, F. P.: Two processes in perceptual learning. *J. Exp. Psych., 36,* 187-211, 1946.
525. Kimble, G. A.: Evidence for the role of motivation in determining the amount of reminiscence in pursuit-rotor learning. *J. Exp. Psych., 40,* 248, 1950.
526. ————: Performance and reminiscence in motor learning as a function of the degree of distribution of practice. *J. Exp. Psych., 39,* 500-510, 1949.
527. ————: Reminiscence in motor learning as a function of interpolated rest. *Am. Psych., 2,* 312, 1947.
528. King, Richard A.: Consolidation of the neural trace in memory: Investigation with one-trial avoidance conditioning and ECS. *J. Comp. & Physiol. Psych., 59,* 283-284, 1965.
529. Kingsley, Howard L.: The development of motor skills. *The Nature and Conditions of Learning.* New York, Prentice-Hall, Inc., 2, 1946.
530. Kirchner, W. K.: Age differences in short-term retention of rapidly changing information. *J. Exp. Psych., 55,* 352-358, 1958.
531. Klein, G. and Krech, D.: Cortical conductivity in the brain injured. *J. Res., 21,* 118-148, 1952.
532. Kline, L. W. and Johannsen, D. E.: Comparative role of the face and face-body-hands as aids in identifying emotions. *J. Ab. & Soc. Psych., 29,* 415-426, 1935.
533. Knapp, Clude and Dixon, Robert: Learning to juggle: I. A study to determine the effects of two different distribution of practice on learning efficiency. *Res. Quart., 21,* 331-336, 1950.
534. ————: Learning to juggle: II. A study of whole and part methods. *Res. Quart., 23,* 389-401, 1952.
535. Kneeland, Natalie: Self-estimates of improvement in repeated tasks. *Arch. Psych., 163,* 1934.
536. Knitz, B. L. and Zaffy, Donna J.: Short-term and long-term retention and task difficulty. *J. Psych., 59,* 229-232, 1965.
537. Koch, H. L.: The influence of mechanical guidance upon maze learning. *Psych. Monographs, 147,* 1923.
538. Koffa, K.: *The Growth of the Mind.* New York, Harcourt Brace, 1929.
539. Kogan, Bernard R. (Ed.): *Darwin and His Critics.* San Francisco, Wadsworth Publishing Company, Inc., 1960.
540. Kohler, W.: *Dynamics in Psychology.* New York, Liveright, 1940.
541. ————: *Gestalt Psychology.* New York, Liveright, 1929.
542. Kohler, W. and Dinnerstein, D.: Figural after-effects in kinesthesis. In *Miscellanea psychologia,* Albert Michotte, Paris: Librarie Philosophique, 196-220, 1947.
543. Koonce, Jefferson M., Chambliss, Davis J., and Irion, Arthur: Long-term reminiscence in the pursuit rotor habit. *J. Exp. Psych., 67,* 498-500, 1964.
544. Kreiger, Jane C.: The influence of figural-ground perception on spatial adjustment in tennis. M.A. Thesis, University of California, Los Angeles, 1962.
545. Krueger, W. C. F.: Further studies in overlearning. *J. Exp. Psych., 13,* 152-163, 1930.
546. Krus, Donald M., Heinz, Werner, and Wagoner, Seymour: Studies in vicariousness: Motor activity and perceived movement. *Am. J. Psych., 66,* 603-609, 1953.

547. Kurz, Ronald B.: Relationship between time imagery and Rorschach human movement responses. *J. Consult. Psych., 27,* 273-276, 1963.
548. Laban, Rudolph: *Effort.* London, London MacDonald Press, 1947.
549. La Barre, Weston: The cultural basis of emotions and gestures. *J. Personal., 16,* 49-68, 1947.
550. Lachman, Sheldon J.: A theory relating learning to electrophysiology of the brain. *J. Psych., 59,* 275-281, 1965.
551. Laidlow, R. W. and Hamilton, M. A.: A study of thresholds in apperception of passive movement among normal subjects. *Bull. Neurol. Inst.,* New York, *6,* 268-273, 1937.
552. Laird, D. A.: Changes in motor control and individual variations under the influence of "razzing." *J. Exp. Psych., 6,* 233-246, 1923.
553. Lambert, Phillip: Practice effect of non-dominant vs. dominant musculature in acquiring two-handed skill. *Res. Quart., 22,* 50-57, 1951.
554. Landauer, Thomas K.: Two hypotheses concerning the biochemical basis of memory. *Psych. Rev., 71:3,* 167-179, 1964.
555. Langdon, J. N. and Yates, E. M.: Experimental investigation into transfer of training in skilled performances. *Br. J. Psych., 18,* 422-437, 1928.
556. Langer, Jonas, Heinz, Werner, and Wapner, Seymour: Apparent speed of walking under conditions of danger. *J. Gen. Psych., 73,* 291-298, 1965.
557. Langfeld, Herbert S.: Voluntary movement under positive and negative instruction. *Psych. Rev., 20,* 459-478, 1913.
558. Langworthy, Orthello: The neurophysiology of motivation. *Am. J. Psychiatry, 122:9,* 1033-1039, March 1966.
559. Lardahl, D. S.: Effect of the weight-contrast illusion on rotary pursuit performance. *Percept. & Mot. Skills, 17,* 87-90, 1963.
560. Lardahl, D. S. and Archer, E. J.: Transfer effects on a rotary pursuit task as a function of first task difficulty. *J. Exp. Psych., 56,* 421-426, 1958.
561. Lasher, Gabriel W. (Ed.): *The Processes of Ongoing Human Evolution.* Detroit, Wayne State University Press, 1960.
562. Lashley, K. S.: The acquisition of skill in archery. Papers from the Department of Marine Biology, Carnegie Institute, Washington, *7,* 105-128, 1915.
563. ————: *Brain Mechanisms and Intelligence.* New York, Dover Publications, Inc., 1963.
564. Latane, Biff and Arrowood, John: Emotional arousal and task performance. *J. Appl. Psych., 47,* 324-327, 1963.
565. Latchaw, Marjorie: Measuring selected motor skills in fourth, fifth, and sixth grades. *Res. Quart., 25,* 439-449, 1954.
566. Lavery, J. J.: The effect of one-trial delay in knowledge of results on the acquisition and retention of a tossing skill. *Am. J. Psych., 77,* 437-443, 1964.
567. ————: Retention of a skill following training with and without instructions to retain. *Percept. & Mot. Skills, 18,* 275-281, 1964.
568. Lavery, J. J. and Suddon, Florence H.: Retention of simple motor skills as a function of the number of trials by which KR is delayed. *Percept. & Mot. Skills, 15,* 231-237, 1962.
569. Lawrence, D. H.: The transfer of a discrimination along a continuum. *J. Comp. & Physiol. Psych., 45,* 511-516, 1952.
570. Lazarus, R. S., Deese, J., and Osler, S. J.: The effects of psychological stress upon performance. *Psych. Bull., 49,* 293-317, 1952.
571. Leakey, L. S. B.: *Adam's Ancestors.* London, Methune & Company Ltd., 1934.
572. Leavitt, H. J. and Schlosberg, H.: The retention of verbal and of motor skills. *J. Exp. Psych., 34,* 404-417, 1944.
573. Leibowitz, H. W. and Lomont, J. F.: *The Effect of Grid Lines in the Field of View Upon Perception of Motion.* Technical Report No. 54-201, March, 1954, Wright-Patterson Air Force Base.
574. ————: *The Effect of Luminance and Exposure Time Upon Perception of Motion.* Technical Report No. 54-78, March, 1954. Wright-Patterson Air Force Base.
575. Leshman, Saul S.: Effects of aspiration and achievement on muscular tension. *J. Exp. Psych., 61,* 133-137, 1961.

576. Leton, Donald A.: Visual-motor capacities and ocular efficiency in reading. *Percept. & Mot. Skills, 15,* 407-432, 1962.
577. Leuba, J. H.: The influence of the duration and of the rate of arm movements upon the judgment of their length. *Am. J. Psych., 20,* 374-385, 1909.
578. Levy, S. L.: This way to self improvement. *Personnel J., 38,* 373-376, 1960.
579. Lewinson, T. S. and Zubin, J.: *Handwriting Analysis.* New York, King's Crown Press, 1942.
580. Lewis, D. and Lowe, W.: Retention of skill on the SAM Complex Coordinator. *Proceeding Iowa Acad. Sci., 63,* 591-599, 1959.
581. Lewis, D., Smitt, P. N., and McAllister, D. E.: Retroactive facilitation and interference in performance on the two-hand coordinator. *J. Exp. Psych., 44,* 44-50, 1952.
582. Lewis, F. H.: Affective characteristics of rhythm. *Psych. Bull., 30,* 679-680, 1933.
583. Lewis, Michael, Wall, A. Martin, and Aronfreed, Justin: Developmental change in the relative values of social and non-social reinforcement. *J. Exp. Psych., 66,* 133-137, 1963.
584. Liddel, E. G. T. and Sherrington, Sir C. S.: Recruitment and some other features of reflex inhibition. *Proceedings of the Royal Society Series: Series B, Biological Sciences, 97,* 488-518, 1925.
585. Lincoln, Robt. S.: Learning a rate of movement. *J. Exp. Psych., 47,* 465-470, 1954.
586. Lincoln, Robt. S. and Smith, K. U.: Transfer of training in tracking performance at different target speeds. *J. Appl. Psych., 35,* 358, 1951.
587. Lindeburg, Franklin A.: A study of the degree of transfer between quickening exercises and other coordinated movements. *Res. Quart., 20,* 180-195, 1949.
588. Lipman, Ronald S. and Spitz, Herman: The relationship between kinesthetic satiation and inhibition in rotary pursuit performance. *J. Exp. Psych., 62:5,* 468-475, 1961.
589. Lipsitt, L. P.: A self concept scale for children and its relationship to the children's form of the manifest anxiety scale. *Child Dev., 29,* 463-472, 1959.
590. Lloyd, Andrei J. and Caldwell, Lee S.: Accuracy of active and passive positioning of the leg on the basis of kinesthetic cures. *J. Comp. & Physiol. Psych., 60,* 102-106, 1965.
591. Locke, E. A.: Interaction of ability and motivation in performance. *Percept. & Mot. Skills, 21,* 719-725, 1965.
592. ————: The relationship of task success to task liking and satisfaction. *J. Appl. Psych.,* No. 5, 379-385, 1965.
593. Locke, John: *Essay Concerning Human Understanding.* 1690.
594. London, Perry and Fuhrer, Marcus: Hypnosis, motivation, and performance. *J. Personal., 29,* 321-333, 1961.
595. Lorge, Irving: Influence of regularly interpolated time intervals upon subsequent learning. *Teachers' College Contributions to Education,* Columbia University, 438, 1930.
596. Lorge, Irving, Fox, David, Davitz, Joel, and Bremer, Marlin: A survey of studies contrasting the quality of group performance and individual performance, 1920-1957. *Psych. Bull., 55,* 1958.
597. Lotter, Willard S.: Interrelationships among reaction times and speed of movement in different limbs. *Res. Quart., 31,* 147-154, 1960.
598. ————: Specificity or generality of speed of systematically related movements. *Res. Quart., 32,* 55-61, 1961.
599. Lovass, O. I.: The relationship of induced muscular tension, tension level, and manifest anxiety in learning. *J. Exp. Psych., 59,* 146-152, 1960.
600. ————: Supplementary report: The relationship of induced muscular tension to manifest anxiety in learning. *J. Exp. Psych., 59,* 205, 1960.
601. Lowe, C. Marshall: The self-concept, fact or artifact? *Psych. Bull., 58,* 325-336, 1961.
602. Lucas, J. D.: The interactive effects of anxiety, failure, and intra-serial duplication. *Am. J. Psych., 65,* 59-66, 1952.

603. Luh, C. W.: The conditions of retention. *Psych. Monographs, 31,* 3, 1922.
604. Lundgate: The effect of manual guidance upon maze learning. *Psych. Rev. Monographs, 33,* 33, 1923.
605. Luttges, M , Johnson, T., Buck, C., Holland, J., and McGaugh, J.: An examination of "Transfer of Learning" by nucleic acid. *Science, 151,* 834-837, 1966.
606. Lyon, Darwin Oliver: *Memory and the Learning Process.* Baltimore, Warwick and York, Inc., 1917.
607. MacArthur, R. S.: The experimental investigation of persistence in secondary school boys. *Canad. J. Psych., 9,* 42-54, 1955.
608. Maccoby, Eleanor E., Dowley, Edith M., and Hagen, John W.: Activity level and intellectual functioning in normal pre-school children. *Child Dev., 36,* 761-769, 1965.
609. Macworth, N. H.: Researches on the measurement of human performance. *Medical Res. Council Special Report Series, No. 268.* London: His Majesty's Stationery Office, 1950.
610. Madsen, K. B.: *Theories of Motivation.* 2nd ed., Cleveland, Howard Allen, 1961.
611. Magoun, H. W.: Darwin and concepts of brain function in *Brain Mechanism and Learning.* A symposium by the Council for Internal Organizations of Medical Sciences, under UNESCO and WHO, J. F. Delafresnaye (Ed.). Springfield, Charles C Thomas, 1961.
612. ———: *The Waking Brain.* Springfield, Charles C Thomas, 1958.
613. Malmo, R. B.: Activation: A neuropsychological dimension. *Psych. Rev., 66,* 367-368, 1959.
614. Malmo, R. B. and Davis, J. F.: Anxiety and behavioral arousal. *Psych. Rev., 64,* 276 287, 1957
615. Mandler, George: The warm-up effect: some further evidence on temporal and task factors. *J. Gen. Psych., 55,* 3-8, 1956.
616. Manzer, C. W.: The effect of verbal suggestion on output and variability of muscular work. *Psych. Clin., 22,* 248-256, 1934.
617. Marriott, R.: *Incentive Payments System, A Review of Research and Opinion.* London, Staples Press, 1961.
618. Marston, Wm., King, C. Daly, and Marston, Elizabeth: *Integrative Psychology.* Kegan, Paul (Ed.), New York, Harcourt Brace & Co., 1931.
619. Martin, Barclay: Reward and punishment associated with the same goal response: A factor in the learning of motives. *Psych. Bull., 60,* 441-451, 1963.
620. Matarazzo, Ruth and Matarazzo, J. D.: Anxiety level and pursuit-meter performance. *J. Consult. Psych., 20,* 70, 1956.
621. Matarazzo, J. D., Ulett, G. A., and Saslow, G.: Human maze performance as a function of increasing levels of anxiety. *J. Gen. Psych., 53,* 79-95, 1955.
622. Matsumoto, M.: Researches on acoustic space. Studies in Yale Psychology Laboratory, 5, 1-75, 1887.
623. Maxwell, Gavin: *Ring of Bright Water.* London, Longmans, Green & Co., 1960.
624. McAllister, D. E.: The effects of various kinds of relevant verbal pretraining on subsequent motor performance. *J. Exp. Psych., 46,* 329-336, 1953.
625. McBride, G., King, M. G., and James, J. W.: Social proximity effects on galvanic skin responses in adult humans. *J. Psych., 61,* 153-157, 1965.
626. McCain, Sam Reid: A comparison of the motion perception fields of athletes and non-athletes. M.A. Thesis, presented to the University of Alabama, 1950.
627. McCaskill, Carra L. and Wellman, Beth L.: A study of common motor achievements at the pre-school ages. *Child Dev., 9,* 141-150, 1938.
628. McClelland, D. C. and Apricella, F. S.: Reminiscence following experimentally induced failure. *J. Exp. Psych., 37,* 159-169, 1947.
629. McCloy, C. H.: An analytical study of the stunt type test as a measure of motor educability. *Res. Quart., 8,* 46-55, 1937.
630. ———: Blocks test of multiple response. *Psychometrike, 7,* 165-169, 1942.
631. McCord, Joan, McCord, William, and Thurber, Emily: Some effects of paternal absence on male children. *J. Ab. & Soc. Psych., 64,* 361-369, 1962.

632. McCormack, P. D., Binding, F. R. S., and McElheran: Effects on reaction time of partial knowledge of results of performance. *Percept. & Mot. Skills, 17,* 279-281, 1963.

633. McCraw, L. W.: Comparative analysis of methods of scoring tests of motor learning. *Res. Quart., 26,* 440-453, 1955.

634. McDougall, W.: *An Introduction to Social Psychology.* 13th ed., Boston, John W. Luce Co., 1918.

635. ———: *An Introduction to Psychology.* Boston, Bruce Humphries, 1926.

636. McGeogh, J. A.: The comparative retention values of a maze habit, of nonsense syllables, and of rational learning. *J. Exp. Psych., 15,* 662-680, 1932.

637. ———: The influence of four different interpolated activities upon retention. *J. Exp. Psych., 14,* 400-413, 1931.

638. McGeogh, J. A. and Irion, A. L.: *The Psychology of Human Learning.* 2nd ed., London, Longmans, Green & Co., 1952.

639. McGeogh, J. A. and Melton, A. W.: The comparative retention values of maze habits and nonsense syllables. *J. Exp. Psych., 12,* 392-414, 1929.

640. McGraw, Myrtle B.: *Growth: A Study of Johnny and Jimmy.* New York, Appleton-Century-Croft, 1935.

641. McGuigan, F. J.: The effect of precision, delay and schedule of knowledge of results on performance. *J. Exp. Psych., 58,* 79-84, 1959.

642. McGuigan, F. J., Hutchens, Carolyn, Eason, Nancy, and Reynolds, Teddy: The retrograde interference of motor activity with knowledge of results. *J. Gen. Psych., 70,* 279-281, 1964.

643. McIntyre, J. and Humphries, M.: Reminiscence in pursuit rotor reaction time. *Percept. & Mot. Skills, 18,* 39-42, 1964.

644. McTeer, A.: Changes in group tension following electric shock in minor tracing. *J. Exp. Psych., 36,* 735-742, 1933.

645. Medinnus, Gene R.: Adolescents' self-acceptance and perceptions of their parents. *J. Consult. Psych., 29,* 150-154, 1965.

646. Melcher, Ruth T.: Children's motor learning, with and without vision. *Child Dev., 4,* 315-350, 1934.

647. Melton, A. W: Learning. In W. S. Munroe (Ed.) *Encyclopedia of Educational Research.* New York, The Macmillan Company, 668-690, 1950.

648. Mendel, Giseld: Children's preferences for differing degrees of novelty. *Child Dev., 36,* 452-464, 1966.

649. Mendryk, Stephen: Reaction time, movement time, and task specificity relationships at ages 12, 33, and 48 years. *Res. Quart., 31,* 156-162, 1960.

650. Menninger, W. C.: Yesterday's war and today's challenge. *Psychiatry in a Troubled World.* New York, The Macmillan Co., 1948.

651. Menzel, Emil: Individual differences in the responsiveness of young chimpanzees to stimulus size and novelty. *Percept. & Mot. Skills, 15,* 127-134, 1962.

652. Menzel, Emil, Davenport, Richard, and Rogers, C. M.: Some aspects of behavior toward novelty in young chimpanzees. *J. Comp. & Physiol. Psych., 54,* 16-19, 1961.

653. Meredith, G. P.: The transfer of training. *Occup. Psych., 15,* 61-76, 1941.

654. Merriman, B. J.: The relationship of personality traits to motor ability. *Res. Quart., 31,* 163-173, 1960.

655. Meyer, D. R.: On the interaction of simultaneous responses. *Psych. Bull., 50,* 204-220, 1953.

656. Meyer, D. R. and Noble, Merrill E.: Summation of manifest anxiety and muscular tension. *J. Exp. Psych., 55,* 599-602, 1958.

657. Michael, Ernest D., Jr.: Stress adaptation through exercise. *Res. Quart., 28,* 50-54, 1957.

658. Michotte, Van den Berch, Albert: Perception and cognition. *Acta Psych., 11,* 70-91, 1955.

659. Miles, W. R.: Age and human ability. *Psych. Rev., 40,* 99-123, 1933.

660. ———: The two-story duplicate maze. *J. Exp. Psych., 10,* 365-377, 1927.

661. Millard, Cecil V.: *Child Growth and Development in the Elementary School Years.* Boston, D. C. Heath & Company.

662. Miller, Donna Mae: The relation between some visual perceptual factors and the degree of success realized by sports performers. Doctoral dissertation, University of Southern California, 1960.
663. Miller, George A., Galanter, Eugene, and Dribham, Karl H.: *Plans and the Structure of Behavior.* New York, Henry Holt & Co., Inc., 1960.
664. Miller, N. E.: Central stimulation and other new approaches to motivation and reward. *Am. Psych., 13,* 100-108, 1958.
665. ————: Experiments on motivation. *Science, 126,* 1271, 1957.
666. ————: Learnable drives and rewards. In S. S. Stevens (Ed.), *Handbook of Experimental Psychology.* New York, John Wiley & Sons, Inc.
667. Mingione, Am Dessinger: Need for achievement in Negro and white children. *J. Consult. Psych., 29,* 108-111, 1965.
668. Mirsky, I. A. and Stein, M.: The secretion of an antidiuretic substance into the circulation in response to noxious stimuli. *Science, 118,* 602, 1953.
669. Missiuro, W.: The development of reflex activity in children. In International Res. in Sport and Phys. Ed., E. Jokl and E. Simon (Eds.). Springfield, Charles C Thomas, 372-383, 1964.
670. Moeller, George and Chattin, Craig P.: The palmar perspiration index and pursuit tracking. *Percept. & Mot. Skills, 15,* 463-473, 1962.
671. Montebello, Robt. A.: The role of stereoscopic vision in some aspects of basketball playing ability. M.A. Thesis, Ohio State University, Columbus, 1953.
672. Montessori, Maria: *Dr. Montessori's Own Handbook.* New York, Frederick A. Stokes, 1914.
673. Morgan, C. T.: Some structural factors in perception. In D. C. Beardslee and Michael Wertheimer, *Readings in Perception.* New York, D. Van Nostrand Co., Inc., 3-36.
674. Morin, R. F., Grant, D. A., and Nystrom, C. O.: *Temporal Predictions of Motion from Intermittently Viewed Light Stimulation.* Technical Report No. 54-69, January 1954. Wright-Patterson Air Force Base.
675. Morrison, Andrew V.: Individual differences in the ability to interpret gestures. Doctoral dissertation, University of California, Los Angeles, 1961.
676. Moss, C. Scott: *Hypnosis in Perspective.* New York, The Macmillan Company, 1965.
677. Mott, Jane Adele: Eye movements during initial learning of motor skills. Doctoral dissertation, University of Southern California, Los Angeles, 1954.
678. Mountcastle, V. B., Poggio, G. F., and Werner, G.: The relation of thalamic cell response to peripheral stimuli varied over an intensive continuum. *J. Neurophysiol., 26,* 804-834, 1963.
679. Moylan, Joseph J.: Kinesthetic figural after-effects: Satiation or contrast. *J. Exp. Psych., 67,* 83-90, 1964.
680. Mukherjee, Bishwa N.: Transfer of two-hand coordination skill as a function of initial ability level. *J. Gen. Psych., 67,* 215-223, 1962.
681. Muller, G. E. and Pilzecker, A.: Experimentelle Beitrage zur Lehre Vom Gedachtniss. *Zsch. F. Psych., 1,* 1-300, 1900.
682. Munn, N. L.: Bilateral transfer of learning. *J. Exp. Psych., 15,* 343-353, 1932.
683. Munsterberg, Hugo: *Psychology, General and Applied.* New York, D. Appleton & Co., 1914.
684. Murray, H. A.: *Explorations in Personality.* New York, Oxford University Press, 1938.
685. Murray, H. A. *in* Hall, Calvin S. and Lindzey, Gardner: *Theories of Personality.* New York, John Wiley & Sons, Inc., 1957.
686. Mussen, Paul H.: Some antecedents and consequences of masculine sex-typing in adolescent boys. *Psych. Monographs, 75,* 2, 1961.
687. Mussen, Paul H. and Jones, M. C.: Self-conceptions, motivations and interpersonal attitudes of late and early maturing boys. *Child Dev., 28,* 243-256, 1957.
688. Namikas, Gediminas and Archer, E. James: Motor skill transfer as a function of inter-task interval and pre-transfer task difficulty. *J. Exp. Psych., 59,* 109-112, 1960.

689. Naylor, James C. and Briggs, George E.: Effect of rehearsal of temporal and spatial aspects on the long-term retention of a procedural skill. *J. Appl. Psych.*, 4, 120-126, 1963.
690. ————: *Long-Term Retention of Learned Skills, a Review of the Literature.* Laboratory of Aviation Psychology, Ohio State University and Ohio State University Research Foundation, August 1961.
691. Nelson, Dale O.: Leadership in sports. *Res. Quart.*, 37, 268-275, 1966.
692. ————: Studies of transfer of learning in gross motor skills. *Res. Quart.*, 28, 364-374, 1957.
693. Nelson, Gaylord A. and Henry, Franklin M.: Age differences and interrelationships between skill and learning in gross motor performance of ten and fifteen-year-old boys. *Res. Quart.*, 27, 162-175, 1956.
694. Nelson, Richard and Fahrney, Richard A.: Relationships between strength and speed of elbow flexion. *Res. Quart.*, 36:4, 455-463, December 1965.
695. Nichols, Robert C.: A factor analysis of parental attitudes of fathers. *Child Dev.*, 33, 791-802, 1962.
696. Nicholson, N. C.: Notes on muscular work during hypnosis. *Johns Hopkins Hosp. Bull.*, 31, 89-91, 1920.
697. Nidever, Jack E.: A factor analytic study of general muscular tension. Doctoral dissertation, University of California, Los Angeles, 1960.
698. Niemeyer, Roy K.: Part versus whole methods and massed versus distributed practice in the learning of selected large muscle activities. Proceed. College Phys. Ed. Assn., 122-125, 1958.
699. Nishi, Tokumichi: A new tentative theory of visual space perception. Part II. *Tohoku Psych. Folio*, 17, 1-20, 1958.
700. Noble, Clyde E.: Amount-set and length difficulty function for a self-paced perceptual motor skill. *J. Exp. Psych.*, 46, 435, 1953.
701. Noble, Clyde E., Baker, Blaine L., and Jones, Thomas A.: Age and sex parameters in psychomotor learning. *Percept. & Mot. Skills*, 19, 935-945, 1964.
702. Noer, David and Whittaker, James: Effects of masculine-feminine ego involvement on the acquisition of a mirror-tracing skill. *J. Psych.*, 56, 15-17, 1963.
703. Norcross, W. H.: Experiments on the transfer of training. *J. Comp. Psych.*, 1, 317-363, 1921.
704. Norris, E. B.: Performance of a motor task as a function of rest at different points in acquisition. *J. Exp. Psych.*, 45, 260-264, 1953.
705. Nystrom, C. O., Morin, R. E., and Grant, D. A.: Transfer effects between automatically-paced training schedules in a perceptual motor task. *J. Gen. Psych.*, 55, 9-18, 1956.
706. Ogilvie, B. C. and Tutko, T. A.: The psychological profile of Olympic champions. Proceedings 1st International Congress of Psychology of Sport, Rome, 1965.
707. Oliver, James: The effects of physical conditioning exercises and activities on the mental characteristics of educationally sub-normal boys. *Br. J. Psych.*, 155-165, June 1958.
708. Olsen, E. A.: Relationship between psychological capacities and success in college athletics. *Res. Quart.*, 27, 79-89, 1956.
709. Oseretsky, N.: Psychomotorik Methoden zur Underschung der Motorik. *Z. angewand Psych.*, 17, 1-58, 1931. (Translation by Elizabeth Lang, Northwestern University, 1949, unpublished manuscript.)
710. O. S. S.: *The Assessment of Men.* New York, Rinehart, 1948.
711. Paillard, Jacques: The patterning of skilled movements. Chapter 67 in *The Handbook of Physiology*, section I, Neurophysiology, 3, John Field (Ed.). American Physiological Society, Washington, D.C. 1960, 1679-1708.
712. Palmer, Robt. D.: Development of a differentiated handedness. *Psych. Bull.*, 62, 257-272, 1964.
713. ————: Hand differentiation and psychological functioning. *J. Personal.*, 31, 446-461, 1963.
714. Parker, James F., Jr. and Fleishman, Edwin A.: Use of analytical information concerning task requirements to increase the effectiveness of skill training. *J. Appl. Psych.*, 45, 295-302, 1961.

715. Parsons, O. A., Phillips, L., and Lane, J. E.: Performance on the same psychomotor task under different stressful conditions. *J. Psych., 38,* 457-466, 1954.

716. Patten, Everett F.: The influence of distribution of repetitions on certain rote learning phenomena. *J. Psych., 5,* 359-374, 1938.

717. Patterson, G. R. and Anderson, D.: Peers as social reinforcers. *Child Dev., 35,* 951-960, 1964.

718. Pavlov, I. P.: *Conditioned Reflexes.* (Translated by G. V. Anrep.) London, Oxford University Press, 1927.

719. Pechstein, Louis A.: Alleged elements of waste in learning a motor problem by the 'part method.' *J. Ed. Psych., 8,* 303-310, 1917.

720. ————: Massed vs. distributed effort in learning. *J. Ed. Psych., 12,* 92-97, 1921.

721. Peiper, Albrecht: *Cerebral Function in Infancy and Childhood.* Consultants Bureau, New York, 1963.

722. Penfield, W. and Roberts, L.: *Speech and Brain Mechanisms.* Princeton, N.J., Princeton University Press, 1959.

723. Perl, Ruth E.: The effect of practice upon individual differences. *Arch. Psych., 159,* 1933.

724. Perrin, F. A. C.: An experimental study of motor ability. *J. Exp. Psych., 4,* 25-57, 1921.

725. Peterson, Joseph: Experiments in ball-tossing: The significance of learning curves. *J. Exp. Psych., 2,* 178-224, 1919.

726. ————: Review of Tolman "purposive behavior in animals and man." *Am. J. Psych., 45,* 177-178, 1933.

727. Phares, E. Jerry: Effects of reinforcement value on expectancy statements in skill and chance situations. *Percept. & Mot. Skills, 20,* 845-852, 1965.

728. Piaget, Jean: *The Construction of Reality in the Child.* New York, Basic Books, Inc., 1954.

729. ————: *Play, Dreams, and Imitation in Childhood.* Translation by C. Gattegno and F. M. Hodgson. New York, Norton, 1951.

730. Pierce, A. H.: *Researches on Acoustic Space.* Studies in Yale Psychology Laboratory, *5,* 1-209, 1901.

731. Pierson, Wm. R.: Comparison of fencers and nonfencers by psychomotor, space perception and anthropometric measures. *Res. Quart., 27,* 1, 1956.

732. ————: The relationship of movement time and reaction time from childhood to senility. *Res. Quart., 30,* 227-230, 1959.

733. Pinneo, Lawrence R.: The effects of induced muscular tension during tracking on level of activation and on performance. *J. Exp. Psych., 62:5,* 523-531, 1961.

734. Plutchik, Robt. and Petti, Rodger D.: Rate of learning on a pursuit rotor task at a constant work-rest ratio with varying work and rest ratios. *Percept. & Mot. Skills, 19,* 227-231, 1964.

735. Postman, L. and Bruner, J. S.: Perception under stress. *Psych. Rev., 55,* 314-323, 1948.

736. Poulton, E. C.: On prediction in skilled movements. *Psych. Bull., 54,* 467-478, 1957.

737. Preyer, W.: Embryonic motility and sensitivity. Monographs of the Society for Research in Child Development (translated from German), *2,* 6, 1937.

738. Pryor, Helen B.: Charts of normal body measurements and revised width-weight tables in graphic form. *J. Pediatrics, 68,* 615-631, 1966.

739. Pryor, Helen B and Stolz, H.: Determining appropriate weight for body build. *J. Pediatrics, 3,* 608-624, 1933.

740. Purdy, Bonnie J. and Lockhart, Aileene: Retention and relearning of gross motor skills after long periods of no practice. *Res. Quart., 33,* 2, 1962.

741. Ragsdale, C. E.: How children learn the motor types of activities. *49th Yearbook.* Chicago, University of Chicago Press, 1952.

742. ————: *The Psychology of Motor Learning.* Ann Arbor, Edward Bros. Press, Inc., 1930.

743. Rasch, Philip J. and Mozee, Gene: Neuroticism and extroversion in weight trainers. *J. Physical and Mental Rehab., 17,* 53-56, 1963.
744. Rathbone, Josephine L.: Relaxation. Bureau of Publications, Teachers' College, Columbia University, New York, 1943.
745. Lord Rayleigh (J. W. Stauttis): Acoustical observations. *Phil. Mag., 5,* 456-464, 1887.
746. Reed, Homer B.: An experiment on the law of effect in learning the maze by humans. *J. Ed. Psych., 26,* 695, 1935.
747. Reiter, Heurz H.: Relation of body build to personal preference among college males. *Percept. & Mot. Skills, 21,* 34, 1965.
748. Renold, Albert *et al.:* Reaction of the adrenal cortex to physical and emotional stress in college oarsmen. *New Engl. J. Medicine, 45,* 754-757, 1951.
749. Maria de Renzende, Naitres: An experiment on the perception of time. *Arch. de Brasil, 2,* 40-55, 1950.
750. Rethlingshafer, Dorothy: *Motivation as Related to Personality.* New York, McGraw-Hill Book Co., 1963.
751. ————: Relationship of tests of persistence to other measures of continuance of activities. *J. Ab. & Soc. Psych., 37,* 71-82, 1942.
752. Reynolds, B. and Bilodeau, I. McD.: Acquisition and retention of three psychomotor tests as a function of distribution of practice during acquisition. *J. Exp. Psych., 44,* 19-26, 1952.
753. Riddoch, G.: Dissociation of visual perception due to occipital injuries with especial reference to appreciation of movement. *Brain, 40,* 15-17, 1917.
754. Rimoldi, H. J. A.: Personal Tempo. *J. Ab. & Soc. Psych., 46,* 283-303, 1951.
755. Riopelle, A. J.: Psychomotor performance and distribution of practice. *J. Exp. Psych., 40,* 390, 1950.
756. Robbins, Melvyn Paul: The Delacato interpretation of neurological organization. *Reading Res. Quart.,* 59-77, 1966.
757. Roe, A. and Simpson, G. G. (Eds.): *Behavior and Evolution.* New Haven, Yale University Press, 1958.
758. Roehrig, Wm. C.: Psychomotor task with perfect recall after 50 weeks of no practice. *Percept. & Mot. Skills, 19,* 547-550, 1964.
759. Roff, Merrill: A factorial study of tests in the perceptual area. *Psychometric Monograph, 41,* 8, 1953.
760. Roffell, Gertrude: Visual and kinesthetic judgments of length. *Am. J. Psych., 48,* 331-334, 1946.
761. Ronco, Paul G.: An experimental quantification of kinesthetic sensation: Extent of arm movement. *J. Psych., 55,* 227-238, 1963.
762. Rose, J. E. and Mountcastle, V. B.: Touch and kinesthesis in j. field (Eg). *Handbook of Physiology,* v. 1, Washington D.C., American Physiological Society, 307-429, 1959.
763. Roseborough, Mary E.: Experimental studies of small groups. *Psych. Bull., 50,* 275-303, 1953.
764. Rosen, Bernard C. and D'Andrade, Roy: The psycho-social origins of achievement motivation. *Sociometry, 22,* 185-218, 1959.
765. Rosenzweig, S.: A dynamic interpretation of psychotherapy oriented towards research. In S. S. Tomkins (Ed.), *Contemporary Psychopathology.* Cambridge, Harvard University Press, 235-243, 1943.
766. Rubin, Edgar: An abridged translation by Michael Wertheimer of *Visuell Wahrgenommene Figuren,* Copenhagen Gyldendalske, 1912.
767. Rubin-Rabson, Grace: Studies in the psychology of memorizing piano music: II. A comparison of massed and distributed practice. *J. Ed. Psych., 31,* 270-284, 1940.
768. ————: Studies on the psychology of memorizing piano music: III. A comparison of the whole and the part approach. *J. Ed. Psych., 31,* 460-476, 1940.
769. ————: Studies in the psychology of memorizing piano music: VII. A comparison of three degrees of overlearning. *J. Ed. Psych., 32,* 688-696, 1941.
770. Ruesch, J. and Kees, W.: *Non-Verbal Communication.* Berkeley, University of California Press, 1956.

771. Russell, J. T.: Relative efficiency of relaxation and tension in performing an act of skill. *J. Gen. Psych., 6,* 330-343, 1932.

772. Russell, W. R.: *Brain, Memory, Learning.* Fair Lawn, N.J., Oxford University Press, Chap. XII, "Hypothalamus: Frontal Lobes," 1959.

773. Ryan, Dean E.: Competitive performance in relation to achievement motivation and anxiety. Paper presented to the National Convention, Minneapolis, Minnesota, May, 1963.

774. ————: Kinesthetic Figural After-effects and Athletic Performance. Speech presented to National Convention of American Assn. of Health, Recreation and Phys. Ed., Chicago, Illinois, 1966.

775. ————: Retention of stabilometer performance over extended periods of time. *Res. Quart., 36,* 46-51, 1965.

776. Ryans, D. G.: An experimental attempt to analyse persistence behavior: I. Measuring traits presumed to involve persistence. *J. Gen. Psych., 19,* 333-353, 1938.

777. Sackett, Gene P.: Manipulatory behavior in monkeys reared under different conditions of early stimulus variation. *Percept. & Mot. Skills, 20,* 985-988, 1965.

778. Sackett, R. S.: The influence of symbolic rehearsal upon the retention of a maze habit. *J. Gen. Psych., 10,* 376-398, 1934.

779. ————: The relationship between amount of symbolic rehearsal and retention of a maze habit. *J. Gen. Psych., 13,* 113-128, 1935.

780. Sanderson, J.: Intention in motor learning. *J. Exp. Psych., 12,* 463-489, 1929.

781. Sarason, Irwin G. and Palola, Ernest G.: The relationship of test and general anxiety, difficulty of task, and experimental instructions to performance. *J. Exp. Psych., 59,* 185-191, 1960.

782. Sarason, S. and Rosenzweig, S.: An experimental study of the triadic hypothesis: Reaction to frustration, ego-defense hypnotizability: II. Thematic Apperception approach. *Character & Personal., 11,* 150-165, 1942.

783. Schafer, V. G. and Gilliland, A. R.: The relationship of time estimations to certain physiological changes. *J. Exp. Psych., 23,* 545-552, 1938.

784. Schendel, Jack: Psychological differences between athletes and non-participants in athletics at three educational levels. *Res. Quart., 36,* 52-67, 1965.

785. Schneider, Carl W. and Bartley, S. Howard: A study of the effects of mechanically induced tension of the neck muscles on the perception of verticality. *J. Psych., 54,* 245-248, 1962.

786. Schonbar, Rosalie A.: The interaction of observer pairs in judging visual extent and movement. *Arch. Psych., 28,* 299, 1945.

787. Scott, M. Gladys: Measurement of kinesthesis. *Res. Quart., 26,* 324-341, 1955.

788. Scott, R. H.: The psychology of the body image. *Br. J. Med. Psych., 24,* 266, 1954.

789. Scripture, E. W.: Cross education. *Pop. Sci. Monthly, 56,* 589-596, 1899.

790. ————: Recent investigations at the Yale Laboratory. *Psych. Rev., 6,* 165, 1899.

791. Scripture, E. W., Smith, T. L., and Brown, E. M.: On the education of muscular control and power. Studies from the Yale Psychological Laboratory, *2,* 114-119, 1894.

792. Seagoe, May V.: Qualitative wholes: A re-evaluation of the whole-part problem. *J. Ed. Psych., 27,* 537-545, 1936.

793. Seashore, H. G.: The development of a beam walking test and its use in measuring development of balance in children. *Res. Quart., 18,* 246-259, 1947.

794. ————: Some relationships of fine and gross motor abilities. *Res. Quart., 13,* 259-274, 1942.

795. Seashore, H. G. and Bavelas, A.: The function of knowledge of results in Thorndike's line drawing experiment. *Psych Rev., 48,* 155-164, 1941.

796. Seashore, R. G.: Individual differences in motor skills. *J. Gen. Psych., 3,* 38-66, 1930.

797. Seashore, R. H.: Work methods: An often neglected factor underlying individual differences. *Psych. Rev., 46,* 123-141, 1939.

798. Secord, Paul F.: Personality in faces. *Genetic Psych. Mono.*, *49*, 231-279, 1954.
799. Seils, Leroy: The relationships between measures of physical growth and gross motor performance of primary grade school children. *Res. Quart.*, *22*, 244-260, 1951.
800. Seligman, C. G.: The vision of the natives of British Guinea. *Report of the Anthropological Expedition to Torres Straits*, 1901, A. C. Haddon (Ed.), Cambridge University Press, 1961.
801. Sells, S. B. and Berry, C. A.: *Human Factors in Jet and Space Travel*. New York, The Ronald Press, 1961.
802. Selye, Hans: *The Stress of Life*. New York, McGraw-Hill Book Co., 324, 1956.
803. Seymour, W. Douglas: Transfer of training in engineering skills. *Percept. & Mot. Skills*, *7*, 235-237, 1957.
804. Shard, Marvin and Blum, J. Michael: Group performance as a function of task difficulty and the group's awareness of member satisfaction. *J. Appl. Psych.*, *49*, 151-154, 1964.
805. Shaw, M. E.: Some motivational factors in cooperation and competition. *J. Personal.*, *26*, 155-169, 1958.
806. Shay, Clayton T.: The progressive-part vs. the whole method of learning motor skills. *Res. Quart.*, *5*, 62-67, 1934.
807. Sheldon, W. H., Dupertuis, C. W., and McDermott, E.: *Atlas of Men:* a guide for somatotyping the adult male at all ages. New York, Harper & Bros., 1954.
808. Sheldon, W. H. and Stevens, S. S.: *The Varieties of Temperament*. New York, Harper & Bros., 1942.
809. Shepard, Alfred, Abbey, D. S., and Humphries, M.: Age and sex in relation to perceptual-motor performance on several control-display relations on the TCC. *Percept. & Mot. Skills*, *14*, 103-118, 1962.
810. Shepard, Alfred and Cook, T. W.: Body orientation and perceptual motor performance. *Percept. & Mot. Skills*, *8*, 327-330, 1958.
811. Sherif, Muzafer: A study of some social factors in perception. *Arch. Psych.*, *8*, 187, 1935.
812. Shirley, M. M.: *The First Two Years*. Vol. 1, Minneapolis, University of Minnesota Press, 1931.
813. ————: Studies in activity: II. Activity rhythms; age and activity; activity after rest. *J. Comp. Psych.*, *8*, 159-186, 1928.
814. Siegal, Arthur I.: A motor hypothesis of perceptual development. *Am. J. Psych.*, *66*, 301-304, 1953.
815. Siipola, Elsa M. and Hayden, Susan D.: Exploring eidetic imagery among retarded. *Percept. & Mot. Skills*, *21*, 275-286, 1965.
816. Silleck, Sidney B., Jr. and Lapha, C. W.: The relative effectiveness of emphasis upon right and wrong responses in human maze learning. *J. Exp. Psych.*, *20*, 195-201, 1937.
817. Silver, A. W.: The self concept: Its relationship to parental and peer acceptance. *Dissertation Abstracts*, *19*, 166, 1958.
818. Silver, R. J.: Effect of amount and distribution of warming-up activity on retention in motor learning. *J. Exp. Psych.*, *44*, 88-95, 1952.
819. Singer, J. L. and Herman, J.: Motor and fantasy correlates of Rorschach human movement responses. *J. Consult. Psych.*, *18*, 325-331, 1954.
820. Singer, Robt. N.: Massed and distributed practice effects on the acquisition and retention of a novel basketball skill. *Res. Quart.*, *36*, 68-77, 1965.
821. ————: Effect of spectators on athletes and non-athletes performing a gross motor task. *Res. Quart.*, *36*, 473-483, 1965.
822. Singleton, W. T.: Age and performance timing on simple skills. In *Old Age and the Modern World*. Edinburgh, C. & S. Livingston, 221-231, 1955.
823. ————: The change of movement timing with age. *Br. J. Psych.*, *65*, 166-172, 1954.
824. Skinner, B. F.: *The Behavior of Organisms*. New York, Appleton-Century-Crofts, 437, 1938.

825. Slater-Hammel, A.: Measurement of kinesthetic perception of muscular force with muscle potential charges. *Res. Quart., 28,* 153-159, 1957.
826. Sloan, W.: The Lincoln-Oseretsky Motor Development Scale. *Genetic Psych. Mono., 51,* 183-252, 1955.
827. Slocum, Helen M.: The effect of fatigue induced by physical activity on certain tests in kinesthesis. *Dissertation Abstracts, 13,* 1084-1085, 1953.
828. Smith, Judith L. and Bozymowski, Margaret E.: Effect of attitude toward warmups on motor performance. *Res. Quart., 36,* 78-85, 1965.
829. Smith, Karl U.: *Cybernetic Principles of Learning and Educational Design.* New York, Holt, Rinehart, & Winston, 1965.
830. ————: Feedback theory and motor learning. Paper presented at the North American Society of Sports Psychology, Chicago, Illinois, 1966.
831. Smith, Karl U. and Smith, William M.: *Perception and Motion.* Philadelphia, W. B. Saunders Co., 1962.
832. Smith, Karl U. and Trebra, Patricia Von: The dimensional analysis of motion: IV. Transfer effects and direction of movement. *J. Appl. Psych., 36,* 348-353, 1952.
833. Smith, Leon E.: Individual differences in maximal speed of muscular contraction and reaction time. *Percept. & Mot. Skills, 21,* 19-22, 1965.
834. Smith, Leon E. and Harrison, John S.: Comparison of the effects of visual, motor, mental, and guided practice upon speed and accuracy of performing a simple eye-hand coordination task. *Res. Quart., 33,* 299-307, 1962.
835. Smith, Olin W.: Developmental studies of spatial judgments by children and adults. *Percept. & Mot. Skills, 22,* 3-73, 1966, Monograph Supplement I-V22.
836. Smith, Patricia Cain and Smith, Alin W.: Ball throwing responses to photographically portrayed targets. *J. Exp. Psych., 62,* 223-233, 1961.
837. Smock, Charles D. and Holt, Bess Gene: Children's reactions to novelty: An experimental study of 'curiosity motivation.' *Child Dev., 33,* 631-642, 1962.
838. Smock, Charles D. and Small, Victor H.: Efficiency of utilization of visual information as a function of induced muscular tension. *Percept. & Mot. Skills, 14,* 39-44, 1962.
839. Smythe, E. and Goldstone, S.: The time sense: a normative genetic study of the development of time perception. *Percept. & Mot. Skills, 7,* 49-59, 1957.
840. Snoddy, G. S.: Evidence for two opposed processes in mental growth. Lancaster, Pa., Science Press, 103, 1935.
841. Snoddy, G. W.: An experimental analysis of a case of trial and error learning in the human subject. *Psych. Monographs, 124,* 28, 78, 1920.
842. Snyder, F. W. and Pronko, N. H.: *Vision with Spatial Inversion.* Wichita, Kansas, University of Wichita Press, 1952.
843. Solley, William H.: The effects of verbal instruction of speed and accuracy upon the learning of a motor skill. *Res. Quart., 23,* 231-240, 1952.
844. Solomons, Gerald and Solomons, Hope C.: Factors affecting motor performance of four-month-old infants. *Child Dev., 35,* 1283-1296, 1964.
845. Spearman, C.: General intelligence objectivity measured and determined. *Am. J. Psych., 15,* 201-293, 1904.
846. Spencer, L. T. and Judd, C. H.: Practice without knowledge of results. *Psych. Rev., 29,* 185-198, 1905.
847. Sperry, R. W.: Cerebral organization and behavior. *Science, 133,* 1749-1757, 1961.
848. Spitz, R. A.: The smiling response: a contribution to the ontogenesis of social relations. *Genetic Psych. Mono., 34,* 57-125, 1946.
849. Spitz, R. A. and Wolf, K. M.: The smiling response: a contribution to the ontogenesis of social relations. *Genetic Psych. Mono., 34,* 57-156, 1946.
850. Starbuck, Wm. H.: Level of aspiration. *Psych. Rev., 70,* 51-60, 1963.
851. Start, K. B.: Relationship between intelligence and the effect of mental practice on the performance of a motor skill. *Res. Quart., 31,* 644-649, 1960.
852. Stauffacher, J. C.: The effect of induced muscular tension upon various phases of the learning process. *J. Exp. Psych., 21,* 26-46, 1937.

853. Stennett, R. G.: The relationships of performance level to level of arousal. *J. Exp. Psych., 54,* 54-61, 1957.

854. Stevenson, H. W.: Social reinforcement with children as a function of CA, sex of E and sex of S. *J. Ab. & Soc. Psych., 63,* 147-154, 1961.

855. Stevenson, H. W. and Allen, Sara: Adult performance as a function of sex of experimenter and sex of subject. *J. Ab. & Soc. Psych., 68,* 214-216, 1964.

856. Stolnick, Robert S., Liebert, Robert M., and Hilgard, Ernest R.: The enhancement of muscular performance in hypnosis through exhortation and involving instructions. *J. Personal., 33,* 37-44, 1965.

857. Stoltz, H. R. and Stoltz, L. M.: Adolescent problems related to somatic variations. In *Adolescence,* 43rd Yearbook N.S.S.E. Part I. Chicago, University of Chicago Press, 1944.

858. Stratton, G. M.: The control of another person by obscure signs. *Psych. Rev., 28,* 801-314, 1921.

859. ————: Vision without inversion of the retinal image. *Psych. Rev., 4,* 341-360; 463-481, 1897.

860. Strickland, Bonnie R.: Need approval and motor steadiness under positive and negative approval conditions. *Percept. & Mot. Skills, 20,* 667-668, 1965.

861. Strickland, Bonnie R. and Jenkins, Orvin: Simple motor performance under positive and negative approval motivation. *Percept. & Mot. Skills, 19,* 599-605, 1964.

862. Strong, Clinton H.: Motivation related to performance of physical fitness tests. *Res. Quart., 34,* 497-507, 1963.

863. Stroud, J. B.: The role of muscuar tension in styus maze learning. *J. Exp. Psych., 14,* 606-631, 1931.

864. Stroup, Francis: Relationship between measurement of the field of motion perception and basketball ability in college men. *Res. Quart., 28,* 113-118, 1957.

865. Stuart, Irving R., Breslow, A., Brechner, S. Ilyus, Rosemary B., and Wolpoff, M.: The question of constitutional influence on perceptual style. *Percept. & Mot. Skills, 20,* 419-420, 1965.

866. Suddon, Florence H.: Paced and self-paced performance on simple motor task. *Percept & Mot. Skills, 16,* 247-254, 1963.

867. Sullivan, E. B.: Attitude in relation to learning. *Psych. Monographs, 36,* 169, 1927.

868. Surwillow, W. W.: A new method of motivating human behavior in laboratory investigations. *Am. J. Psych., 71,* 432-436, 1958.

869. Swift, E. J.: Memory of a complex skillful act. *Am. J. Psych., 16,* 131-133, 1905.

870. ————: Memory of skillful movements. *Psych. Bull., 3,* 185-187, 1906.

871. ————: Relearning a skillful act: An experimental study in neuro-muscular memory. *Psych. Bull., 7,* 17-19, 1910.

872. ————: Studies in the psychology and physiology of learning. *Am. J. Psych., 14,* 201-251, 1903.

873. Szafran, J.: Changes in age and with exclusion of vision in performance at an aiming task. *J. Exp. Psych., 44,* 111-118, 1951.

874. ————: Experiments on the greater use of vision by older adults. In *Old Age in the Modern World.* Edinburgh, E. &. S. Livingstone, Ltd., 231-235.

875. Szfran, J. and Welford, A. T.: On the relation between transfer and difficulty of initial task. *Quart. J. Exp. Psych., 2,* 88-94, 1950.

876. Taylor, J. A.: A personality test for manifest anxiety. *J. Ab. & Soc. Psych., 48,* 285-290, 1953.

877. Taylor, J. A. and Spence, K. W.: The relationship of anxiety level to performance in serial learning. *J. Exp. Psych., 44,* 61-66, 1952.

878. Teuber, Hans Lukas: Some alterations in behavior after cerebral lesions in man. In *Evolution of Nervous Control from Primitive Organisms to Man.* Allan D. Bass (Ed.), American Association for the Advancement of Science, Washington, D.C., *52,* 157-194, 1959.

879. Thompson, Merrell E.: A study of reliabilities of selected gross muscular coordination test items. Hum. Resour. Res. Cent. Res. Bull., 52, 1952.
880. Thorndike, E. L.: A note on the accuracy of discrimination of weights and lengths. Psych. Rev., 16, 340-346, 1909.
881. ———: Fundamentals of Learning. New York, New York Teachers College, 1935.
882. ———: The Psychology of Wants, Interests and Attitudes. New York, D. Appleton-Century Co., 1935.
883. Thorndike, E. L. and Woodworth, R. S.: The influence of improvement in one mental function upon the efficiency of other functions. Psych. Rev., 8, 247-261, 1901.
884. Thornton, G. R.: A factor analysis of tests designed to measure persistence. Psych. Monographs, 51, 1-42, 1939.
885. Thune, John B.: Personality of weightlifters. Res. Quart., 20, 296-306, 1949.
886. Thurstone, L. L.: The perceptual factor. Psychometrike, 3, 1-17, 1938.
887. ———: Some primary abilities in visual thinking. Chicago, University of Chicago, Psychometric Laboratory Report, 59, 1950.
888. ———: The vectors of the mind. Psych. Rev., 41, 1-32, 1934.
889. Tibbits, Clark and Donahue, Wilma: Aging in Today's Society. Englewood Cliffs, N.J., Prentice-Hall, Inc., 1960.
890. Tichener, E. B.: A Beginner's Psychology. New York, The Macmillan Co., 1916.
891. Tolman, Edward C.: Purposeful Behavior in Animals and Men. New York, The Century Co., 463, 1932.
892. ———: There is more than one kind of learning. Psych. Rev., 56, 144-155, 1940.
893. Toppen, J. T.: Effect of size and frequency of money reinforcement on human operant (work) behavior. Percept. & Mot. Skills, 20, 259-269, 1965.
894. ———: Money reinforcement and human operant (work) behavior in piecework-payment and time-payment comparisons. Percept. & Mot. Skills, 21, 907-913, 1965.
895. Tower, S. S.: In The Precentral Motor Cortex. 2nd ed., P. C. Bucy (Ed.). Urbana, University of Illinois Press, 149, 1949.
896. Travis, L. E.: The effect of a small audience upon hand-eye coordination. J. Ab. & Soc. Psych., 20, 142-146, 1925.
897. Triplett, Norman: The dynamogenic factors in pacemaking and competition. Am. J. Psych., 9, 507-533, 1897-98.
898. Tsai, J. C.: Shifting of distribution of practice in maze learning. J. Exp. Psych., 40, 639, 1950.
899. Tschermak, Seysengg S.: Uber Parallaktoskopie. Pfleig. Arch. Ges. Physiol., 241, 454-469, 1939.
900. Twining, W. E.: Mental practice and physical practice in learning a motor skill. Res. Quart., 20, 432-435, 1949.
901. Ulrich, Celeste: Measurement of stress evidenced by college women in situations involving competition. Res. Quart., 28, 160-172, 1957.
902. Underwood, B. J.: Experimental Psychology. New York, Appleton-Century-Crofts, 1949.
903. Updegraff, Ruth: The visual perception of distance in young children and adults, a comparative study. University of Iowa Studies, Studies in Child Welfare, 4, 4.
904. U.S. Department of the Army: A factor analysis of spatial relations items. Personal Res. Br. Rep., 31, 978, 1952.
905. Vandell, Roland A., Davis, R. A., and Clugston, H. A.: The function of mental practice in the acquisition of motor skills. J. Gen. Psych., 29, 243-250, 1943.
906. Vandenberg, Steven G.: Factor analytic studies of the Lincoln-Oseretsky test of motor proficiency. Percept. & Mot. Skills, 19, 23-41, 1964.
907. Van der Lugt, M. J. A.: Adult Psychomotor Test Series of the Measurement of Manual Ability. New York, New York University, 1948.

908. Van Tilborg, Paul W.: The retention of mental and finger maze habits. *J. Exp. Psych., 19,* 334-341, 1936.
909. Vernon, M. D.: *A Further Study of Visual Perception.* New York, Cambridge University Press, 1954.
910. Vernon, P. E.: *Personality Tests and Assessments.* London, Methune, 1963.
911. ————: *The Structure of Human Abilities.* London, Methune, 1953.
912. Vickers, Vernette, Poynyz, Lillian, and Baum, Mabel: The brace scale used with young children. *Res. Quart., 13,* 299-308, 1942.
913. Von Neumann, J.: *The Computer and the Brain.* New Haven, Conn., Yale University Press, 1958.
914. Walk, Richard D. and Gibson, Eleanor J.: A comparative and analytic study of visual depth perception. *Psych. Monographs, 75,* 15, 519, 1961.
915. Walker, Richard N.: Body-build and behavior in young children. Body-build and nursery school teacher's ratings. *Mono. of the Society for the Res. in Child Dev.,* Gesell Institute of Child Development, *3,* 27, 84, 1952.
916. ————: Measuring masculinity and femininity by children's game choices. *Child Dev., 35,* 961-971, 1964.
917. Wallace, Melvin and Albertt, Robin: Temporal experience. *Psych. Bull., 57,* 213-236, 1960.
918. Wallach, H.: The role of head movements and vestibular and visual cues in sound localization. *J. Exp. Psych., 27,* 339-368, 1940.
919. Walsh, Marzas: Prediction of motor skill attainment from early learning. *Percept. & Mot. Skills, 17,* 263-266, 1963.
920. Walters, C. Etta: Prediction of postnatal development from fetal activity. *Child Dev., 33,* 801-808, 1965.
921. Wang, T. L.: Influence of tuition in the acquisition of skill. *Psych. Monographs, 34,* 154, 1925.
922. Wapner, Seymour and Heinz, Werner: *Perceptual Development, An Investigation Within the Framework of Sensory-Tonic Field Theory.* Clark University Press, 1957.
923. Warden, C. J.: The distribution of practice in animal learning. *Comp. Psych. Mono., 1,* 2, 1923.
924. ————: The relative economy of various modes of attack in the mastery of a stylus maze. *J. Exp. Psych., 7,* 243-275, 1924.
925. Wardweel, Elinor: Children's reactions to being watched during success and failure. Unpublished Doctoral Thesis, Cornell University, 1960.
926. Washburn, Sherwood L.: The new physical anthropology. *Transactions of the New York Academy of Sciences,* Series 2, v. XIII, No. 7, 298-304.
927. Washburn, Wilbur C.: The effects of physique and intra-family tension on self-concepts in adolescent males. *J. Consult. Psych., 26,* 460-466, 1962.
928. Wassenaar, G. M. C.: The effect of general anxiety as an index of lability on the performance of various psychomotor tasks. *J. Gen. Psych., 71,* 351-357, 1964.
929. Waterland, Joan C. and Hellenbrandt, F. A.: Involuntary patterning associated with willed movement performed against progressively increasing resistance. *Am. J. Phys. Med., 43,* 13-30, 1964.
930. Waters, R. H. and Poole, G. B.: The relative retention values of stylus and mental habits. *J. Exp. Psych., 16,* 429-434, 1933.
931. Watson, J. B.: Experimental studies on the growth of emotions. *Ped. Sem., 32,* 328-348, 1925.
932. Weatherly, Donald: Self-perceived rate of physical maturation and personality in late adolescence. *Child Dev., 35,* 1197-1210, 1964.
933. Webb, Walter W.: Massed versus distributed practice in pursuitmeter learning. *J. Gen. Psych., 8,* 272-278, 1933.
934. Weber, A. O.: Estimation of time. *Psych. Bull., 30,* 233-252, 1933.
935. Weber, C. O.: The properties of space and time in kinesthetic field of force. *Am. J. Psych., 38,* 597-606, 1927.
936. Weber, Mary Ellen: Development of a conceptual model of human movement from endocrine and perceptual theory with analysis of the effects of aberrations on movement. Ed.D. dissertation, University of California, Los Angeles, 1960.

937. Wechsler, D. R. Hartogs: The clinical measurement of anxiety. *Psychiatric Quart., 19,* 618, 1945.
938. Weinberg, Dorothe R., Guy, Donald E., and Tupper, Ronald W.: Variation of past feedback interval in simple motor learning. *J. Exp. Psych., 67,* 98-99, 1964.
939. Weinstein, C.: Tactile sensitivity of the phalanges. *Percept. & Mot. Skills, 14,* 351-354, 1962.
940. Weissman, Albert: Retrograde amnesia effect of supramaximal electroconvulsive shock on one-trial acquisition in rats. *J. Comp. & Physiol. Psych., 57,* 248-250, 1964.
941. Weitzman, Bernard: A figural after-effect produced by a phenomenal dichotomy in a uniform contour. *J. Exp. Psych., 66,* 195-200, 1963.
942. Weitzenhoffer, Andre M.: *Hypnotism, An Objective Study in Suggestibility.* New York, John Wiley & Sons, Inc.
943. Welford, A. T.: *Aging and Human Skill.* New York, Oxford University Press, 1958.
944. ————: *Skill and Age, An Experimental Approach.* The Nuffield Foundation, Oxford University Press, 1951.
945. Welker, W. I.: Effects of age and experience on play and exploration of young chimpanzees. *J. Comp. & Physiol. Psych., 49,* 223-234, 1956.
946. ————: Some determinants of play and exploration in chimpanzees. *J. Comp. & Physiol. Psych., 49,* 84-90, 1956.
947. Wellman, Beth: The development of motor coordination in young children, an experimental study in the control of hand and arm movements. University of Iowa Studies in Child Welfare, 3, 4.
948. Wells, W. R.: Expectancy versus performance in hypnosis. *J. Gen. Psych., 35,* 99-119, 1947.
949. Wenger, M. A.: An attempt to appraise individual differences in level of muscular tension. *J. Exp. Psych., 32,* 213-225, 1943.
950. ————: Muscular processes and personality. *Child Dev., 9,* 261-276, 1938.
951. Wenger, M. A., Jones, F. N., and Jones, M. H.: *Physiological Psychology.* New York, Holt, Rinehart & Winston, 1956.
952. Werner, Heinz: Motion and motion perception: a study on vicarious functioning. *J. Psych., 19,* 317-327, 1945.
953. Werner, Heinz and Wapner, W.: Sensory-tonic field theory of perception. *J. Personal., 18,* 88-107, 1949.
954. ————: Toward a general theory of perception. *Psych. Rev., 59,* 324-338, 1952.
955. Werner, H., Wapner, W., and Chandler, K. A.: Experiments on sensory-tonic field theory of perception. II. Effect of supported and unsupported tilt of body on the visual perception of verticality. *J. Exp. Psych., 42,* 346-350, 1951.
956. Wertheimer, M.: Untersuchunger zur Lehre von der Gestalt, II. *Psychol. Forsch., 4,* 301-350, 1923.
957. Wertheimer, M. and Leventhal, C. M.: Permanent satiation phenomena with kinesthetic figural after-effects. *J. Exp. Psych., 55,* 255-257, 1958.
958. Wetzel, Norman C.: Assessing the physical condition of children. *J. Ped., 22,* 82-110, 1943.
959. Weybrew, Benjamin B.: Accuracy of time estimation and muscular tension. *Percept. & Mot. Skills, 17,* 118, 1963.
960. Weyner, Norma and Zeaman, D.: Team and individual performances on a motor learning task. *J. Gen. Psych., 55,* 127-142, 1956.
961. Wiebe, Vernon R.: A factor analysis of tests of kinesthesis. Doctoral dissertation, University of Iowa, 1956.
962. Wieg, E. L.: Bilateral transfer in the motor learning of young children and adults. *Child Dev., 3,* 247-267, 1932.
963. Wiener, Norbert: *Cybernetics.* 2nd ed., New York, MIT Press, 1961.
964. Wiest, W. M., Porter, L. W., and Grisselli, E. E.: Individual proficiency and team performance. *J. Appl. Psych., 45,* 435-440, 1961.
965. Wild, Monica R.: The behavior pattern of throwing and some observations concerning its course of development in children. *Res. Quart., 9,* 20-24, 1938.

966. Williams, G. W.: The effect of hypnosis on muscular fatigue. *J. Ab. & Soc. Psych., 24,* 318-329, 1929.
967. Willington, Anna M. and Strickland, Bonnie R.: Need for approval and simple motor performance. *Percept. & Mot. Skills, 21,* 879, 884.
968. Wilson, Martha, Wilson, William A., Jr., and Chiang, Henry Min: Formation of Tactile Learning Sets. *J. Comp. & Physiol. Psych., 56,* 732-734, 1963.
969. Winograd, Samuel: Relationship of timing and vision to baseball performance. *Res. Quart., 13,* 481-493, 1942.
970. Witkin, H. A.: Perception of body position and of the position of the visual field. *Psych. Monographs, 63*:7, 1949.
971. ————: The nature and importance of individual differences in perception. *J. Personal., 18,* 145-170, 1949.
972. ————: Perception of the upright when the force acting on the body is changed. *J. Exp. Psych., 40,* 93-106, 1950.
973. ————: Further studies of perception of the upright when the force acting on the body is changed. *J. Exp. Psych., 43,* 9-20, 1952.
974. Witkin, H. A. and Asch, S. E.: Studies in space orientation. IV. Further experiments on perception of the upright with displaced visual fields. *J. Exp. Psych., 38,* 762-782, 1948.
975. Witkin, H. A., Lewis, H. B., Herzman, M., Mackover, K., Meissner, P. B., and Wapner, S.: *Personality Through Perception.* New York, Harper & Rowe, 1954.
976. Wolf, S., Cardon, P. V., Shepard, E. M., and Wolff, H. G.: *Life Stress and Essential Hypertension, A Study of Circulatory Adjustments in Man.* Baltimore, The Williams & Wilkins Co., 1955.
977. Woodruff, Burton and Helson, Harry: Torque: A new dimension in tactile-kinesthetic activity. *Am. J. Psych., 78,* 271-277, 1965.
978. Wooldridge, Dean E.: *The Machinery of the Brain.* New York, McGraw-Hill Book Company, 1963.
979. Woodson, Wesley E.: *Human Engineering Guide for Equipment Design.* Berkeley, University of California Press, 1956.
980. Woodward, Patricia: Experimental study of transfer of training in motor learning. *J. Appl. Psych., 27,* 12-32, 1943.
981. Woodworth, R. S.: Accuracy of voluntary movement. *Psych. Monographs, 3,* 3, 1899.
982. ————: *Dynamics of Behavior.* New York, Henry Holt & Co., 403, 1958.
983. ————: *Experimental Psychology.* New York, Henry Holt & Co., 1938.
984. Wundt, W. M.: *Physiological Psychology,* 1874.
985. Wysocki, Boleslaw A. and Whitney, Eleanor: Body image of crippled children as seen in draw-a-person test behavior. *Percept. & Mot. Skills, 21,* 499-504, 1965.
986. Yensen, Roy: A factor influencing motor overflow. *Percept. & Mot. Skills, 20,* 967-968, 1965.
987. Young, Olive G.: Rate of learning in relation to spacing of practice periods in archery and badminton. *Res. Quart., 25,* 231, 1954.
988. Young, Paul T.: *Motivation and Emotion.* New York, John Wiley & Sons, Inc., 1961.
989. Zamora, Emil N. and Kaelbling, Rudolph: Memory and electroconvulsive therapy. *Am. J. Psychiatry, 64,* 122, 1965.
990. Zarron, Leon J.: Maternal deprivation: Toward an empirical and conceptual evaluation. *Psych. Bull., 58,* 459-490, 1961.
991. Zartman, E. N. and Cason, H.: The influence of an increase in muscular tension on mental efficiency. *J. Exp. Psych., 17,* 671-679, 1934.
992. Zeaman, D. and Kaufman, H.: Individual differences and theory in a motor learning task. *Psych. Monographs, 69,* 14, 1955.
993. Zegers, R. T.: Monocular movement—parallax thresholds as functions of field size, field position and speed of stimulus movement. *J. Psych., 26,* 477-498, 1948.
994. Zeigarnik, Bluma: Ulber das Behalten von erledigten und unerledigten Handlungen. *Psych. Forsch., 9,* 1-85, 1927.

995. Zigler, Edward and Kanzer, Paul: The effectiveness of two classes of reinforcers on the performance of middle and lower class children. *J. Personal.*,
30, 155-163, 1962.

996. Zigler, M J. and Barrett, Rebecca: A further contribution to the tactual perception of form. *J. Exp. Psych.*, *10*, 184-192, 1927.

997. Zimmerman, Wayne: Hypothesis concerning the nature of the spatial factors.
Ed. & Psych. Meas., *14*, 396-400, 1954.

998. Zipf, Sheila G.: Effects of probability of reward and speed requirements on
human performance. *J. Exp. Psych.*, *65*, 106-107.

999. Zuckerman, John V.: Effects of variations in commentary upon the learning
of perceptual-motor tasks from sound motion pictures. *The American Psychologist*, *5*, 363-364, 1950.

1000. Zunich, Michael: Child behavior and parental attitudes. *J. Psych.*, *62*, 41-46,
1966.

Index